Tales for Shakespeare

D1302481

Tales for Shakespeare

Stories That Inspired the Plays

Edited by

Thomas G. Olsen

**Cambridge
Scholars**
Publishing

Tales for Shakespeare: Stories That Inspired the Plays

Edited by Thomas G. Olsen

This book first published 2020. The present binding first published 2021.

Cambridge Scholars Publishing

Lady Stephenson Library, Newcastle upon Tyne, NE6 2PA, UK

British Library Cataloguing in Publication Data
A catalogue record for this book is available from the British Library

ISBN (10): 1-5275-7156-4
ISBN (13): 978-1-5275-7156-3

For Marinella, again and always

TABLE OF CONTENTS

ACKNOWLEDGEMENTS

This project has been helped by many colleagues and friends who read and commented on various sections of the book, shared a detail, or offered useful suggestions at various points in its development: Brendan Burns, Christopher Chalifoux, Andy Evans, Thomas Festa, Charles Houser, Daniel Kempton, Andy and Deb Mousley, Cyrus Mulready, Stephen Parks, June Schlueter, and Anders Winroth. My late, lamented colleague and cycling companion Peter Kaufman heard a lot about *Tales for Shakespeare* as we rode many miles together. Over the years he made many suggestions and offered a good deal of encouragement, as did my writing group partners Andy Evans and Cyrus Mulready.

I would like also to thank The State University of New York at New Paltz for sabbatical time and research support, and to acknowledge my many students who have seen versions of these stories in their Shakespeare classes and helped me shape the project. My two wonderful research students, Russell Dembin and Jahna Romano, worked on early stages of the project with me, bringing their intelligence and curiosity to my endeavours. Parts of the General Introduction were delivered to audiences at the Fairleigh Dickinson University Shakespeare Colloquium and the Elizabethan Club at Yale University. I thank the Beinecke Rare Book and Manuscript Library, the Elizabethan Club of Yale University, the Huntington Library, and the Wikimedia Foundation for permission to reprint the images of several title pages.

ILLUSTRATIONS

Figure 1-1. The title page of Gerard Laingbaine's *Momus Triumphans: Or, The Plagiaries of the English Stage* (London: for N. C., 1688). Image courtesy of the Beinecke Rare Book and Manuscript Library, Yale University.

Figure 1-2. The title page of the falsely dated quarto of *Sir John Oldcastle* (London: T[homas] P[avier], 1600, but really 1619), erroneously bearing Shakespeare's name as author. Image courtesy of The Elizabethan Club of Yale University.

Figure 2.1. The title page of Matteo Bandello's *La Prima Parte de le Novelle del Bandello*, published by Vincenzo Busdrago (Lucca, 1554). Image courtesy of the Beinecke Rare Book and Manuscript Library, Yale University.

Figure 6-1. The title page of the first edition of Robert Greene's *Pandosto. The Triumph of Time* (London: Thomas Orwin for Thomas Cadman, 1588). Image courtesy of the Wikimedia Foundation.

Figure 7-1. The title page of *The True Chronicle History of King Leir and His Three Daughters, Gonorill, Ragan, and Cordella* (London: Simon Stafford for John Wright, 1605). Image courtesy of the Huntington Library.

INTRODUCTION

> All the world's a stage,
> And all the men and women merely players.
> They have their exits and their entrances,
> And one man in his time plays many parts,
> His acts being seven ages. At first the infant,
> Mewling and puking in the nurse's arms;
> And then the whining schoolboy with his satchel
> And shining morning face, creeping like snail
> Unwillingly to school. And then the lover,
> Sighing like furnace, with a woeful ballad
> Made to his mistress' eyebrow. Then a soldier,
> Full of strange oaths and bearded like the pard,
> Jealous in honor, sudden and quick in quarrel,
> Seeking the bubble reputation
> Even in the cannon's mouth. And then the justice,
> In fair round belly with good capon lined,
> With eyes severe and beard of formal cut,
> Full of wise saws and modern instances,
> And so he plays his part. The sixth age shifts
> Into the lean and slippered pantaloon,
> With spectacles on nose and pouch on side,
> His youthful hose, well saved, a world too wide
> For his shrunk shank; and his big manly voice,
> Turning again toward childish treble, pipes
> And whistles in his sound. Last scene of all,
> That ends this strange eventful history,
> Is second childishness and mere oblivion,
> Sans teeth, sans eyes, sans taste, sans everything.

Let's begin with one of the most frequently quoted and beloved of Shakespeare's speeches, from *As You Like It*: a humane, comprehensive, and eminently memorable pronouncement on the human life cycle. It's Shakespeare at his best, as he develops an exquisite metaphor of actors playing roles to a seemingly basic truth about the "stages" of our finite time on earth. No wonder Shakespeare is almost universally considered great.[1]

The only problem is, this great speech did not originate with Shakespeare. Not even the basic idea. Neither the actors-as-people metaphor, nor the idea of life-as-a role we play, nor the division of our lives into seven ages or acts, nor even the specifics of each of those stages is his original creation. He borrowed it all, tapping into a vast storehouse of ancient, medieval, and contemporary sources that had already expressed these ideas. They were entirely commonplace by the late 1590s, when he composed *As You Like It*.

William Shakespeare, Plagiarist?

What are we to make of this phenomenon of outright borrowing, maybe stealing, which occurs over and over in the Shakespeare canon? By modern standards William Shakespeare was a plagiarist. As a matter of fact, he would certainly qualify as one of the most notoriously successful ones in the history of the English language. On the strength of his dramatic writings, and especially on the public performances of them, he became famous in his own lifetime and eventually wealthy, too. And in countless editions, performances, and adaptations of his plays and poems he achieved a posthumous fame that no other English writer enjoys. And he's been good to others as well: as one scholar notes, his writings have provided the publishing industry with its most profitable, enduring, royalty-free "cash cow" ever.[2]

But the plays that made him rich and famous were, in almost every instance, significantly based upon other authors' works that he mined for their story lines, for their characters, and in some cases even for their verbal expression. As the playwright and critic (and cranky admirer of Shakespeare) George Bernard Shaw once quipped, Shakespeare had a tremendous "gift of telling a story (provided some one else told it to him first)."[3] This is hardly the image most readers want in their minds when thinking about a poet and playwright who has brought great pleasure and challenges to more than twenty generations of admiring readers, scholars, thespians, and theatre patrons across the world.

Before rushing to apply modern ideas about plagiarism and artistic originality to the case of Shakespeare, modern readers need to understand much more about what people in his age understood the creative process to be, what they considered legitimate and illegitimate literary borrowing, and what ethical standards and legal structures were in place in their time. In other words, we actually cannot be so sure that Shakespeare was a plagiarist even if everything we *think* we know about plagiarism would seem to apply to his artistic processes and to the literary works that remain as his legacy.

Contemporary readers also need to consider the general human desire to retell and adapt stories, for that is what Shakespeare did in nearly everything he wrote. In this regard, he ends up looking like almost any other storyteller who relies on the stories of the past, rather than a singular case of either a creative genius or a literary thief. As Linda Hutcheon writes—herself adapting an idea expressed in Walter Benjamin's seminal 1923 essay "The Translator's Task"—storytelling is always and has always been the art of repeating the stories told to us: "art is derived from other art; stories are born of other stories."[4] We need to keep in mind this basic human impulse to retell and to make new as we approach the question of Shakespeare's "plagiarism."

What is a Plagiarist?

First, some definitions. The English word *plagiarism* is derived from a classical Latin root, *plagium*, literally meaning kidnapping. In Shakespeare's youth and for about the first half of his literary career, which as far as scholars can reconstruct began sometime about 1590 and ended sometime about 1612, the term was used in its restricted, literal sense, as in this excerpt from a sermon published in 1577: "and yet man-stealing is most sharply forbidden. Now they commit the offence called Plagium, that is to say, man-stealing."[5] What's evident in this brief example is how anxious the author seems to be to define a Latin term in words more familiar to English speakers: "the offence *called* Plagium"—a phrase that suggests that the author anticipates a certain cognitive gap between his readers' prior experience and the new word. And so he is quick to define the term using the more tangible, usual Anglo-Saxon synonym "man-stealing."[6]

From about the middle of Shakespeare's career the literal concept of "man-stealing" and the variety of Latinate *plagia-* words used to express it slowly became naturalised in the language. But these terms also began to change meanings, gradually taking on the figurative sense with which we are now most familiar. In 1598, as Shakespeare was enjoying success with his cycle of English history plays and several now-perennial favourites such as *Romeo and Juliet*, *The Merchant of Venice*, and *A Midsummer Night's Dream*, Bishop Joseph Hall turned the word from the legal to the literary sphere by referring to the theft of "old Petrarch's spright [spirit] unto a plagiary sonnet-wright."[7] Although Hall's figurative application of the crime of man-stealing to that of literary theft was not altogether new in Western letters—the Roman poet Martial had used the same image in accusing his fellow poet Fidentius of stealing his verses—it was by no means a common figure of speech. It still had the power of a fresh metaphor.

This is so because literary imitation was not routinely considered criminal. In fact, for most of Western literary history an author's ability to absorb and rework the stories of the past constituted not only a good practice but a necessary one. In the much-followed advice of the Roman poet

Horace, younger poets were encouraged to mine the *publica materies*, a concept that equates roughly to our modern notion of public domain or creative commons, for their ideas. Literary creation was not understood to be the development from scratch of new stories, but rather the creative re-working of old and familiar ones.[8] In 1601 Shakespeare's friend and rival poet-playwright Ben Jonson used Martial's image on three occasions in his play *The Poetaster*. During a heated exchange between rival poets, the following accusation flies: "Why, the ditty's all borrowed; 'tis Horace's: hang him, plagiary!" The image is repeated twice more in the play in two parallel constructions: "poetaster and plagiary" and "play-dresser and plagiary."[9] These were terms of disparagement: a poetaster is an inferior, second-rate poet, the thing that every aspiring poet dreads becoming; a play-dresser was a contemporary term used to describe someone who helped produce plays, not write them, and so in this context, an inferior artist. Jonson was a very self-consciously learned poet and playwright, a classicist vitally interested in his own status as an author and in the relationship of authors to each other and to their literary forebears. Unlike Shakespeare, he was highly protective of his own literary reputation and worried about a range of intellectual property issues with which most of his fellow playwrights rarely bothered. And so it seems fitting for him to be the only English playwright of the period to apply Martial's fifteen-hundred year-old metaphor to English letters, and to do so in a play largely taken from Horace, whose plot revolves around the reputations and careers of rival poets.

What goes around comes around. Within seventy years Jonson was in turn called out by poet and critic John Dryden, who wrote in his *An Essay of Dramatick Poesie* (1668) that Jonson "was not onely a professed Imitator of *Horace*, but a learned Plagiary of all the others; you can track him every where in their Snow." But Dryden hardly faulted Jonson for his habit of borrowing. Indeed, he singled him out among the poets as the "greatest man of the last age" even while he noted the many ways that Jonson borrowed from other writers.[10]

Another twenty years would pass before the adjective would actually be used, again by Bishop Hall in reference to a minister caught cribbing from another theologian: "the plagiary priest having stolen this whole passage . . . verbatim out of Bellarmine."[11] A generation later, in 1646, the idiosyncratic polymath Sir Thomas Browne used the same word, but this time as a noun: "plagiary had not its nativity with printing, but began in times when thefts were difficult."[12] Browne's assertion here is revealing, as it points specifically to the relationship between ideas and published writings. He offers a long list of classical authors who pillaged their forebears, arguing that plagiarism predates the enormous power of the printing press to disseminate ideas, whether they are original or borrowed. The very fact that Browne senses the need to advance this argument reveals that something was changing in English literary thought in the seventeenth century: a belief that "plagiary" and publishing somehow belong together. And indeed, the printing press, able to produce editions in hundreds and eventually thousands of essentially identical copies, greatly increased the potential for a writer's literary theft to make itself known as wider and wider circles of readers had opportunities to identify borrowed words and ideas.[13] But even more significant is that Browne is not arguing that the press gave birth to plagiarism, which he calls "translation" or "transcription," but rather that the practice predated the invention of a technology that exposed borrowing much more easily and widely. And he is at pains not to characterise what we would call plagiarism as criminal: "the Ancients were but men, even like our selves. The practice of transcription in our days, was no Monster in theirs...."[14]

Indeed, an assertion of criminality within the sphere of literary production is not something a writer of Shakespeare's age would have easily understood. It took more than sixty years after the end of his literary career and fifty after his death before English authors began routinely to apply the term *plagiary* to literary theft in the sense that we see in Dryden's comment on Jonson. During a period that also saw a massive increase in the power and reach of the periodical press—which offered even more frequent opportunities for authors to borrow from others, and to be discovered by a larger and larger reading public doing so—the now-familiar definition of plagiarism began to take hold in the language.

Plagiarist and *plagiarism*, the terms best known to us now, have an even more interesting history. The noun *plagiarist*, meaning specifically a writer who steals another's literary works, appears for the first time in 1674. And although a religious controversialist used the word in 1621, writing "Were you afraid to be challenged for plagiarism," nearly one hundred years elapse before we find another recorded use of the now-familiar noun form *plagiarism*.[15] For many years thereafter *plagiary* remained the preferred term of English writers, rather than *plagiarism*, and by the mid-seventeenth century its literal sense of man-stealing was in clear competition with the emergent figurative sense of word-stealing.

What is interesting about this history is how far into the future this modern sense of literary plagiarism was with respect to Shakespeare's career. Beginning in the 1670s and 1680s we begin to find clearer and more frequent complaints about literary thefts—as in phrases such as "Plagiaries and depredations" and even in book titles such as Gerald Langbaine's 1688 *Momus Triumphans: Or, The Plagiaries of the English Stage* (see Figure 1-

1). His monumental title, typical of the period and ending with idea of *stolen* plots, tells us a great deal about the shifting definition of this evolving word.[16]

Essential to these linguistic changes is an important underlying cultural principle. To be the victim of theft an author had first to *own* something. This basic assumption about the nature and definition of literary "property" has to be accepted and shared by a culture before the slow process of creating legal protections for this kind of ownership can follow. All parties have to concur that an author originates and produces something so distinctively his or her own (by the late seventeenth century we can confidently speak of some notable women writing for a public) as to constitute something that can be possessed or owned. Once a culture accepts that an intangible "product" such as words strung together can constitute a form of property, it is on its way to imagining a way to protect that product's maker and "owner" through legal structures. This is what was occurring in the last decades of the seventeenth and first years of the eighteenth centuries.

In the decades before the all-important Statute of Anne of 1710, prominent writers such as Thomas Hobbes, John Locke, Joseph Addison, and Daniel Defoe began to make increasingly sophisticated legal and moral arguments in favour of copyright protections.[17] In bringing his *Paradise Lost* to press, John Milton left us our oldest surviving contract between an author and publisher—for the now quaint-sounding sum of £5 and promise of more if the book were to sell well.[18] This gradual movement toward distinguishing legitimate from illegitimate borrowing and toward establishing an author as a category of property-owner was much more than just a few key authors rallying to protect themselves and their fellow writers, however. It signals the start of a profound transformation in the dominant ideas of originality and creativity in English letters, in the basic assumptions governing literary writing, and in the principles upon which that society and its legal system operated.

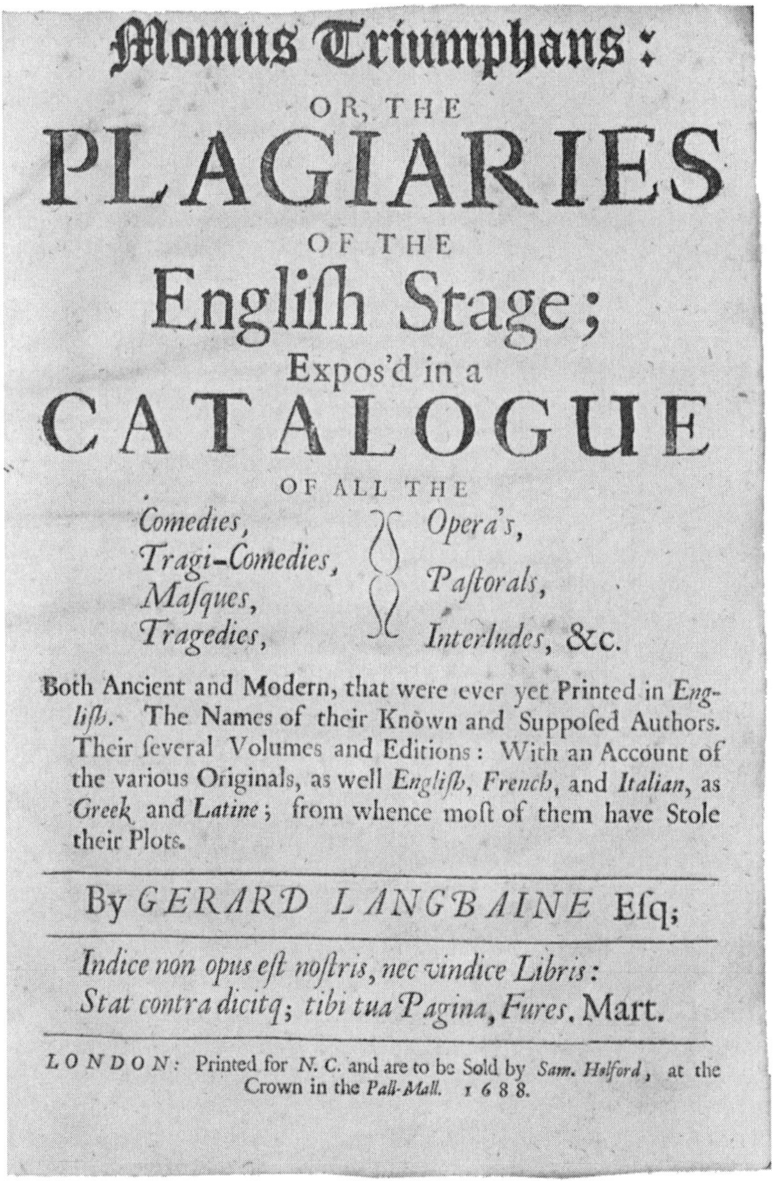

Momus Triumphans:

OR, THE

PLAGIARIES

OF THE

Englifh Stage;

Expos'd in a

CATALOGUE

OF ALL THE

Comedies,	Opera's,
Tragi-Comedies,	Paftorals,
Mafques,	
Tragedies,	Interludes, &c.

Both Ancient and Modern, that were ever yet Printed in Englifh. The Names of their Known and Suppofed Authors.
Their feveral Volumes and Editions: With an Account of
the various Originals, as well Englifh, French, and Italian, as
Greek and Latine; from whence moft of them have Stole
their Plots.

By GERARD LANGBAINE Efq;

Indice non opus eft noftris, nec vindice Libris:
Stat contra dicitq; tibi tua Pagina, Fures. Mart.

LONDON: Printed for N. C. and are to be Sold by Sam. Holford, at the
Crown in the Pall-Mall. 1688.

Fig. 1-1. The title page of Gerard Langbaine's *Momus Triumphans*

The Statute of Anne, formally titled *An Act for the Encouragement of Learning, by Vesting the Copies of Printed Books in the Author's or Purchasers of Such Copies* is a monumental event in the history of the evolving ideas concerning plagiarism in England and eventually North America. Prior to its passage, legal protections, such as they were, resided with the publisher, not the author. What was protected—quite imperfectly, to be sure—was not the intangible intellectual labour of developing and arguing one's original ideas or telling a good story, but the financial investment of publishers, who, unlike single scribes making individual copies of manuscripts, faced very significant up-front material and labour costs when they produced a printed edition. Since the sixteenth century English publishers had operated under a loose system of royal patents, monopolies, and licences that protected those investments; bibles, prayer books, ABCs, legal statutes, and other highly profitable works proved especially lucrative to publishers lucky enough to enter into such arrangements. In granting such exclusive rights to certain publishers, the Crown also exercised a significant oversight and even censorship power; since monopolies and patents could be withdrawn or left to expire, publishers were cautious not to draw royal ire by publishing the wrong works. It was a system that had something in it for certain publishers and a great advantage for a government that used regulation of the press to manage dissent and to control the diffusion of ideas and art.

Not all protections proceeded from the top downward, however: the London Company of Stationers, a powerful trade guild to which early modern publishers belonged, regulated the printing business in the capital and exercised significant control over its own members by granting to them licences to publish specific works. Although there are some notable cases of rogue publishers pirating works "owned" by others, and many other cases of disputed claims to these rights, the system functioned reasonably well for many decades. Since a licence to publish certain types of works could secure very significant financial rewards for publishers, it probably also contributed to a kind of de facto censorship over what was published. According to historian of copyright law Mark Rose, over the course of the seventeenth century the language used in these licences gradually evolved away from an emphasis upon the *action* of the specific Stationers' grant to an emphasis upon the *rights* of ownership of the publisher—another sign that something was changing in the culture of authorship. He concludes that "a gap was beginning to develop between the institution of the stationers' copyright, which was based upon a traditional conception of society as a community bound by ties of fidelity and service, and the emergent ideology of possessive individualism." The emerging conception of publishers' *proprietary* rights over their products was in the ascendency over a residual idea of a primarily regulatory or supervisory public benefit.[19] As interesting as these changes are, we must remember that by the time they begin to emerge in English institutions like the printing trade and the legal system, Shakespeare's career was long over. None bear directly on how he would have thought about his own creative process.

Before going forward, let us consider an important question. Could it be that just because writers of Shakespeare's era did not routinely use the word *plagiarise* or its related terms to refer to literary theft they had no concept of it? Of course not. Then, as now, authors took due pride in making original work and felt entitled to credit for it. But the meaning of "original work" has changed radically over the last four hundred years, and so this definition needs careful examination. John Kerrigan studied the evolution of early modern ideas of originality, concluding that in the lexicon of Shakespeare's time, an "original work" was one from which copies were made, which is to say, a pattern or prototype for a new but derivative work. This was the sense of originality that had been in use since at least the time of Chaucer, and it was not until well into the middle of the eighteenth century that our modern idea of an original work as origin*ating* with a new author came into use.[20] Shakespeare's generation operated under the cultural assumption that originality was a successful form of copying.

In fact, soon after Shakespeare's early plays achieved popular success and he received some measure of notice, he drew the wrath of a rival playwright on precisely this question. Robert Greene, a university-educated London hack writer and minor playwright some six years older than Shakespeare, complained in a 1592 pamphlet that "there is an upstart Crow, beautified with our feathers, that with his *Tygers hart wrapt in a Players hyde*, supposes he is as well able to bombast out a blank verse as the best of you: and being an absolute *Johannes fac totum*, is in his own conceit the only Shake-scene in a country."[21] The implication behind Greene's snub on young Shakespeare centres on the complaint that he gained his new fame from borrowing from his contemporaries ("beautified with *our* feathers").

Greene's diatribe alludes to a famous fable usually attributed to Aesop (but in fact not original to him—the more one looks for literary appropriation, the more one finds it!) in which a plain bird borrows the feathers of a beautifully plumed one and vainly parades around in them, only to get his comeuppance. Would Greene have charged Shakespeare with literary "man-stealing" if the younger playwright had not, apparently, been so proud of his accomplishments? Was this a matter of class or seniority more than literary borrowing? Perhaps it was a dig at Shakespeare's lack of university education? Greene's metaphor, following the logic of the fable, seems more to complain about Shakespeare's arrogance and presumption, or perhaps irritating sense of singularity (he is an "upstart crow") than any particular act of illicit or unethical literary borrowing. What is interesting about Greene's diatribe is how unclear the metaphor of borrowed feathers is: does he mean Shakespeare's literary borrowing or does he mean his tendency to outshine his fellow writers? And in a delightful irony, Greene even alludes to Shakespeare's image of "a tiger's heart, wrapped in a woman's hide" from *Henry VI, part 3*—in a sense stealing from the very author he intends to insult.

Today most people are acutely aware of the concept of intellectual property in everything from textbooks and bestselling fiction, to pop music, television commercials, and print advertising: who produces it, who markets it, who consumes it, and how it's protected through increasingly complex global legal structures such as brand registration, trademarks, copyright, and digital stamps. Writers of Shakespeare's generation and before enjoyed almost none of the legal protections that modern authors and publishers assume today and that now govern our individual and institutional attitudes toward plagiarism. The principles of copyright as they are now defined did not exist, the court system was not set up to decide cases of intellectual property, and as we have just seen, the very concept of intellectual property claimed on the basis of originality was deeply fraught with subtleties and contradictions that authors and early modern courts would have been equally ill-prepared to deal with.[22]

Modern conceptions of authorship as an existential category are largely a product of Romantic thought that privileged originality in a way that it had never before been defined or privileged in prior ages. Even the protections afforded by the Statute of Anne in 1710 did little to advance the interests of the creators of what we now call intellectual and creative property, as opposed to the publishers who took the financial and administrative risks of bringing their ideas to a public.

Shakespeare's Borrowing

Although very successful, Shakespeare was only one participant in a system of assumptions and practices that stretched back to classical literature, defined literary production in the Middle Ages, and still governed the ways early modern writers thought about their writing processes. Well before the age of Shakespeare and Jonson, Chaucer reworked Boccaccio, and before him Dante took from Virgil, and Virgil took from Homer. Homer, really more a composite than real author, took from oral traditions. In each case, an author's creativity was inherently and primarily a collaboration with the authors of the past, a matter of standing—as the old truism attributed to Sir Isaac Newton (but not original to him) has it—like a dwarf on the shoulders of the giants who came before.[23] Literary originality meant building upon the works of the past rather than breaking from them. As the time-honoured medieval conception of authorship had it, God is the only author and everyone we now call an author merely a scribe.[24] Or in the words of C. S. Lewis, "Touching up something that was already there was almost the characteristically medieval method of composition."[25]

Three aspects of Shakespeare's particular forms of "plagiarism" deserve comment. Perhaps the first and most important is that he was remarkably uninhibited and refreshingly unprejudiced in his choice of source material, unfettered by received ideas concerning the kinds of literary works that could ennoble a serious author. He certainly resorted to the classics, Ovid's *Metamorphoses* above all, and he drew freely from an inheritance of what modern readers now broadly accept as great literary works handed down as part of a cultural heritage from ancient Rome and to a more limited degree from ancient Greece. Works as different from each other as *Titus Andronicus*, *Venus and Adonis*, and *A Midsummer Night's Dream* all have roots in Ovid, while Plutarch and other favourite classical authors provided story lines for the plays set in ancient times: *Antony and Cleopatra*, *Coriolanus*, *Julius Caesar*, and *Timon of Athens*.[26]

But Shakespeare also ranged in and borrowed, apparently without shame, from a wide range of contemporary popular fiction, pamphlets, and sensational news stories. One such example, Robert Greene's *Pandosto: The Triumph of Time*, provided the basis for his *The Winter's Tale*. (This is the same Robert Greene who had called him an upstart crow. Maybe he had a point about Shakespeare's borrowed feathers?) Though his biographers usually conclude that Shakespeare did have a grammar-school education as a boy, he was not a university-trained scholar and sometimes, but not always, took the easy route by reading ancient and modern European source works in translation rather than in the original.[27] Just as important was his listening: he listened to the speech patterns and ideas of common people in London and in the English countryside. As plays such as *Henry IV Part I*, *As You Like It*, *A Midsummer Night's Dream, Measure for Measure, Julius Caesar,* and *Coriolanus* vividly demonstrate, he also had a keen and often sympathetic ear for the rich, evocative language of the habitués of drinking establishments and brothels, simple shepherds, and angry mobs. He knew the names of many plants, their properties, and the rude nicknames that country people sometimes gave them. All these voices existed well outside the bounds of what many more conventionally learned or tradition-bound early modern authors considered acceptable source material.

Second, within any particular source text—usefully called *hypotexts* by the French theorist Gérard Genette—Shakespeare was also remarkably unbound by pre-ordained ideas about what was important or valuable; he took only what he wanted from his sources, often leaving aside major plot points and characters, and routinely manipulating major details of approach, tone, action, and meaning to fit artistic designs of his own.[28] He was inherently a *synthesising* artist, again and again employing an eclectic, recombinant style of borrowing in which he fused together elements from multiple sources and never produced straight, slavish, or superficial rewritings of any one source, even in cases where he retained major plot lines and characters from a single story.

In the very useful distinction offered by E. M. Forster in his *Aspects of the Novel* (1927), there is a fundamental difference between a story and a plot, and this distinction is central to understanding how Shakespeare borrowed and what he did with his borrowing. In Forster's words, a story is merely "a narrative of events arranged in their time-sequence," while a plot is "also a narrative of events, the emphasis falling on causality." He illustrates his point with this now-famous juxtaposition: "'The king died and then the queen died' is a story. 'The king died and then the queen died of grief' is a plot." In a plot, the emphasis of what is being told to us shifts from events to causes, and to what may underlie those causes. Linear time is less important than what stimulates the reader's imagination: we begin to ask "why" rather than "and then?"[29] Forster's maxim is a point of particular importance to Shakespeare's methods, for time after time, we see that his engagement with a prior narrative is often at the level of story, for its framework and sequence of events, while the plot comes from his imagination: he supplies motives where motives are unclear or absent in the source, he explores human desires and anxieties at key points where the prior text is silent, and he shows little restraint in changing the details of a story when doing so improves it. Sometimes, as in the case of his King Lear and several other protagonists, he achieves psychological effect by suppressing or denying motives that are explicit in his sources.

At this point I want to make clear a basic principle about Shakespeare's habits of composition: knowing one major source story for a Shakespeare play, even the source that most recognizably served him for his story lines, never fully accounts for his borrowing. Not only did he routinely combine more than one story, but he also drew from the language of the English Bible, made allusions to topical political events, and summoned the spirit of works, like Marlowe's *The Jew of Malta*, without necessarily copying the stories' narrative events. He synthesised and recombined material, even non-literary in nature, to change a received story into a plot. The collection of stories you now have before you does not attempt to present all the sources that went into a single play, but many of those sources can be tracked down and consulted as you understand more about how and where Shakespeare drew inspiration for his works.[30]

To these two observations can be added a third, perhaps better left to be discovered through the reading experiences of individuals than pronounced upon at great length here: Shakespeare consistently showed a remarkable ability to discover within his source stories the psychology lying latent in other writers' characters, as well as opportunities to explore emotional conflict and inner turmoil that his sources often underplayed or simply ignored. This tendency appears not only in his dramatic works, but also in his two narrative poems, *Venus and Adonis* and *The Rape of Lucrece*, published in 1593 and 1594, respectively. In these poems and in his nearly forty plays, what is especially striking is Shakespeare's habit of teasing out and developing human passions and the workings of the human mind, creating out of mere words the impression that a real person is opening up his or her soul. Sometimes, as we will see, he did so on the basis of almost no textual precedent because early modern authors often made little of the psychology of their characters. See, for example, how you respond to the sources stories for *The Merchant of Venice*, *Hamlet*, *Othello*, and *The Winter's Tale* and note what happens in the transition from the prior story to the second telling. Shakespeare had a knack for discovering or inventing the psychology behind the actions narrated in someone else's plot—recall George Bernard Shaw's quip that the playwright could tell a great story so long as someone told it to him first. One of the ways he developed his own stories was by emphasizing the psychological dimensions of characters he found in the pages of others.

In the enthusiastic analysis of one influential contemporary critic, Shakespeare is judged to have "invented" what it is to be human and to have shown audiences for the first time in history what human psychology looked like when dramatised.[31] Although this claim has been the subject of a number of highly sceptical and sometimes hostile responses,[32] most readers of Shakespeare do come to admire his ability to deliver characters of remarkable depth and truthfulness. To give just one notable example: the textual basis for the almost larger-than-life character Lady Macbeth is extremely thin. Despite her enormous presence in Shakespeare's play, she gets nothing more than a parenthetical mention in his main source, Raphael Holinshed's *Chronicle of England, Scotland and Ireland* (1587). In Shakespeare's telling of the story, however, we get fiery speeches and astonishing feats of emotional blackmail as she chides, cajoles, and demands her way into her husband's consciousness. Lady Macbeth's transformation can be very instructive: where Holinshed contents himself with a passing reference that leaves readers with practically no lasting image of her and certainly nothing that would allow them to draw any conclusions about her motivations or passions, Shakespeare spotted an opportunity to explore a very minor character's psychology. In doing so, he deepened the psychology of his protagonist as well. By heightening and intensifying Macbeth's wife's presence in the story, Shakespeare created one of the great husband-wife stories of all time: her overwhelming ambition, followed by her precipitous fall into guilt, madness, and eventual suicide complements Macbeth's own psychological complex of ambition and restraint. In the final acts of the play she offers a sharply defined foil for his descent into paranoia and cruelty, creating and enriching the story as audiences become a party to the couple's shared fantasies, ambitions, hesitations, guilt, and ultimately separation and death.

Where did Shakespeare find or discover the material to do so? Geoffrey Bullough's discussion of his creative process in writing *Macbeth* is helpful: "Lady Macbeth's character is almost entirely created by Shakespeare both in its internal convolutions and in its outward manifestations. The ambitious wives in Holinshed and other possible chronicle sources provided merely a sketchy outline which he filled in."[33] Specifically, Shakespeare may also have remembered Queen Medea, who murdered her own children, from Thomas Newton's 1581 *Seneca His Tenne Tragedies*. He may have drawn some details from Hector Boece's *The Description of Scotland*, a source used by Holinshed, in which Scottish wives are vividly described as breastfeeding their young children for fear that they would degenerate if left to wet-nurses, but at the same time given to the custom of dipping their swords in and drinking the blood of their freshly slain enemies. Details such as these may have combined into the details of Lady Macbeth's bloodlust and the image of her dashing out the brains of her own toothless child while it was nursing. Shakespeare may also have transferred some of the qualities of King Duff's ambitious wife, using details given in Holinshed's *Chronicle*, to his newly developed character.[34] The conclusion we should arrive at through this example is that although Shakespeare took the *Macbeth* story from Holinshed, he radically transformed almost every important aspect of it to create, in effect, an original work.

Women and the marginalised—wives, daughters, gardeners and other manual labourers, prostitutes and pimps, thieves, foreigners, and servants—all come in for special attention in the works of Shakespeare. This is one of his particular features as an author: a knack for discovering in these usually minor characters psychological and emotional depths that his historical and literary sources almost always deny them or never report. One contemporary critic calls this quality a "compulsive habit of creative interiorization"—the ability to imagine and creatively render as believable the inner lives of even his minor characters, while another argues that Shakespeare "is able to embody different perspectives" to produce authentic representations of human experience, converting "'selves' or possible selves . . . into ways of being and living."[35] The development of Lady Macbeth from almost no textual antecedents serves as a prime example of this aspect of Shakespeare's technique as a playwright.

Adaptation and Appropriation: A Human Constant

According to Richard Dawkins, our human capacity to pass on elements of culture from one generation to another is almost as constitutive of our nature as is our biology.[36] In a study first published in 1976 he offered a brief overview of his theory of cultural "memes": units of culture analogous to genetic data, but in fact even more enduring across human evolution than our genetic distinctiveness. He argues that memes are the basic elements of human culture—tunes, ideas, catch-phrases, clothes, fashions, ways of making pots or building arches—that propagate themselves, much like genetic traits across generations, by an ongoing and almost inexorable process of imitation and repetition.[37] To the Internet generation, of course, memes are most commonly thought of as the web-based jokes and parodies that circulate and change with amazing speed and variety over social media networks.[38] This modern sense builds upon the root definition offered by Dawkins: in broad cultural terms, all forms of memes function and have meaning because one generation or group passes its cultural distinctiveness to another by transmitting its thought, its techniques, and its material and cultural products, and even its jokes, via previously circulated forms. Like genetic code, memes can combine, associate and adapt; and thus they evolve, producing a cultural heritage that is both distinctive and open to variation. And that is the principal strength of memes according to Dawkins: a combination of durability and adaptability.

His theory takes us to the very heart of an important aspect of Shakespeare's "plagiarism," for what he routinely did as an author was to engage with a literary tradition comprised of many interwoven memes that he replicated in modified and fresh forms. Shakespeare's originality consisted not in inventing new stories but in discovering in his hypotexts something latent or unspoken.[39] Examples include basic plot details such as the struggle of young love against familial pressures in *Romeo and Juliet*, Hamlet's inner quest to avenge his murdered father, or the ill-fated love-test that King Lear puts to his three daughters. All these individual units of human narrative tradition—these memes—resonate with timeless, folkloristic, or fairy-tale qualities that are immediately recognizable as belonging to some deep human reservoir of stories much larger and older even than the various Western literary repositories from which Shakespeare borrowed.

Central to the theory of memes is the principle that cultural transmission benefits, somewhat paradoxically, from variation. In other words, a unit of culture that holds to a straight, unchanging line of transmission, just like a genetic trait that never mutates, is likely to die out within a few generations. An unchanging unit of cultural meaning eventually becomes irrelevant or obscure to later audiences, but a cultural trait that absorbs and accommodates new stimuli has much greater chances of surviving. In the case of human stories, this means that old stories must be made new so as to be relevant to generations that have different interests, concerns, or challenges; they must both retain something of their essence and renew themselves. The stories most open to imitation are the ones that stand the best chance of surviving into the future.[40]

All of this sounds a lot like what occurs in contemporary fan fiction circles, where amateur authors, usually with the help of social media outlets and the wide reach of the Internet, give new life to familiar stories, whether those of Homer, Jane Austen, or J. K. Rowling. In a literary category called by one critic "a genre fundamentally based on appropriation . . . . a form of cultural production that is essentially derivative," fan fiction authors set well-known characters or plot lines in new time frames, sometimes imagining scenes, characters, or plot events not in the original work, often mashing together characters or episodes from two or more source stories.[41] At times their efforts also cross platforms, drawing from television, video games, or cinema to fiction, or vice-versa.[42] Indeed, the explosion of fan fiction in the last generation or so is merely an accelerated, obvious, and cross-media version of what has occurred over the whole course of Western literature, where prior stories functioned as prompts and invitations for generations of subsequent authors to create their own literary and cultural productions in a more gradual but equally interactive and participatory way.

What this line of thinking suggests is that modern readers and audiences need to look at Shakespeare's habits of borrowing as just one instance in a broad, on-going human process of cultural replication and renewal, and not as simple or single acts of source-stealing. Like contemporary fan fiction authors, Shakespeare took old stories and gave them new life, often changing the method of presentation from prose or verse narrative, which are *telling modes*, to that of drama, which is primarily a presentational or *showing* mode.[43] Some examples of this process contained in the following pages of this collection include his reworking of the legendary Romeo and

Juliet story, taken from Arthur Brooke (who took it from other sources in a long line of borrowing), the Othello story of Cinthio, and others. In some of these cases, as in his use of François Belleforest's version of the Hamlet story or Ser Giovanni Fiorentino's *Il Pecorone* for *The Merchant of Venice*, one source text was combined wholesale with other major sources in a process of co-adaptation that demonstrates the basic principle espoused by Dawkins, that memes replicate themselves in human culture by being fundamentally open to variation and adaptation.[44]

In other cases, he reworked a previously staged dramatic work of his fellow London playwrights. *The True Chronicle History of King Leir and His Three Daughters, Gonorill, Ragan, and Cordella*, published in 1605 but first performed about a decade earlier, became the blueprint for his own *King Lear*. In *The Merchant of Venice*, published twice in 1600 but probably first acted a few years before that, he cribbed only a few specific lines from Christopher Marlowe's hugely successful play *The Jew of Malta* (and also grabbed some from Marlowe's *Tamburlaine the Great*). But he also responded on a very deep level, a level irrespective of exact verbal borrowings and plot details, to key elements of that play's spirit.[45] In still other cases, he mined historical narratives in search of glimpses into the minds and spirits of characters from the ancient world such as Julius Caesar and Coriolanus, and of kings and queens of his native England such as King John, Richard II, Prince Hal, Henry IV, and Richard III. His principal sources for his English history plays were Raphael Holinshed's massive prose *Chronicles of England, Scotland, and Ireland* (1587 edition) and Edward Hall's *Union of the Two Noble and Illustre Families* (1548). For his plays based on classical history he resorted principally to Sir Thomas North's *The Lives of the Noble Grecians and Romanes* (1579), an ambitious tome (itself a translation from the French) which contained a wealth of stories that inspired Shakespeare's imagination.

We can better understand Shakespeare's particular case by considering what some of the best minds interested in the human impulse to adapt stories have said about the process and the effects of adaptation in general. Among the most important points argued by Linda Hutcheon, one of the leading contemporary theorists in this field, is that audiences and readers derive— and seem always to have derived—great satisfaction from the combination of familiar and new elements that adaptations provide. An adaptation appeals to audiences and readers precisely because it is both familiar—it's a story that they already know—and fresh—it's not *exactly* the story they remember. Something new piques their interest, while at the same time something already comfortable grounds them and makes them feel at home.[46]

Underlying and supporting these theories of the familiar and the new is the time-honoured Aristotelian principle of imitation, or as he called it, *mimesis*. Aristotle's theory posits that part of the pleasure of engaging with dramatic stories about others is that we, as spectators, find pleasure in seeing actions and characters that in some way resemble aspects of our own lives. Aristotle was not making the claim that audiences experience anything like a perfect one-to-one correspondence between what they see and what they live—he was, after all, using Sophocles' tragedy *Oedipus Rex* as his primary text and that play does not offer up a life story to be desired by anyone. Rather, he suggested that aspects of what theatrical audiences witness stimulate the basic human emotions of fear and pity and bring about "the proper purgation of these emotions" that encourages some form of self-awareness.[47]

Modern genres such as the novel or the personal memoir, to say nothing of film or televised mass-audience sporting events, which Aristotle did not know anything about and could not even anticipate, have the same potential as drama to excite in readers and viewers the human emotions he describes. Fiction and creative non-fiction have an enormous capacity to present an imitation of life to readers as they become engaged with stories they read rather than see performed. Cinema presents another narrative genre that Aristotle could never have imagined, but which works very effectively on our emotions: because of the particular characteristics of its medium (the darkened room, the potential for highly realistic camera-work, the layering of music over images and voices, and so on), film has a special power to focus viewers' attention, in much the way that concentrated reading can, both forms creating a diegesis (the fictional "reality" that setting, characters, and actions present to us) so compelling that the world around us can slip away and time can seem suspended.

Even though Aristotle's *Poetics*, the source of this theory of mimesis, was imperfectly known in Shakespeare's time, the principle of literature's capacity to represent real life and show it to readers in a recognizable form had a defining effect on the way that literary works were created in Shakespeare's time. The concept of mimesis promoted imitation as a foundational principle of artistic creation during the early modern period and even before. Imitation of prior works actually *constituted* creativity; it was expected that writers would engage with the stories of the past, modifying or amplifying those narratives, all the while imitating them and thus creating for readers something that—following Hutcheon's principle— was both familiar and new. Not only was imitation expected by audiences, it was regarded as a sign of virtuosity for literary authors to insert themselves into this tradition (in this period, "herself" only occasionally applies) and make a claim on it by offering a new version of a well-worn or previously written tale. Contemporaries of Shakespeare's such as Ben Jonson and Edmund Spenser, both much more eager than Shakespeare to claim status as literary authors, deliberately and conspicuously announced their debts to prior authors, even as they created something new out of old forms and old stories.[48] So did John Milton in *Paradise Lost* (1667), published more than half a century after Shakespeare's career ended. As one theorist of modern plagiarism summarises, "mimesis was the means whereby Western writers established their authority, and textual collaboration was their method of composition."[49] To be a great writer was to take one's place in a line of great writers, and the acknowledged way to do that was to crib from them and imitate them: to create an implied collaboration with a prior author and pre-existing hypotexts—in effect, to graft a new story unto old ones.[50]

Early modern educational methods encouraged precisely these attitudes, and they were instilled into even very young students. Repetition, rote-memorisation, and constant attention to the individual style of classical authors chosen for their distinctive command of Latin drove the grammar-school curriculum; it was some version of this approach, we can surmise, that the young William Shakespeare would have been trained up in at grammar school in Stratford-upon-Avon.[51] As students of Shakespeare's time developed their skills, they might even be taught by their schoolmasters to use Roger Ascham's so-called double-translation method, by which they would translate Latin into English, and then, without the original Latin before them, attempt to recast from their English the Latin of the original, coming as close possible to it.[52] Clearly, a curriculum that made such exercises an educational priority and held literary modelling in such high regard was one that certainly valued imitation as an art form.

According to one recent analysis, the Elizabethan curriculum's emphasis on memorization created the perfect conditions for Shakespeare's creative imagination to reconstruct creatively what he imperfectly remembered from his school texts, as well as for him to develop an especially good ear for the different registers and variants of his native language.[53] Indeed, this has been a consistent theme in Shakespeare criticism over the centuries: he has often been credited with a "natural" or "native" genius and a freshness of language and character development at odds with formal and received ideas of literary propriety.[54]

Shakespeare as a Source

Not only was Shakespeare a habitual adaptor of others' works, but over the four centuries since the end of his career, his own works have served as sources for thousands and thousands of stage productions across the globe and at all levels of amateurism and professionalism. Since every production is an interpretation, each one of these is in a sense an adaptation of a prior Shakespearean hypotext, but even more obviously so are thousands of novels, poems, children's books, paintings, sculptures, films, TV episodes, video games, as well as countless literary allusions that pick up and run with some aspect of his stories.

As an example, let us consider the liner notes of the Oscar Peterson Trio's album *West Side Story*. Released in 1962, this seven-track LP appeared almost exactly 400 years after the birth of Shakespeare and just five years after the first stage production of the Leonard Bernstein-Stephen Sondheim-Arthur Laurents musical *West Side Story*, a re-telling of the *Romeo and Juliet* story set in contemporary New York, where Shakespeare's Capulets and Montagues become rival street gangs. Between recording sessions Peterson commented, "Basically I would say this is the first album of its type of the music from *West Side Story* . . . It is a very different album . . . because this music is an arranger's delight . . . This goes along with my belief that anything within the jazz medium should contain proper room for improvisation, or what we call creative impact."[55]

We would be hard-pressed to find a better instance of Richard Dawkins's theory that cultural memes best propagate themselves through adaptation than we have here in Peterson's comments. At the time, nearly everyone in the jazz world, and outside it ("practically every kind of musical organization in every kind of context except, perhaps, as a suite of marches," the liner notes observe), was trying his or her hand at new arrangements of the Bernstein score.[56] Familiar and currently popular show-tunes took on a new face as jazz musicians riffed (and capitalised) on the enormous success of the production and the soundtrack LP, but they gave it new freshness by imprinting the source with their own artistic stamp. The comfort of the familiar combined with the appeal of the new.

And *West Side Story* was nothing short of an international runaway hit: the Broadway musical ran for over 700 performances and garnered two Tony awards before setting out on a long American tour. A European production opened in England in 1958 and ran for over 1,000 performances; tours of Scandinavia, Israel, Africa, and the Near East followed, as did regional productions in the United States. A film version was released in 1961, extending the original stage production to even wider cinema audiences literally across the world (and winning an astonishing ten Oscars out of an equally astonishing eleven nominations). Soundtrack albums from both the stage production and the film garnered top awards and critical plaudits.

As Dawkins's theory suggests, we have here an instance of a deeply rooted cultural narrative. The story of Tony and Maria's star-crossed love, with Romeo and Juliet's story behind it, changed form and found new audiences as musical theatre spawned musical soundtrack and then feature film. Jazz (and other) musical adaptations followed show tunes, as did countless regional, amateur, high school and college productions that took their cues from the original but did not duplicate it. A rich tradition of film and television parodies, including amusing spoofs on *Saturday Night Live*, *Scrubs*, *The Simpsons*, *Family Guy*, *Glee*, and many tongue-in-cheek print and television advertisements have provided ongoing endorsements of the show's deep and lasting cultural importance.[57]

All these creative variations on a theme ultimately pointed back to Shakespeare as their source because *West Side Story* was such an obvious appropriation of *Romeo and Juliet*, with nearly perfect character-to-character parallels and a plot structure that closely followed Shakespeare's. But this was also Shakespeare with a contemporary twist: a very significant change in the dynamic of the Montague-Capulet rivalry spoke pointedly to the troubled state of contemporary American race relations, immigration policies, and the many social ills that accompanied the formation of mid-century American urban ghettos that grew up along with the problems of intransigent poverty. Mixed in with the musical's finger-snapping songs and director-choreographer Jerome Robbins's balletic fight scenes were some surprisingly honest insights into some of the grittier contemporary realities of the American city, and somehow these, too, captivated audiences across the world. But even with its timeliness and frankness about these problems—the results of adaptive processes sometimes called proximation and indigenization[58]—*West Side Story* also enjoyed an added dimension of cultural prestige among audiences of the era because it "came from Shakespeare."

Or did it? We know better: as we will see in the pages that follow, Shakespeare himself was just one stopping point in the much longer cultural history of the Romeo and Juliet story. He borrowed very directly from Arthur Brooke's 1562 version of the story, but by the time Brooke took up his pen the tale had already been often retold in the fifteenth and sixteenth centuries, with many printed versions in Italian, French, and English. And even after Brooke's translation from a French source, published versions other than Shakespeare's appeared in English. It was a story whose basic outlines reached back hundreds of years before Shakespeare and has continued hundreds of years after him.

As an American scholar spending a sabbatical year in Italy, I listened to the Oscar Peterson album I borrowed from my local library and was made all the more acutely aware of how Richard Dawkins's theory of memes accounts for our basic human desire to retell stories and to make culture out of culture. Working backwards, we can trace this evolutionary process. First, we have a Canadian-born musician translating one distinctively American form, the musical, to another distinctively American form, jazz. But the American musical itself is not a new or even purely indigenous form, either: it has its roots in the English comic opera and the central European operetta traditions of the nineteenth century, both of which mingled with the conventions of mid-nineteenth century American minstrel shows and music hall revues. These in turn drew upon pre-existing vernacular American song traditions. Beginning around the time of World War I, this mix took on a more distinctly native flavour, but it remained a hybrid form for many decades. And jazz, too, has its own complex and still-debated evolution out of a mixture of West African musical idioms, antebellum popular music, African-American spirituals, and European instrumentation.[59]

Musically, our example offers an excellent instance of interwoven styles and traditions that cross and re-cross in multiple forms, just as the Romeo and Juliet story did in the fifteenth and sixteenth centuries in Europe. In terms of narrative, we have a sixteenth-century English stage play adapted for a twentieth-century American audience; that play was taken from a sixteenth-century English poem—and not the only one that century—which in turn derives from an Italian source that located the action in "fair Verona," some sixty kilometres from the library from which I borrowed Peterson's album and where I first drafted this introduction. The Italian version of Luigi da Porto (c. 1530) that located the action in Verona derived from previously published versions that set the story, variously, in other cities in Italy and even in the near east. But the roots of the Romeo and Juliet story are even deeper than that, with a version of the sleep potion-tragic death theme appearing as early as the fifth century CE and a version very close to the Romeo and Juliet story appearing in an Italian printed edition in 1476.[60] That an American recording of 1962, now migrated from LP to CD format, has made its way back to a northern Italian public library just an hour from Romeo and Juliet's Verona says something very significant about the flow and the power of cultural memes as they change form and become new cultural signifiers even as they also keep very old stories alive in our collective cultural memory.

Clearly, the strategies of appropriation and adaptation that Shakespeare used in creating his works did not begin or end with him. Far from it. In fact, even within his own lifetime playwrights and other writers responded directly to his works. Two brief examples can serve to illustrate major strands within this cultural process. The first is this one: in 1609-10, during Shakespeare's own theatrical career, a play by John Fletcher appeared, called *The Tamer Tamed; Or, The Woman's Prize*, an obvious and self-conscious sequel to *The Taming of the Shrew*.[61] In it, Shakespeare's Petruccio, the "tamer" character, remarries after the death of his wife Katherina, but soon finds his new wife Maria to be an even more resistant and defiant partner, ready to organise her fellow women into a sex-strike à la Aristophanes' *Lysistrata* and to humiliate her husband personally and publicly. The story concludes with a dryly ironic comic resolution and a message of mutuality between the sexes, but it also amusingly picks up on some major themes of the Shakespearean hypotext (animal training, the withholding of food) and inverts the trope of his domination over his female partner.

The appearance of this sequel, especially so close to the early performances of Shakespeare's own play, suggests that a work of art such as *The Taming of the Shrew* quickly entered into a kind of public domain and became available for updating and re-imagining by others. Rather than a story that definitively closes with Petruccio's final assertion that he has mastered his wife ("'Twas I won the wager, though you hit the white / And being a winner, God give you good night!" he boasts), the story actually remains open for further adaptations, amplifications, and revisions. Fletcher seems to be responding to the uncertainty suggested by the closing lines of the play:

> HORTENSIO. Now go thy ways, thou hast tamed a curst shrew.
> LUCENTIO. 'Tis a wonder, by your leave, she will be tamed so.
> (5.2.190-93)

This last exchange, so at odds with Petruccio's show of confidence just two lines before, seems almost to invite a response. Is Lucentio's wonder merely marvelling or does it express a polite doubt about his friend's proclaimed success? Does it undermine the supposed conclusion of a mission Petruccio has just declared complete? The door seems left wide open for a re-make or sequel, with clever playwrights like Fletcher invited in.[62]

The firſt part

Of the true & hono-
rable hiſtory, of the Life of
Sir Iohn Old-caſtle, the good
Lord Cobham.

*As it hath bene lately acted by the Right
honorable the Earle of Notingham
Lord High Admirall of England,
his Seruants.*

Written by William Shakeſpeare.

London printed for T.P.
1600.

Fig. 1-2. The falsely dated quarto of *Sir John Oldcastle*

A second example tells us something about the cultural authority that Shakespeare enjoyed during and after his lifetime. As described in a prior section of this introduction, early in his dramatic career Shakespeare was charged by Robert Greene with puffing himself up by using the borrowed feathers of his fellow Elizabethan writers (recall that it was Greene who called him "an upstart Crow, beautified with our feathers"). Some of the next generation of writers—or at least publishers—were happy to borrow Shakespeare's feathers once he had made a name for himself. As is evident from examples such as *The London Prodigall* (1605), *Sir John Old-Castle* (1619, but falsely dated 1600), and *Fair Em* (1631), Shakespeare's name on a title page lent dignity (and more to the point, commercial appeal) to plays that were not written by him. Even by the early seventeenth century Shakespeare had become a brand—his name vulnerable to appropriation and exploitation by those who sought to cash in on it, but also a signal of emerging ideas of authorship that would develop later in the seventeenth century.[63]

Just as Shakespeare showed keen business acumen when he retold stories that had already proved winners with English readers and audiences, for more than four hundred years subsequent writers and other creative minds have been happy to cash in on Shakespeare's prior successes. A notable instance occurred in the 1790s: a notorious forgery scandal surrounding *Vortigern and Rowena*, a purportedly lost Shakespeare play that was claimed as a new discovery by the book collector and minor writer William Henry Ireland in 1794 and performed—only once—in 1796. Ireland grew up in a literary and antiquarian household, surrounded by rare books, manuscripts, and letters collected by his writer-collector father Samuel. The exact nature of the father-son plot, if indeed they did collaborate in the forgery, is lost to history now, but it is clear that the younger Ireland began first to forge Shakespearean ephemera such as letters and legal documents before moving on to fragments and then full texts of both known (*Hamlet* and *King Lear*) and supposedly undiscovered plays like *Vortigern and Rowena*.[64] After being exposed by a number of England's literary elite, Ireland eventually confessed his hoax, moved to France, and pieced together a meagre existence for the rest of his days.

As noteworthy—and sad—as this example is, the vast majority of Shakespeare's adaptors and respondents over the centuries have had objectives other than passing off forgeries as genuine Shakespeare. Most have been basically "straight" theatrical productions, with no particular political or cultural motives. However, in the last several decades we have also seen a strong counter-current, offering up much more confrontational responses both to the cultural values thought to reside in his works and to

Shakespeare as a cultural figure.[65] As an economically secure white European male, he has been the target of critical and cultural re-examinations that in one way or another follow Adrienne Rich's now-famous 1971 definition of *re-vision*: "the act of looking back, of seeing with fresh eyes, of entering an old text from a new critical direction." Rich goes on to explain that "we need to know the writing of the past, and know it differently than we have ever known it, not to pass on a tradition but to break its hold over us."[66]

Although Shakespeare's works have often been re-envisioned since the Restoration, when a number of England's most important contemporary playwrights radically rewrote his works to suit what they considered the tastes of the age or to bring out what they considered the latent political messages contained within them, Rich speaks to an altogether different kind of approach that charges authors to write in a way that "talks back" directly to power structures. Although her specific topic was women readers and writers within a masculinist literary tradition, her idea has been generalised to other dispossessed or marginalised groups. In re-writing a culturally powerful or esteemed canonical writer's works, adapters and re-writers re-inscribe the truths generally believed to reside in those hypotexts—all with the goal of breaking the "hold" these texts have over us.

Within this tradition are a number of very important creative re-visions of Shakespeare's works. Let us focus on the example of *King Lear*, a play that, as we will see in the following pages, has a long pre-Shakespearean cultural history that was radically transformed by Shakespeare when he wrote his version of an already well-worn story. Although Nahum Tate's 1681 revision ("reviv'd with alterations," the title page proclaims—and not a typo for "revis'd") changed a great deal about the play, most notably its ending, it did not question its underlying assumptions about masculine power, the emotional state of King Lear, or the moral status of Goneril, Regan, and Cordelia. That kind of revision would come, however, in late nineteenth-century New York with a Yiddish-language adaptation entitled *Miriele Efros* (first titled *The Jewish Queen Lear*) and even more pointedly in Gordon Bottomley's *King Lear's Wife*, first performed and published in England 1915. Bottomley offered his audiences a selfish and promiscuous king who cavorts openly with his dying wife's servant and presides over a dysfunctional family full of mutual mistrust and rancour. The play suggests that the problems in both the family and the kingdom proceed from Lear's enormous egotism and his sexual drive—a sharp blow to prevailing interpretations of King Lear as a man who, in the words of the monarch himself, is "more sinn'd against than sinning" (3.2.57-58).

The London-based Women's Theatre Group's 1987 *Lear's Daughters* and Jane Smiley's 1991 novel *A Thousand Acres* follow this thread, even more explicitly exposing and interrogating King Lear's sexual pathologies and his oppressive exercise of masculine power as the root cause of the tragedy that follows. In the case of *A Thousand Acres*, Smiley very self-consciously exploits the technical features of prose fiction to shift the point of view from the *showing* mode of drama to the *telling* mode of narrated fiction in an effort to exonerate the narrator Ginny (Goneril), if not all three daughters, and to re-focus her readers' sense of reality and their sympathies with respect to her underlying hypotext.[67] The contemporary playwright Young Jean Lee's *LEAR* (2010) completely excludes the character of King Lear from this stage adaptation, in a very deliberate provocation that re-focuses the story on his daughters.[68] Despite the prominence of female power in the daughters, the play is in constant dialogue with its hypotext as it revisits but sharply re-imagines some of the tensest emotional moments of interaction between the aged king and his daughters.

Another strand of creative re-vision, more focused upon the political undercurrents of Shakespeare's *King Lear* than on gender-as-power questions emerged in the last half of the twentieth century. Most conspicuously, Edward Bond's *Lear* (1971) re-imagines King Lear as a pitiless totalitarian dictator and his kingdom a brutal police state. The play is a dark, unrelenting mash-up of *King Lear* and post-Hitler, post-Stalin Europe. Adrian Mitchell's 1985 one-act *The Tragedy of King Real* was published just in the wake of initiatives of the grassroots Campaign for Nuclear Disarmament to block the placement of American cruise missiles on British soil. It presents a capricious King Lear figure (King Real), who has control over a nuclear arsenal but ultimately is persuaded by his daughter Cloudella (Cordelia) to relinquish the keys to it and save the planet.[69] Despite the ominous topic of nuclear warfare, Mitchell's tone in the play is a good deal lighter than Bond's and his appropriation of the King Lear story a good deal looser. Indeed, he uses Shakespeare's story principally as ready-made framework, much like a pantomime troupe typically selects a well-known fairy tale on which to hang its annual show to save audiences the trouble of having to understand a new plot along with a new message.

Whether deeply engaged or not, serious or light-hearted, re-visions such as these—and there are many, many other responses to *King Lear*, just as there are many others to other Shakespeare plays—remind us that stories have a way of living on, adapting, and becoming something new and vital with each new iteration. Just as organisms benefit from an evolutionary process of adaptation, the culturally and artistically familiar provides the genetic basis, as it were, for new offspring that will inhabit new worlds filled with new issues, whether those are the rise of totalitarianism or the threat of nuclear annihilation. As the often-quoted observation of genre critic Northrop Frye runs, "poetry can only be made out of other poems; novels out of other novels."[70] New art emerges with each new generation and sometimes it seems to offer something never seen before. But perhaps there really is nothing new under the sun.

So . . . Was Shakespeare a Plagiarist?

Was Shakespeare a plagiarist? The simple answer is *no*, not in any way that he or his contemporaries could have understood. The other equally simple answer is *yes*: he certainly took freely and liberally from the writings of others, and did so without crediting them. The first would be his culture's answer; the second would be our culture's. But I would like to propose a third way that neither charges Shakespeare with a creative crime that was not yet defined as a crime nor gives him credit for originality that was not his. This is why modern readers and critics need to understand principles, terminology, and expectations in both Shakespeare's time and our own: the categories with which we now approach questions of literary originality and literary theft simply will not fit the case of Shakespeare, just as the prevailing definition of originality in his day makes little sense to us now.

What lies between these two essentially irreconcilable paradigms is over four hundred years of changing ideas concerning all the major topics discussed in this introduction: the fundamental principle of mimesis in our engagement with stories and in the ways they are written; the way that the "memes" of human culture transmit themselves by an evolutionary process; the mix of familiar and new that might explain our appreciation for twice- or thrice-told tales; the value a society places on imitation versus originality as a marker of artistic accomplishment; the relatively new Romantic conception of the author as an autonomous and original agent versus the traditional idea of author as a participant in an organic and ongoing social process of human storytelling; and the legal and ethical strictures that protect authors and those who invest in their creations. All these elements are conditioned and affected by larger social and institutional forces that have differently defined what originality is—what it means to write one's "own" or "original" work.

Even now, largely because words, images, music, and other information travel from one digital repository to another so freely via the Internet, plagiarism is very much a matter for new ethical and legal debates on college campuses and beyond. A lively new academic interest in "plagiarism studies" has grown up around the world, with professional conferences and articles, testimonials, letters to editors, case studies, blog discussions, calls for updating our definitions, and proposals for change appearing in leading periodical publications. Most students are familiar with the now ubiquitous plagiarism-detection software that schools and colleges have made an integral part of their grading systems, but they may not know that some contemporary thinkers working on the topic of plagiarism now argue that we need to re-think our assumptions about the rules that regulate (and often punish) plagiarism in schools and universities: its history, its ethics, its relationship to authorship, and even its very definition. New questions focused on its control in schools and on campuses have followed, as have new debates about its definition in spheres such as public life, where political speeches routinely borrow heavily from previous ones and in many cases are ghost-written, and the sciences, where not only reputations but in some cases quite a lot of money can be won or lost on the strength of claims to originality. Online plagiarism of creative writing, too, is a constant drain on the time and mental energy of authors who find their work stolen and republished elsewhere on the web.[71]

These radically changing ideas about originality and creativity put Shakespeare into a long line of author-borrowers that begins before Martial (c. 38 - c. 103 CE) and includes many luminaries of our literary and cultural heritage: Geoffrey Chaucer, Ben Jonson, Alexander Pope, Laurence Sterne, Benjamin Franklin, Samuel Taylor Coleridge, Oscar Wilde, Ernest Hemingway, Martin Luther King, Jr., Martin Amis, Graham Swift, and many others whose originality has been questioned in one way or another. Taking cues from theoretical discussions of authorship such as Roland Barthes' 1968 landmark essay "The Death of the Author," and Michel Foucault's 1979 response "What Is an Author?" modern theorists and thinkers often argue that authorship and intellectual property are comparatively recent, socially constructed categories, and that schools, universities, and other institutions cling to policies that fundamentally misunderstand both the historical development of authorship and the nature of the composition process. Some call for a complete revision of the way institutions of learning look at the process of writing and the legal and ethical issues that surround it.[72]

This new thinking will certainly influence future understanding of authorship and creativity within the field of Shakespeare studies. For now, a well-known maxim of T. S. Eliot may serve as a closing idea: "Immature poets imitate; mature poets steal." What is essential when reading or seeing Shakespeare is that we recognise how integral his ingrained habit of stealing others' literature was to his process of creating literature—and how in his day doing so was a sign of literary maturity. But Eliot also wrote that "No poet, no artist of any kind, has his complete meaning alone. His significance, his appreciation is the appreciation of his relation to the dead poets and artists. You cannot value him alone; you must set him, for contrast and comparison, among the dead."[73] Perhaps we should be thankful that Shakespeare also drew upon the energies and ideas of living and recent authors, happy to stand on the shoulders of not just giants.

Borrowing is the life-blood of creativity, and in the end Shakespeare offers us one of the best examples of this principle: creative he certainly was, but we best appreciate how and why when we understand what creativity meant in his own age, as well as how and why our ideas around creativity and plagiarism have evolved. Only then do we know the whole story of what it means to be English literature's most revered author. Or plagiarist.

Notes

[1] All citations from Shakespeare are from *The Norton Shakespeare*, ed. Stephen Greenblatt et al. 3rd ed. (New York: Norton, 2015).

[2] David Scott Kastan, *Shakespeare and the Book* (Cambridge: Cambridge University Press, 2001), 11, and see also 111.

[3] George Bernard Shaw, "Blaming the Bard' *Saturday Review* 26 September, 1896. Reprinted https://archive.org/stream/BlamingTheBard/shaw_george_bernard_blaming_the_b ard_djvu.txt. (paragraph 3).

[4] Linda Hutcheon with Siobhan O'Flynn, *A Theory of Adaptation,* 2nd ed. (New York: Routledge, 2013), 2, citing Walter Benjamin, "The Task of the Translator" in *Theories of Translation*, ed. Rainer Schulte and John Biguenet (Chicago: University of Chicago Press, 1992), 90.

[5] *Oxford English Dictionary* 2nd ed. (Oxford: Oxford University Press, 1989), "Plagium," def. 1. (hereafter cited as *OED*). I have modernised the spelling and punctuation of this and subsequent citations from the *OED*.

[6] On linguistic changes during this period, see Seth Lerer, "A Universal Hubbub Wild: New Words and Worlds in Early Modern English," chapter 10 (141-152) in his *Inventing English: A Portable History of the Language* (New York: Columbia University Press, 2007); and Melvyn Bragg, *The Adventure of English: The Biography of a Language*, esp. chapter 12 "Shakespeare's English" (132-143).

[7] *OED*, "Plagiary," def. 1. *The Collected Poems of Joseph Hall, Bishop of Exeter and Norwich*, ed. A. Davenport (Liverpool: At the University Press, 1949), 57. See also Scott McGill, *Plagiarism in Latin Poetry* (Cambridge: Cambridge University Press, 2013).

[8] Horace, *Art of Poetry*, lines 131-35. The text is widely available in many editions and online sites, for example https://www.poetryintranslation.com/PITBR/Latin/HoraceArsPoetica.php.

[9] Ben Jonson, *The Poetaster*, 4.3.95-96 and 5.3.218-20 in *Ben Jonson*, ed. C. H. Herford and Percy Simpson (Oxford: Clarendon Press, 1932), 268, 304.

[10] John Dryden, "An Essay of Dramatick Poesie." *The Works of John Dryden*, ed. Samuel Holt Monk et al. (Berkeley and Los Angeles: University of California Press, 1971), 17:21. Dryden also commented that Jonson was "deeply conversant in the Ancients, both Greek and Latine, and he borrowed boldly from them: there is scarce a Poet or Historian of those times whom he has not translated in *Sejanus* and *Catiline* [two plays by Jonson]. But he has done his Robberies so openly, that one may see he fears not to be taxed by any Law. He invades Authours like a Monarch, and what would be theft in other Poets, is onely victory in him" (57).

[11] *OED*, s. v. "Plagiary," def. 1. *The Works of the Right Reverend Joseph Hall*, ed. Philip Wynter. New Edition (Oxford: At the University Press, 1868) 8:545.

[12] *OED*, s. v. "Plagiary," def. 1. I quote from the sixth edition of Sir Thomas Browne, *Pseudodoxia Epidemica* (London, 1672), 22. This edition is the final one overseen by Browne himself.

[13] In actual practice, printed copies often varied within a press run since proofreading and correction were typically done while the press was printing. Different "states" of a single edition resulted when these "stop-press" corrections were carried out, often several times during an entire press run, thus producing multiple variations within a single edition.

[14] Browne, *Pseudodoxia Epidemica*, 22.

[15] *OED*, s.v. "Plagiarism," def. 1.

[16] Gerald Langbaine, *Momus Triumphans: or, The plagiaries of the English stage: expos'd in a catalogue of all the comedies, tragi-comedies, masques, tragedies, opera's, pastorals, interludes, &c., both ancient and modern, that were ever yet printed in English* (London, 1688). Cited in *OED*, s.v. "Plagiary," def. 3.b.

[17] The best survey is Mark Rose, *Authors and Owners: The Invention of Copyright* (Cambridge, MA: Harvard University Press, 1993), especially his preface and chapters 1-3. See also Lyman Ray Patterson, *Copyright in Historical Perspective* (Nashville: Vanderbilt University Press, 1968) and Benjamin Kaplan, *An Unhurried View of Copyright* (New York: Columbia University Press, 1967), both formative studies for Rose. For Hobbes, see his *Leviathan* (Harmondsworth: Penguin, 1974), 217.

[18] Barbara K. Lewalski, *The Life of John Milton* (Oxford: Blackwell, 2000), 453.

[19] Rose, *Authors and Owners*, 14-15. See also Sean Burke, *The Death and Return of the Author: Criticism and Subjectivity in Barthes, Foucault and Derrida*, 2nd ed. (Edinburgh: Edinburgh University Press, 1998).

[20] John Kerrigan, *Shakespeare's Originality* (Oxford: Oxford University Press, 2018), 1-2; see also 3-18 passim.

[21] Robert Greene, *A Groats-vvorth of witte, bought with a million of repentance.* (London, 1592.), ed. G. B. Harrison (New York: Barnes and Noble, 1966), 45. I have left the quotation (from Shakespeare's *Henry VI, part* 3) in its original spelling; the rest of the passage has been modernised.

[22] Peter W. M. Blayney, *The Stationer's Company and the Printers of London 1501-1557* (Cambridge: Cambridge University Press, 2013). Even modern courts, to say nothing of the court of popular opinion, often struggle with the subtleties of intellectual property cases. For example, a famous controversy surrounded no less a figure than Martin Luther King, Jr. In the late 1980s scholars working on his papers

discovered that significant sections of his graduate work at Boston University, including his dissertation, were taken without proper acknowledgement from other sources, including the work of other students. *New York Times*, "Boston U Panel Finds Plagiarism by Dr. King" October 11, 1991.

[23] For an amusing and informative historical survey of the "shoulders of giants" trope, see http://www.aerospaceweb.org/question/history/q0162b.shtml.

[24] Alistair Minnis, *Medieval Theory of Authorship: Scholastic Literary Attitudes in the Later Middle Ages*, 2nd ed. (Philadelphia: University of Pennsylvania Press, 1988), 94-101; Ernst Robert Curtius, *European Literature and the Latin Middle Ages* (New York: Harper & Row, 1963), 310, 314-15, citing scriptural passages and Alcuin of York.

[25] C. S. Lewis, Introduction. *Selections from Layamon's* Brut, ed. G. L. Brook. (Oxford: Clarendon Press, 1963), vii. See also Richard Posner, *Law and Literature* (Cambridge, MA: Harvard University Press, 1998), 529-30, and see Giles Constable, "Forgery and Plagiarism in the Middle Ages" *Archiv für Diplomatik, Schriftgeschite, Siegel- und Wappenkunde* 29 (1983): 1-41, especially page 39, and Stephen Orgel, "The Renaissance Artist as Plagiarist" *ELH* 48, no. 3 (Fall 1981): 476-95.

[26] Colin Burrow, "Shakespeare and Humanistic Culture" in *Shakespeare and the Classics*, ed. Charles Martindale and A. B. Taylor (Cambridge: Cambridge University Press, 2004), 9ff. The *locus classicus* concerning Shakespeare's studies and the Elizabethan school curriculum, T. W. Baldwin, *William Shakespere's Small Latine & Lesse Greeke* 2 vols. (Champaign-Urbana, IL: University of Illinois Press, 1944), contains a wealth of information. It is also available online, with a useful search function: http://durer.press.illinois.edu/baldwin/index.html.

[27] Naseem Shaheen, "Shakespeare's Knowledge of Italian" *Shakespeare Survey* 47 (1994): 161-69.

[28] Gérard Genette, *Palimpsests: Literature in the Second Degree*, trans. Channa Newman and Claude Doubinsky (Lincoln, NE: University of Nebraska Press, 1997), 309.

[29] E. M. Forster, *Aspects of the Novel* (New York: Harcourt Brace Jovanovich, 1927), 86.

[30] See Geoffrey Bullough's eight-volume *Narrative and Dramatic Sources of Shakespeare* (1957-75) for a broader picture of sources and analogues that went into, or might have gone into, any single work (see also the "Further Reading" section).

[31] Harold Bloom, *Shakespeare: The Invention of the Human* (New York: Riverhead, 1998).

[32] An excellent example is Karen Newman's review essay "Charactery," reprinted in her *Essaying Shakespeare* (Minneapolis, MN: University of Minnesota Press, 2009), 111-22.

[33] Bullough, *Narrative and Dramatic Sources*, 7:448.

[34] Bullough, *Narrative and Dramatic Sources,* 7:447-48.

[35] Graham Bradshaw, *Misrepresentations: Shakespeare and the Materialists* (Ithaca: Cornell University Press, 1993), 132, cited in Posner, *Law and Literature*, 28. Andy Mousley, *Re-humanising Shakespeare: Literary Humanism, Wisdom and Modernity* (Edinburgh: Edinburgh University Press, 2007), 40.

[36] Richard Dawkins, *The Selfish Gene*. 30th Anniversary Edition. (Oxford: Oxford University Press, 2006), chapter 11. See Hutcheon and O'Flynn, *A Theory of Adaptation*, 31-32.

[37] Dawkins, *Selfish Gene*, 192.

[38] On Internet-based memes, see http://en.wikipedia.org/wiki/Internet_meme. Archives of popular memes include sites such as http://knowyourmeme.com and dork.com.

[39] Kerrigan, *Shakespeare's Originality*, 1-18.

[40] Dawkins estimates that with each new generation about one half of our individual genetic contribution is lost: within three generations our genetic particularity has disappeared into the general gene pool. Not so with memes: "if you contribute to the world's culture, if you have a good idea, compose a tune, invent a sparking plug, write a poem, it may live on, intact, long after your genes have dissolved into the common pool" (*Selfish Gene*, 199).

[41] Abigail De Kosnik, "Should Fan Fiction Be Free?" *Cinema Journal* 48, no.4 (Summer 2009): 120.

[42] See examples at www.fanfiction.net.

[43] This distinction is discussed at some length in Hutcheon and O'Flynn, *A Theory of Adaptation*, especially chapter 2.

[44] Dawkins, *Selfish Gene*, 199.

[45] Robert A. Logan makes a compelling case for the pervasiveness of Marlowe's spirit in the works of Shakespeare, despite (in the case of *The Merchant of Venice*) rather limited direct verbal borrowings: *Shakespeare's Marlowe: The Influence of Christopher Marlowe on Shakespeare's Artistry* (Aldershot, Hamps.: Ashgate, 2007), chapter 5. See also Laurie McGuire and Emma Smith, "What is a Source? Or, How Shakespeare Read His Marlowe" *Shakespeare Survey* 68 (2015): 15-31 and Gary Taylor and John V. Nance, "Imitation or Collaboration? Marlowe and the Early Shakespeare Canon" *Shakespeare Survey* 68 (2015): 32-47.

[46] Hutcheon and O'Flynn, *A Theory of Adaptation*, especially preface, 4, 8, 116. See also Genette, *Palimpsests*, 5-6.

[47] I quote from the S. H. Butcher translation of Aristotle, *Poetics*, available online at http://classics.mit.edu/Aristotle/poetics.mb.txt.

[48] Both authors are discussed at length in Richard Helgerson, *Self-Crowned Laureates: Spenser, Jonson, Milton, and the Literary System* (Berkeley: University of California Press, 1983).

[49] Rebecca Moore Howard, "Plagiarisms, Authorships, and the Academic Death Penalty" *College English* 57, no.7 (November 1995): 789.

[50] Genette's term *grafting* neatly expresses this sense of collaborative creation (*Palimpsests*, ix).

[51] Because essential records are lost, we have no direct evidence that Shakespeare attended grammar school, but all circumstantial evidence of time, place, social class, and local custom points toward the conclusion that he did. See Samuel Schoenbaum, *William Shakespeare: A Compact Documentary Life*, rev. ed. (New York: Oxford University Press, 1987), 62-72. Schoenbaum also usefully summarises the content and pace of the Elizabethan curriculum.

[52] As described in Book II of *The Scholemaster* (London, 1570): *Roger Ascham: English Works*, ed. William Aldis Wright (Cambridge: Cambridge University Press, 1970), 238-302.

[53] Burrow, "Shakespeare and Humanistic Culture," 14-17. See also Baldwin, *Small Latine and Lesse Greeke*, chapters 33-37.

[54] One such example comes from Samuel Johnson's *Preface to Shakespeare* (1755): "Shakespeare is above all writers, at least above all modern writers, the poet of nature; the poet that holds up to his readers a faithful mirror of manners and of life. His characters are not modified by the customs of particular places, unpractised by the rest of the world: by the peculiarities of studies or professions, which can operate but upon small numbers; or by the accidents of transient fashions or temporary opinions: they are the genuine progeny of common humanity, such as the world will always supply, and observation will always find. His persons act and speak by the influence of those general passions and principles by which all minds are agitated, and the whole system of life is continued in motion. In the writings of other poets a character is too often an individual; in those of Shakespeare it is commonly a species." (http://www.gutenberg.org/cache/epub/5429/pg5429-images.html).

[55] Dom Cerulli, Liner Notes to Oscar Peterson Trio, *West Side Story*. M. G. M. Records, 1962. PolyGram Records, 1984. Verve Records 821 575-2, page 1.

[56] Cerulli, Liner Notes, 1.

[57] For an amusing survey of TV and film parodies see the 15 November 2011 article on www.slate.com (http://www.slate.com/blogs/browbeat/2011/11/15/west_side_story_50th_annivers ary_50_years_of_spoofs.html). See also Keith Garebian, *The Making of "West Side Story"* (Toronto: ECW Press, 1994. Reprint Mosaic Press, 2010) and the Official *West Side Story* Website (http://www.westsidestory.com/).

[58] *Proximation* originates with Gérard Genette; it refers to the process of updating and making older literature more culturally current; see *Palimpsests*, 304. *Indigenization* is the coinage of anthropologist Susan Stanford Friedman, describing the inevitable accommodations of meaning and emphasis that occur when a work of art travels across time and culture. See Hutcheon and O'Flynn, *A Theory of Adaptation*, 28, 150.

[59] On the history of American musical theatre, see John Bush Jones, *Our Musicals, Ourselves: A Social History of the American Musical Theatre* (Hanover, N.H: Brandeis University Press/University Press of New England, 2003), 1-51. On the origins of Jazz, see *The New Grove Dictionary of Jazz*, ed. Barry Dean Kernfeld (New York: Grove, 2002), 2:361-69.

[60] On the story's pre-Shakespearean history as prose narrative, poem, and play, see Bullough, *Narrative and Dramatic Sources*, 1:269-76.

[61] See the Revels Student Edition of *The Tamer Tamed; Or, The Woman's Prize*, ed. Celia R. Daileader and Gary Taylor (Manchester: Manchester University Press, 2006). The play was very popular in the seventeenth century and was played at least three times in the eighteenth, but then fell out of favour. After a long hiatus, the play was revived several times in the late twentieth century, most notably in the Royal

Shakespeare Company's 2003 production, which played in repertory with *The Taming of the Shrew*, using the same cast (Daileader and Taylor, 25-31).

[62] *The Taming of the Shrew* has a close relationship to a play called *The Taming of A Shrew*, published in 1594. A great deal of scholarly energy has been spent trying to establish the relationship between the two plays, with very little consensus about even basic questions such as who authored *A Shrew* and which play preceded the other.

[63] Kastan, *Shakespeare and the Book*, 30-41, 57.

[64] On the Ireland forgeries, see Jeffrey Kahan, *Reforging Shakespeare: The Story of a Theatrical Scandal* (Bethlehem, PA: Lehigh University Press, 1998), Patricia Pierce, *The Great Shakespeare Fraud: The Strange, True Story of William-Henry Ireland* (Phoenix Mill, Glous., 2004), and Doug Stewart. *The Boy Who Would Be Shakespeare: A Tale of Forgery and Folly* (Cambridge, MA: Da Capo Press, 2010).

[65] A number of seminal studies of Shakespeare's cultural authority are contained within the essay collection *The Shakespeare Myth*, ed. Graham Holderness (Manchester: Manchester University Press, 1988).

[66] Adrienne Rich, "When We Dead Re-Awaken: Writing as Re-Vision" *College English* 34, no.1 (October 1972): 18-19.

[67] A number of studies of Jane Smiley's *A Thousand Acres* (New York: Fawcett, 1991) have appeared, including a keynote lecture by Smiley herself: "Shakespeare in Iceland" in *Transforming Shakespeare: Contemporary Women's Re-Visions in Literature and Performance*, ed. Marianne Novy (New York: St. Martin's Press, 1999), 159-79.

[68] Young Jean Lee, *The Shipment and LEAR* (New York: Theatre Communications Group, 2010), 82-83.

[69] Edward Bond, *Lear* (London: Eyre Methuen, 1972), and Adrian Mitchell, "The Tragedy of King Real" in his *Peace Plays* (London and New York: Methuen, 1985), 1-41.

[70] Northrop Frye, *The Anatomy of Criticism*, (Princeton: Princeton University Press, 1957), 97. He is cited in Hutcheon and O'Flynn, *A Theory of Adaptation*, 2 and quoted in Posner, *Law and Literature*, 533.

[71] See, for example, the watchdog and advocacy website www.plagiarismtoday.com.

[72] Barthes' and Foucault's essays are widely available in different print and online translations. Some representative examples of "apologist" arguments for new definitions of creativity and plagiarism include Rebecca Moore Howard, *Standing in the Shadow of Giants: Plagiarists, Authors, Collaborators* (Stamford, CT: Ablex, 1999); Margaret Price, "Beyond 'Gotcha'": Situating Plagiarism in Policy and Pedagogy." *College Composition and Communication* 54, no. 1 (September 2002): 88-115; and Sean Zwagerman, "The Scarlet P: Plagiarism, Panopticism, and the Rhetoric of Academic Integrity" *College Composition and Communication* 59, no. 4 (June 2008): 676-710.

[73] The quotations come, respectively, from Eliot's essays "Philip Massinger" and "Tradition and the Individual Talent" published in *The Sacred Wood and Other Essays* (1920). This important collection is reprinted in a budget edition: T. S. Eliot, *The Sacred Wood and Major Early Essays* (Mineola, NY: Dover, 1998), 72, 28.

MATTEO BANDELLO, "TIMBREO AND FENICIA" FROM HIS *NOVELLE* (1554)

MUCH ADO ABOUT NOTHING

Fig. 2-1. The title page of the 1554 edition of Bandello's *Novelle*

For the major plot structure of *Much Ado About Nothing* Shakespeare drew upon the story of Sir Timbreo and the lady Fenicia, by the Italian author Matteo Bandello (c. 1485-1561). The tale was included in his 1554 *La Prima Parte de le Novelle* (*The First Part of the Tales*), published in Lucca by Vincenzo Busdrago. Bandello's story shares similarities with an earlier version written by the Italian epic poet Ludovico Ariosto in his *Orlando Furioso*, first published in 1516 and translated into English verse by Sir Harington in 1591. It is likely that Shakespeare also read the Ariosto story since a few plot details in *Much Ado About Nothing* seem to be derived from that version of the tale rather than Bandello's.

The Ariosto-Bandello story provided the basic structure of the Claudio-Hero plot, but as we shall see, Shakespeare embellished this story in significant ways by adding a second plot strand and changing several emphases of his original. In many ways, his use of Bandello's story is typical of the way Shakespeare engaged with his reading: whether using a text from a revered classical author such as Ovid or a popular contemporary storyteller such as Bandello, he often retained elements of what he read and sometimes years later would recycle them in plays not directly based on these sources.

Bandello was a popular author in the sixteenth century, widely read and widely translated. Geoffrey Bullough identified the Claudio-Hero plot as "one of the most admired stories of the sixteenth century" and noted that its basic outline is much older even than Ariosto, with Spanish and Greek versions prior to his own. Bandello's stories tapped into a growing appetite for vernacular literature at a time when literacy was spreading quickly throughout Europe and the cost of books was dropping precipitously as paper—the most expensive element of book publishing at the time— became cheaper. The sixteenth-century publishing trade as a whole became more efficient at producing popular reading material for a populace increasingly interested in buying it. And these buyers often wanted stories that spoke to some aspect of their own lives, as well as classic stories of heroes, knights, kings, emperors, and other larger-than-life figures from ancient history or the annals of mythology.

Although Shakespeare's re-make of Bandello's tale of the Sir Timbreo and Fenicia story is in many ways characteristic of how he remembered and re-purposed a story, it is also among the most complicated and interesting examples of how he encountered, remembered, and used a published source. He returned to elements of the basic plot of this story over and over across his career, transforming the original narrative into several variations on a theme. On the one hand, it is interesting to note that he relied upon Bandello's story only partially in *Much Ado About Nothing*, filling out some details of the Claudio-Hero story by using a section of Ariosto's *Orlando Furioso*. On the other hand, he was clearly fascinated with the archetype of a sleeping beauty figure who awakes—or in some cases, only seems to awake—from a death-like slumber. This element of Bandello's story served Shakespeare throughout his career as a playwright, most notably in his portrayals of Juliet in *Romeo and Juliet* in the mid-1590s, as well as Imogen in *Cymbeline* and Hermione in *The Winter's Tale*, just before his retirement from theatrical life in London. Traces of the motif can also be observed in Desdemona in *Othello* and Cordelia in *King Lear*, two "sleeping beauties" who, tragically, never revive.

But Shakespeare also greatly expanded the scope of the story, adding the Beatrice and Benedict strand of the plot, it appears, principally from his own imagination. Although scholars have diligently sought to find a clear, direct source or sources for this element of the story, and although literary history provides many analogues to the "merry war" of words Beatrice and Benedict wage with each other throughout the play, no consensus has ever formed around what story or stories Shakespeare might have drawn upon in creating one of his great romantic comedies. And it is a very important element of the play, for Beatrice and Benedict form a lively contrasting couple to Hero and Claudio, mirroring their relationship as a pair of would-be lovers, while at the same time offering revealing differences. Claudio is a willing, but inexperienced lover, while Benedict is resistant and cynical; their differences accentuate and sharpen the broad questions about love, loyalty, and imagination with which the play deals. Likewise, Hero is demure and submissive—attributes conventionally expected of women of her time. But she is also something of a cipher as a personality, while Beatrice leads with her sharp tongue and her sharp wit. Her aggressive language and especially her craving for revenge in Act 4 suggest that she is comfortable in a world associated with men and masculine power, a sphere quite apart from Hero's experience. Shakespeare diminished the role of Lady Fenicia as he changed her into Hero. Was he perhaps doing so to make space for the larger-than-life energy of his own comic creation, Beatrice?

These two plot strands, one derived from Bandello and one probably invented by Shakespeare, are in the experience of many readers and theatre-goers over the years a strange and perhaps even uncomfortable fusion: the main narrative strand centres on Claudio's sudden and brief wooing and then brutal rejection of Hero, her presumed death, and her eventual "resurrection" and reunion with him. Structurally, that story line more or less initiates the action of the play and provides the basis of the story's all-important happy ending (though it is a valid question to ask how happy this surprise conclusion really is).

But as audiences and critics have noticed for centuries, despite their centrality in the main plot, Hero and Claudio generally do not excite the kind of interest that the structurally parallel but infinitely more interesting pair of lovers Beatrice and Benedict do. In nearly every production their witty verbal exchanges and all-too human capitulation to love assure that they always seem to steal the show. Despite their structurally peripheral positions in the story, they fill in the affective gaps of the rather dry and ethically ambiguous Claudio-Hero story. They usually become the centre of the play, emotionally and experientially, for readers and playgoers. Looking into Shakespeare's strategies of adaptation can tell us a lot about why this effect seems to be almost universal among readers and audiences.

The trouble with settling on Bandello's text as a clear source for the Claudio-Hero plot is that no English version of the story was available in Shakespeare's time and we do not know with certainty that Shakespeare could read Italian. Internal evidence suggests that he did not use a 1569 French translation by François de Belleforest (who was possibly his source for *Hamlet*) or extracts of the story published in an earlier French edition by Pierre Boaistuau (1559) that would also have been available to him. So how did he know the story of Sir Timbreo and Fenicia? One theory credits Shakespeare with the ability to read Italian. Based on Shakespeare's intense interest in Italian stories and Italian settings in his own plays, this seems a reasonable, if unprovable, hypothesis. A second theory suggests that he might have seen an English translation of this famous story in manuscript—another reasonable hypothesis, but even less likely to be provable, unless one day such a manuscript emerges.

As you read Bandello's story in light of *Much Ado About Nothing*, you will notice something extraordinary: the Claudio character, Sir Timbreo, feels great pangs of conscience and doubt as he reflects upon Fenicia's supposed death. He hesitates and ponders, and he berates himself in a variety of ways before and after the shaming of Fenicia, but he does not follow the rash course that his second self, Claudio, does in Shakespeare's version of the story. Nor does he deliberately create a scene equivalent to the disastrous marriage ceremony of Act 4, scene 1, in which Claudio cruelly and aggressively exposes and repudiates Hero on her own wedding day. And instead of Fenicia's family writing her epitaph, as in Bandello, Shakespeare transfers the act of writing it to Claudio, the man who publicly shamed her. In making all these changes, Shakespeare creates a character whose psychology and motives are largely hidden from us—a reversal of the playwright's more typical movement from the psychological vagueness usually seen in his source stories to the attention to his characters' interiority we find in the plays.

Some other notable differences between Bandello's story and Shakespeare's play deserve mention. Don John, the play's villainous instigator, his henchmen Borachio and Conrad, and the bumbling officers of the watch who eventually expose him, are not in Bandello's story. Why did Shakespeare add them, and what did he expect to gain by making these changes to his source? Structurally, they are essential to the plot of *Much Ado About Nothing*, especially to its comic resolution.

In addition, Bandello's story dwells at some length upon the class differences that impede the course of true love between Sir Timbreo and Fenicia, as well as a rivalry between Sir Timbreo and his friend Sir Girondo for Fenicia's love. Both of these details are omitted from *Much Ado About Nothing*. The lovers are social equals in Shakespeare's version, or at least social class distinctions do not seem to be very important to the conflict. Somewhat counter-intuitively, the play is a *more* psychologically provocative story that explores how friendship, desire, suspicion, and persuasion operate in human life because one of its leading male characters, Claudio, is less demonstrative and expressive than Sir Timbreo, his conscience-struck original. In addition, since some of the usual conventions of comedy, such as overcoming social class differences, are omitted we focus upon the psychology of failed love, not the social barriers that thwart it. For as many have noted, *Much Ado* is an unusual comedy in that the impediments to the lovers' unions are they themselves and not the usual "blocking" forces such as parents, factions, or social norms. The play is unusual in making the obstacles to a happy resolution psychological and internal rather than social and external.

Shakespeare's decision to tone down the effects of Claudio's interior consciousness is a significant transformation to the prior story, whose central theme of guilt leading to epiphany (and then on to reunion and marriage) provided the central theme of a sentimental tale that captivated sixteenth-century readers across all Europe. By denying the affective centre of the prior story, Shakespeare seems to have created room for another story line, which he filled with the lively new characters Beatrice and Benedict— thereby introducing a classic comedy of the sexes into a story that did not originally contain this crowd-pleasing comic feature. In fact, so popular were Beatrice and Benedict as the stars of this show that King Charles I of England wrote their names next to the title of the play in his copy of the Second Folio; for many years after the play was known to audiences by the shorthand of just their two names, and to some degree still is. Music lovers may recall that in 1862 Hector Berlioz transformed the play into a still-performed comic opera with the revealing title *Béatrice et Bénédict*.

But we do not even know where Shakespeare got the Beatrice and
Benedict story line; no obvious or direct source has ever emerged. This
transformation to his source material rivals what he did with the story of
Prince Hal—largely inventing Falstaff, one of his greatest comic characters,
and placing him within a well-known story drawn from historical sources—
or with *King Lear*, where he added the entire Gloucester subplot, taken from
completely other sources than the ones he used for the already well-known
King Leir plot, to create perhaps his greatest tragedy and his most
sophisticated double-plot storyline.

Shakespeare's changes to Bandello's story allow us to make three
important observations about his habits of borrowing. First, he had a
remarkable appetite and appreciation for what we might now call middle-
brow literature: Bandello's story is light, sentimental, and many readers
today feel it lacks comic edge because it is too invested in a mixture of piety
and titillation that we now find odd, but which quite evidently pleased
sixteenth-century readers. But Shakespeare saw something in this
sentimental old tale that inspired him to turn it into a much more robust and
varied story. And he did this over and over again, in *Julius Caesar*, *Richard
II*, *As You Like It*, *The Winter's Tale*, *Othello*, and many other plays—taking
often dry middle-of-the road historical accounts, prose stories, plays, and
poems that showed people as they should be and not as they really are, and
inserting them into situations that put the psychological complexities of
human consciousness and social interactions front and centre.

Second, we must remember that Shakespeare's storytelling talent was
always a recombinant one; he thrived on picking out elements from his
sources that he then fit into some new design. *Much Ado About Nothing* has
been a favourite among readers and playgoers for four hundred years—and
it has provided choice roles for actors lucky enough to be cast as Beatrice
and Benedict—in part because he did *not* simply retell Bandello's story, but
augmented and amplified it with an additional story line that appears to be
of his own invention, as well as many changes to the tone and texture of his
source.

Third, Shakespeare's interest was always in the psychological features
of a story: whatever his sources offered in terms of the workings of the
human mind and the human soul, he typically discovered more, or invented
more. His fundamental interest was in portraying human individuals and the
societies they create for themselves. More often than not, he achieved these
changes by adding psychological dimensionality and expanding our access
to the inner workings of characters' minds. But in *Much Ado*, he does so
by—remarkably—*denying* us access to Claudio, the Sir Timbreo character,
and leaving us to ponder what might make him turn so suddenly and

viciously on his once beloved Hero. In the end, the play is a comic triumph as one set of believable lovers at last find their soul-mates, while the lovers of the original seem destined to a marriage that promises much ado.

A Note on the Text

The story of Sir Timbreo and Fenicia appears in the translation of John Payne, which was included in his *The Novels of Matteo Bandello, Bishop of Agen* (London: Villon Society, 1890). Payne's translation offers readers a spirited example of the literary tastes of the late nineteenth century and its fascination with medieval culture. In a few places I silently amended some of the translator's punctuation, removed or amended his footnotes, and added many new notes. Frequently repeated archaic words are footnoted on their first occurrence and thereafter noted with °, which refers readers to the glossary at the end of this volume.

Matteo Bandello, the Twentieth Story from
La Prima Parte de le Novelle (1554)

SIGNOR SCIPIONE ATTELLANO TELLTH HOW SIGNOR
TIMBREO DI CARDONA, BEING WITH KING PEDRO OF
ARRAGON IN MESSINA, BECAME ENAMOURED OF FENICIA
LIONATA AND OF THE VARIOUS AND UNLOOKED-FOR
CHANCES WHICH BEFELL, BEFORE HE TOOK HER TO WIFE.

In the course of the year one thousand two hundred fourscore and three of
our salvation, the Sicilians, them-seeming[1] they might no longer brook the
domination of the French, one day at the hour of vespers, with unheard of
cruelty massacred all who were in the island, for so was it treacherously
concerted[2] throughout all Sicily; nor did they slay men and women only of
French extraction, but every Sicilian woman, who might be conceived to be
with child by any Frenchman, they butchered that same day; nay, thereafterward, if any were proved to have been gotten with child by a
Frenchman, she was put to death without mercy; whence arose the infamous
renown of the Sicilian Vespers.[3] King Pedro of Aragon, having advice of
this, came straightway thither with his power and seized the sovereignty of
the island, for that Pope Nicholas the Third urged him thereto, telling him
that the island belonged unto him, as husband of Constanza, daughter of
King Manfred. The said King Pedro held his court many days in Palermo
on right royal and magnificent wise[4] and made high festival for the
acquisition of the island. Presently, hearing that King Charles the Second,
son of King Charles the First, who held the kingdom of Naples, came by sea
with a great armament to expel him from Sicily, he went out against him
with such ships and galleys as he had and joined the battle with him,
whereupon sore was the melee and cruel the slaughter. In the end King
Pedro defeated King Charles his fleet and took himself[5] prisoner; after
which, the better to prosecute the war, he removed with his whole court to

---

[1] The archaic form *them-seeming* ("it seemed to them") is used frequently in the
story, as are related forms such as *themseemed, himseemed, himseeming.*
[2] conspired, plotted
[3] Bandello accurately describes the historical "Sicilian Vespers" in the opening of
this fictional tale. On the eve of Easter in 1282 Sicilians rebelled violently
against their French governors, slaughtering some 3,000 people within the
course of about six weeks and driving the French king from Sicily.
[4] in a royal and grand manner (*wise*: see glossary)
[5] King Charles II

Messina, as to that city which is next overagainst[1] Italy and whence one may speedily pass into Calabria.

There, what while he held a right royal court and all was joy and gladness for the gotten victory, joustings being made and balls holden daily,[2] one of his knights, a baron of high repute, by name Don Timbreo di Cardona, whom King Pedro supremely loved, for that he was doughty[3] of his person and had still borne himself valiantly in the past wars, fell passionately in love with a young lady hight[4] Fenicia, the daughter of Messer Lionato de' Lionati, a gentleman of Messina, lovesome,[5] debonair and fair over every other of the country, and little by little became so inflamed for her that he knew not nor wished to live without her sweet sight. Now the baron aforesaid, having from his childhood still served King Pedro by land and by sea, had been mighty richly guerdoned[6] of him, for that, besides gifts without number which he had gotten, the king had then late bestowed upon him the county of Colisano, together with other lands, so that his revenues, over and above the entertainment which he had of the crown, were more than twelve thousand ducats. Don Timbreo, then, fell to passing daily before the young lady's house, accounting himself happy what day he saw her, and Fenicia, who, though but a girl, was quick-witted, and well-advised, speedily perceived the cause of the gentleman's continual passings to and fro. It was notorious[7] that Don Timbreo was one of the king's favourites and that there were few of such avail as he at court; wherefore[8] he was honoured of all. Accordingly Fenicia, seeing him, over and above that which had heard tell of him, apparelled on very lordly[9] and with a worshipful following and noting, to boot, that he was a very handsome young man and seemed mighty well bred, began in her turn to look graciously upon him and to do him honourable reverence. The gentleman waxed daily more enkindled and the more he looked upon her, the more he felt his flame increase and this new fire being grown to such a height in his heart that he felt himself all consumed with love of the fair damsel, he determined to have her by every possible means. But all was in vain, for that unto all the letters and messages he sent her, she never

---

[1] next to
[2] formal dances held daily
[3] strong or brave
[4] named
[5] both beautiful and worthy of love
[6] rewarded (see glossary)
[7] widely known by others
[8] for that reason (see glossary)
[9] dressed in a way befitting a lord or nobleman

answered other what than that she meant to keep her maidenhead inviolate
for him who should be given her to husband; wherefore the poor lover abode
sore disconsolate,[1] more by token that he had never been able to prevail with
her to receive or letters or gifts.[2] Algates,[3] being resolved to have her and
seeing her constancy to be such that, an[4] he would possess her, needs must
he take her to wife, he concluded, after long debatement of the matter in
himself, to demand her of her father to wife. And albeit himseemed he[5]
greatly abased himself in seeking such an alliance, yet, knowing her to be
of ancient and very noble blood, he determined, such was the love he bore
the girl, to use no more delay about the matter.

Having come to this decision, he sought out a gentleman of Messina,
with whom he was very familiar, and to him opened his mind, possessing
him of that which he would have him do with Messer Lionato. The
Messinese[6] accordingly betook himself to the latter and did his errand to
him even as it had been committed unto him by his friend. Messer Lionato,
hearing such good news and knowing Don Timbreo's rank and
consideration, tarried not to take counsel with kinsfolk or friends, but by a
most gracious reply discovered how agreeable it was to him that the
gentleman should deign to ally himself with him and going home,
acquainted his wife and Fenicia with the promise he had made of the latter's
hand. The thing was extremely pleasing to Fenicia, who thanked God with
a devout heart that He vouchsafed her so glorious an issue to her chaste love
and showed her gladness by her countenance. But fortune, which ceaseth
never to cross folk's weal,[7] found an extraordinary means of hindering
nuptials so desired of both parties; and hear how.

It was published abroad in Messina how Don Timbreo di Cardona was
in a few days to espouse Fenicia dei Lionati, which news was generally
pleasing to all the Messinese, for that Messer Lionato was a gentleman who
made himself loved of all, as one who sought to do hurt unto none and
succoured all as most he might, so that all showed great satisfaction at such
an alliance. Now there was in Messina another cavalier, young and nobly
born, by the name Signor Girondo Olerio Valentiano, who had approved

---

[1] For that reason the poor lover remained quite discouraged (see glossary).
[2] either letters or gifts (a usual but now archaic form)
[3] in any case, anyway (used several times throughout the story, often as a narrative
    bridging device; see glossary)
[4] if
[5] he thought himself
[6] inhabitant of Messina
[7] frustrate people's well-being

himself exceeding doughty[1] of his person in the late wars and was moreover one of the most magnificent and liberal[2] gentlemen of the court. He, hearing this news, abode° beyond measure chagrined, for that he had a little before fallen enamoured of Fenicia's charms and so sore was he stricken of love's shafts that he thought for certain to die, except he had her to wife. Accordingly, he had resolved to ask her in marriage of her father and hearing the promise made to Don Timbreo, thought to swoon for dolour; then, finding no remedy for that his pain, he fell into such a frenzy that, overmastered with amorous passion and having no regard unto any manner of reason, he suffered himself to be carried away into doing a thing blameworthy in any one and much more so in a knight and a gentleman such as he was. He had in all their warlike enterprises been well-nigh always Don Timbreo's comrade and there was a brotherly friendship between them, but of this love, whatever might have been the cause thereof, they had still forborne to discover themselves to each other.

Signor Girondo, then, bethought himself to sow such discord between Don Timbreo and his mistress that the match should be broken off, in which case, demanding her of her father to wife, he hoped to have her; nor did he tarry to give effect to this mad conceit[3] and having found a man apt unto the service of his blind and unbridled appetite, he diligently acquainted him with his mind. This man, whom Signor Girondo had taken unto himself for confidant and minister of his wickedness, was a young courtier, a man of little account, to whom evil was more pleasing than good and who, being fully instructed of that which he was to do, went next morning to visit Don Timbreo, who had not yet left the house, but went walking all alone for his pleasure in a garden of his hostelry.[4] The young man entered the garden and Don Timbreo, seeing him make for himself,[5] received him courteously; then, after the wonted[6] salutations, the new-comer bespoke Don Timbreo, saying, "My lord, I come at this hour to speak with thee of matters of the utmost importance, which concern thine honour and well-being, and for that I may chance to say somewhat[7] which will peradventure offend thee, I prithee pardon it to me; nay, let my friendly devotion excuse me in thine eyes and believe that I have bestirred myself to a good end. Algates, this I know, that this which I shall presently tell thee will, if thou be still that noble

---

[1] showed himself brave, forceful
[2] open-handed, generous
[3] idea, notion
[4] lodging
[5] move toward him
[6] customary
[7] something

gentleman which thou hast ever been, be of very great service to thee; and to come to the fact, I must tell thee I heard yesterday that thou hast agreed with Messer Lionato de' Lionati to espouse Fenicia his daughter to thy wife. Look, now, my lord, what thou dost and have regard unto thine honour. This I say to thee for that a gentleman, a friend of mine, goeth well-nigh twice or thrice a week to lie with her and hath enjoyment of her love; nay, this very evening he is to go thither, as of wont,[1] and I shall accompany him, as I use to do on such occasions. Now, an[2] thou wilt pledge me thy word and swear to me not to molest me nor my friend, I will cause thee see the place and all; and that thou mayest know the whole, my friend hath enjoyed her these many months past. The regard I have for thee and the many pleasures which thou of thy favour hast done me induce me to discover this to thee; so now thou wilt do that which shall seem to thee most to thy profit. It sufficeth me to have done thee that office[3] in the matter which pertaineth unto my duty towards thee."

At these words Signor Timbreo was all confounded and was like to take leave of his senses; then, after he had abidden[4] awhile, revolving a thousand things in himself, the bitter and (to his seeming) just despite[5] which possessed him availing more with him than the fervent and loyal love he bore the fair Fenicia, he with a sigh answered the young man on this wise,° saying, "My friend, I cannot nor should but abide[6] eternally obliged to thee, seeing how lovingly thou concernest thyself for me and for mine honour, and I will one day give thee to know effectually how much I am beholden to thee. Algates, for this present I render thee, as most I know and may, the heartiest thanks in my power, and since thou freely profferest thyself to cause me see that which I should never have imagined for myself, I beseech thee, by that loving kindness which hath moved thee to advertise[7] me of this matter, that thou stint not to bear thy friend company and I pledge thee my faith, as a true knight, that I will offer neither thee nor him any manner of hurt or hindrance and will still keep the matter secret, so he may enjoy this his love in peace, for that I should from the first have been better advised and should, with well-opened eyes, have made diligent and curious enquiry of the whole." Whereupon quoth the young man to him, "Do you, then, my lord, betake yourself this night at the third hour to the neighbourhood of

---

[1] as is his habit
[2] if
[3] service
[4] remained, waited
[5] justified anger
[6] remain
[7] warn (see glossary)

Messer Lionato's house and ambush[1] yourself in the ruins overagainst the garden."

Now there abutted upon these ruins a face of Messer Lionato's house, wherein there was an old saloon,[2] whose windows stood open day and night, and there Fenicia was bytimes used to show herself,[3] for that from that quarter the beauty of the garden was better to be enjoyed; but Messer Lionato and his family abode° in the other part of the palace, which was ancient and very great and might have sufficed for a prince's court, not to say a gentleman's household. This settled, the deceitful youth took his leave and returned to his patron, to whom he reported that which he had appointed[4] with Don Timbreo; whereat the perfidious Girondo was mightily rejoiced, himseeming his device succeeded to his wish. Accordingly, the hour come, he clad one of his serving-men on worshipful wise[5] and perfumed him with the sweetest of essences, having lessoned[6] him beforehand of that which he was to do; and the disguised servant set out in company with the youth who had bespoken Don Timbreo, followed by another, with a step-ladder on his shoulder. Now, what was Don Timbreo's state of mind and what and how many were the thoughts which passed through his mind all that day, who might avail to recount at full? I for my part know that I should weary myself in vain; suffice it to say that the over-credulous and ill-fortuned gentleman, blinded with the veil of jealousy, ate little or nothing that day and whoso looked him in the face accounted him more dead than alive. Half an hour before the appointed time he went to hide himself in that ruined place, on such wise° that he might very well see whoso passed there, himseeming yet impossible that Fenicia should have yielded herself unto another. However, he said in himself that girls are fickle, light, unstable, humoursome[7] and greedy of new things, and on this wise, now condemning and now excusing her, he abode° intent upon every movement.

The night was not very dark but exceeding still, and presently he heard the noise of coming feet and eke[8] some broken word or two. By and by he saw the three pass and recognised the youth who had that morning

---

[1] conceal and lie in wait
[2] a salon or reception room
[3] Fenicia habitually appeared
[4] arranged, plotted
[5] he dressed one of his servants in a proper way (wise)
[6] taught
[7] subject to changes in fancy
[8] also (see glossary)

advertised[1] him, but could not recall the faces of the other twain. As they passed before him, he heard the perfumed one, him who played the lover, say to him who bore the ladder, "Look thou set the ladder featly[2] to the window, so it makes no noise, for, when we were last here, my lady Fenicia told me that thou lettest it fall over-heavily. Do it adroitly and quietly." Don Timbreo plainly heard these words, which were to his heart as so many sharp spears, and albeit he was alone and had none other arms than his sword, whilst those who passed had two partisans and most like were armoured to the boot,[3] nevertheless such and so poignant was the jealousy which gnawed at his heart and so sore the despite which inflamed him that he was like to issue forth of his ambush and falling fiercely on the three conspirators, to slaughter him whom he judged to Fenicia's lover or else, abiding dead himself, at one stroke to end the anguish and misery he suffered for excess of dolour. However, remembering him[4] of his plighted faith and esteeming it overgreat baseness and wickedness to assail those who had the assurance of his word, he awaited the issue of the matter, all full of choler and despite and gnawing his heart for rage and fury.

The three, then, coming under Messer Lionato's windows, on the side aforesaid, set the ladder very softly against the balcony and he who played the lover climbed up by it and entered the house, as if he had intelligence within. The which when the disconsolate Don Timbreo saw, firmly believing that he who climbed up went to lie with Fenicia, he was overcome with the cruellest anguish and felt himself all aswoon. However, just despite (as he deemed it) availed so much in him that, doing away all jealousy, it not only altogether quenched the sincere and ardent love which he bore Fenicia, but converted it into cruel hatred; wherefore, caring not to await his rival's coming forth, he departed the place where he was ambushed and returned to his lodging. The youth saw him depart and recognizing him, deemed that of him which was in effect the case; whereupon not long after he made a certain signal and the servant who had gone up coming down, they all repaired in company to the house of Signor Girondo, to whom they related all that had passed; whereat he was marvellously rejoiced and himseemed he was already possessed of the fair Fenicia.

On the morrow, Don Timbreo, who had slept very little that night, arose betimes[5] in the morning, and sending for the townsman, by whom he had

[1] warned (see glossary)
[2] skilfully, carefully
[3] Partisans are long-handled spear-like weapons; in this context, "to the boot" means to advantage, fully.
[4] remembering to himself
[5] early (see glossary)

demanded Fenicia in marriage of her father, acquainted him with that which he would have him do. The Messinese, fully informed of his mind and will, betook himself, at his instance, towards dinner-time, to the house of Messer Lionato, whom he found walking in the saloon, against dinner should be ready,[1] and there likewise was the innocent Fenicia, who wrought certain broideries of hers in silk, in company of her mother and of two sisters of hers, younger than herself. The citizen was graciously received by Messer Lionato, to whom said he, "Messer Lionato, I have a message to deliver to you, to your lady and to Fenicia on the part of Don Timbreo." "You are welcome," replied he; "what is to do? Wife and thou, Fenicia, come and hear with me that which Don Timbreo giveth us to understand." Quoth the messenger, "It is commonly said that an ambassador, in delivering that wherewithal he is charged, should not incur any penalty. I come to you, sent by another, and it grieveth me infinitely to bring you news which may afflict you. Don Timbreo di Cardona sendeth unto you, Messer Lionato, and unto your lady, bidding you provide yourselves with another son-in-law, inasmuch as he purposeth not to have you to parents-in-law, not indeed for any default of yourselves, whom he believeth and holdeth to be loyal and worthy, but for that he hath with his own eyes seen a thing in Fenicia which he could never have believed, and therefore he leaveth it unto you to provide for you occasions. To thee, Fenicia, he saith that the love he bore thee merited not the requital which thou hast made him therefor[2] and biddeth thee provide thyself with another husband, even as thou hast provided thyself with another lover, or better, take him to whom thou hast given thy virginity, for that he purposeth not to have any manner if dealing with thee, since thou hast before marriage made him a burgess of Corneto."[3]

Fenicia, hearing this bitter and shameful message, abode° as she were dead and on like wise° did Messer Lionato and his lady. Nevertheless, taking heart and breath, which had well-nigh failed him for amazement, Messer Lionato thus replied to the messenger, saying, "Brother, I still misdoubted, from the first moment when thou bespokest me of this marriage, that Don Timbreo would not abide constant to his demand, well knowing myself, as I did and do, to be but a poor gentleman and none of his peer. Algates, meseemeth that, an[4] he repented him of taking my daughter to wife, it should have sufficed him to say that he would none of her and not (as he doth) cast upon her so shameful an impeachment as that of harlotry. True it is that all things are possible, but I know how she hath been reared

---

[1] waiting for dinner to be ready
[2] in response
[3] a citizen of the imaginary town of Cuckold (a sardonic joke about infidelity)
[4] if

and what her usances[1] are. God the Just Judge will one day, I trust, make
known the truth." With this reply the gentleman took his leave and Messer
Lionato abode° persuaded that Don Timbreo had repented him of the
proposed alliance, himseeming it were overmuch condescension and
derogation[2] on his part. Now Messer Lionato's family was one of the oldest
in Messina and both noble and of high repute; but his wealth was only that
of a private gentleman, albeit it was matter of record that his forefathers had
anciently owned many lands and castles, with a most ample jurisdiction;
but, through the various revolutions of the island and the civil wars which
had betided,[3] they had (as is seen in many other families) been dispossessed
of their seignoiries;[4] wherefore the good old man, having never seen aught
in his daughter other than most honourable, concluded that Don Timbreo
had taken their poverty and present ill fortune in disdain.

On the other hand, Fenicia, hearing herself thus wrongfully impeached,
was sore disordered for excess of dolour and heart-sickness and abandoning
herself to despair, like a tender and delicate maid as she was and unused to
the blows of perverse fortune, had tendered death dearer than life;
wherefore, overtaken with grievous and poignant anguish, she let herself
fall as one dead and of a sudden losing her natural colour, resembled a
marble statue rather than a live woman. She was taken up and laid upon a
bed, where with hot cloths and other remedies her strayed spirits were
presently recalled to her, and the doctors being sent for, the report spread
throughout Messina how Messer Lionato's daughter Fenicia was fallen so
grievously sick that she abode in the peril of her life. At this news there
came many ladies, kinswomen, and friends, to visit the disconsolate damsel
and learning the cause of her sickness, studied, as best they knew, to console
her; wherefore, as is wont to betide° among a multitude of women, they said
various things concerning so piteous a case and all of one accord severely
blamed Don Timbreo. They were for the most part about the bed of the sick
girl, who presently, having plainly apprehended that which was said,
collected all her strength and seeing that well-nigh all wept for pity of her,
besought them with a feeble voice to forebear; then silence being made, she
spoke thus on languid wise,° saying, "My honoured mother and sisters, I
pray you dry these tears, for that they avail you not, while to me they are an
occasion of fresh dolour and profit nothing for the case betided.° Thus hath
it pleased our Lord God and it behoveth us have patience. The bitterest of
the dolour which I suffer and which goeth little by little wearing away the

---

[1] habits
[2] excessive social self-abasement
[3] occurred (see glossary)
[4] lands (and so also their source of revenue and status)

thread of life in me, is not that I am repudiated, albeit that is a source of infinite grief to me, but the manner of this repudiation it is cutteth me even to the quick and afflicteth my heart beyond remedy. Don Timbreo might have said that I pleased him not to wife and all had been well; but, through the fashion of his rejection of me, I know that I incur everlasting reproach in the eyes of all the Messinese and shall still pass for guilty of that which not only I never did, but which assuredly I never yet thought to do; nay, I shall still be pointed at with the finger of scorn for a strumpet. I have ever confessed and do anew confess myself no match for such a knight and lord as Don Timbreo; for that my parents' little means sought not to marry me in such high place. But, in the matter of nobility and antiquity of blood, the Lionati are known as the most ancient and noble of all this island, we being descended from a most noble Roman house which flourished before our Lord Jesus Christ took flesh, as is testified by very ancient writings. Now, even as for lack of wealth I confess myself unworthy of so great a gentleman, so on like wise° I say that I am most unworthily repudiated, seeing it is a very manifest thing that I have never thought to give any man that of myself which right willeth should be reserved unto my husband. God (whose holy name be still praised and revered) knoweth that I say sooth;[1] and who knoweth but the Divine Majesty would save me by this means? For that, belike, being so nobly married, I had been swollen up with pride and waxed arrogant, contemning this one and that, and had peradventure been less mindful of God's goodness towards me. Now may He do with me that which most pleaseth Him and vouchsafe me that this my tribulation may enure to[2] the welfare of my soul. Moreover, with all my heart I do most devoutly beseech Him to open Don Timbreo his eyes, not that he may take me again to bride—for I feel myself dying little by little—but that he, to whom my faith hath been of little price, may, together with all the world, know that I never committed that mad and shameful default, whereof, against all reason, I am impeached; so that, if I die in this infamy, I may ere[3] long abide justified. Let him enjoy another lady unto whom God hath destined him and live long with her in peace; for me, in a few hours six feet of earth will suffice me. Let my father and my mother and all our friends and kinsfolk have at the least this scantling[4] of comfort in this so great affliction that I am altogether innocent of the infamy which is laid to my charge and take to witness my faith, which I here plight them, as behoveth an obedient daughter; for that weightier pledge or testimony I cannot

---

[1] truth
[2] benefit
[3] before (see glossary)
[4] scrap, shred

presently give. Suffice it me to be before Christ's just tribunal acknowledged innocent of such wickedness; and so unto Him who gave it me I commit my soul, the which, desirous of quitting this earthly prison, taketh flight towards Him."

This said, such was the greatness of the anguish which beset her heart and so sorely did it straiten[1] it that, offering to say I know not what more, she began to lose power of speech and to falter out broken words, which were understood of none, and all at once there spread an ice-cold sweat over her every limb, on such wise° that, crossing her hands upon her breast, she let herself go for dead. The physicians, who were yet there, unable to find any remedy for so grievous a case, gave her up for lost, saying that the fierceness of the pain had burst her heart in sunder, and so they went their ways; nor had Fenicia long abidden, all cold and pulseless, in the arms of those her friends and kinswomen than she was of all accounted dead, and one of the physicians, being called back and finding no pulse in her, declared her to have given up the ghost. What cruel lamentations were made over her, what tears were shed and what piteous sighs heaved, I leave it to you, compassionate ladies, to conceive. The wretched tearful father and the dishevelled and woebegone mother would have made stones weep, whilst the other ladies and all who were there kept up a piteous lamentation. From five to six hours were now past and the burial was appointed for the ensuing day; wherefore the mother, more dead than alive, after the multitude of women had departed, kept with her a kinswoman of hers, the brother's wife of Messer Lionato, and the twain, letting set[2] water on the fire, shut themselves up in a chamber, without other person; then, stripping Fenicia naked, they full[3] to washing her with warm water.

Fenicia's strayed spirits had now been near seven hours abroad, whenas, what while the cold limbs were in bathing, they returned to their accustomed office[4] and the damsel, giving manifest signs of life, began to open her eyes. Her mother and kinswoman were like to cry out; however, plucking up courage, they laid their hands on her heart and felt it make some movement; wherefore they were certified that the damsel was alive and accordingly, without making any stir, they plied her on such wise° with hot cloths and other remedies that she returned well-nigh altogether to herself and opening wide her eyes, said with a heavy sigh, "Alack, where am I?" Quoth her mother, "Seest thou not that thou art here with me and with thine aunt? There had so sore a swoon overcome thee that we deemed thee dead, but

---

[1] squeeze
[2] having servants put water on the fire, to boil or warm it
[3] fell
[4] function, activity

(praised be God) thou art e'en alive." Whereupon, "Alas," replied Fenicia, "how much better were it that I were dead and quit of such sore afflictions!" "Daughter mine," rejoined her mother and aunt, "it behoveth thee live, since God so willeth it, and all shall yet be set right." Then the mother, concealing the joy she felt, opened the chamber-door a little and let call Messer Lionato, who came incontinent.[1] When he saw his daughter restored to herself, it booteth not[2] to ask if he were glad, and many things having been debated between them, he willed, in the first place, that none should know aught of the fact, purposing to send Fenicia forth of Messina to the country-house of his brother, whose wife was there present. Then, the damsel being recruited with delicate viands[3] and wines of price and restored to her former beauty and strength, he sent for his brother and fully instructed him of that which he purposed to do. Accordingly, in pursuance of the ordinance concerted[4] between them, Messer Girolamo (for so was Messer Lionato's brother named) carried Fenicia that same night to his own house in Messina and there kept her very secretly in his wife's company. Then, having made the necessary provision at his country-house, he one morning betimes° despatched his wife thither with Fenicia (who was now sixteen years old), a sister of hers of from thirteen to fourteen and a daughter of his own; and this he did, to the intent that, Fenicia growing and changing looks, as one doth with age, they might in two or three years' time marry her under another name.

The day after the accident, it being reported throughout all Messina that Fenicia was dead, Messer Lionato let order her obsequies[5] according to her rank and caused make a coffin, wherein, unperceived of any, her mother, willing not that any should meddle therewith, laid I know not what; then, shutting the lid, she nailed it and luted[6] it with pitch, on such wise° that all held it for certain that the damsel's body was therewithin. At eventide Messer Lionato and his wife and kinsfolk, clad all in black, escorted[7] the coffin to the church, making such a show of extreme grief as if they had in very deed followed their daughter's body to the tomb; the which moved everyone to pity, for that, the occasion of Fenicia's supposed death having gotten wind, all the Messinese held it for certain that Don Timbreo had forged the story aforesaid for his own ends. The coffin was accordingly

---

[1] immediately, in a rush
[2] it profits not
[3] revived with delicate foods
[4] agreed upon
[5] commissioned her funeral
[6] sealed
[7] accompanied

interred, with general mourning of the whole city, and thereover was set a monument of stone, emblazoned with the ensigns of the Lionati, whereon Messer Lionato let grave[1] this epitaph:

> Fenicia hight I.[2] As ill-fortune bade,
> I was affianced to a cruel knight,
> Who, soon repenting him of nuptial plight,
> Unto my charge a foul transgression laid.
>
> I, as an innocent and tender maid,
> Seeing myself impeached with such unright,
> Chose rather die than live in men's sight
> Shown for a strumpet. Sword or dagger's blade
>
> There needed none, alack, to me to die;
> Sharp grief was deadlier than steel, forsooth,
> Whenas I heard me slandered causelessly.
>
> With my last breath I prayed God of His ruth[3]
> To show the world their error by and by,
> Since my vowed bridegroom recked[4] not of my truth.

The tearful obsequies made and it being freely spoken everywhere of the cause of Fenicia's death and various things discoursed thereupon and all showing compassion of so piteous a case, as of a thing which had been feigned, Don Timbreo began to suffer exceeding great chagrin, together with a certain oppression of the heart, for that he knew not what to believe. Himseemed indeed he should not be blamed, having himself seen a man go up by the ladder to enter the house; but, presently, better considering that which he had seen (more by token that his despite was now in great part cooled and reason began to open his eyes), he bethought himself that he who had entered the house might belike[5] have climbed up thither, either for some other woman or to steal. Moreover, he called to mind that Messer Lionato's house was very great and that none abode whereas[6] the man had gone up; nay, that Fenicia, sleeping with her sister in a chamber within that of her father and mother, might not have availed to come to that side, it behoving

---

[1] had engraved
[2] Fenicia I am called
[3] pity (see glossary)
[4] considered, thought
[5] possibly
[6] no one lived where

her pass through her father's chamber; and so, assailed and tormented by conflicting thoughts, he could find no repose.

On like wise,° Signor Girondo, hearing the manner of Fenicia's death and knowing himself to have been her murderer, felt his heart like to burst for excess of dolour, as well because he was passionately enamoured of her as also for that he had been the true cause of so great a scandal, and was like twice or thrice for despair to have plunged a poniard[1] into his own breast. Unable either to eat or drink, he abode° as he were an idiot, nay, rather, a man possessed, and could take neither rest nor repose. Ultimately, it being the seventh day after Fenicia's funeral and himseeming he might live no longer, if he discovered not to Don Timbreo the wickedness he had done, he betook himself to the palace, at the hour when all went home to dine, and encountering the knight on his way to his hostelry, said to him, "Signor Timbreo, let it not irk you to come with me hard by[2] on an occasion of mine." Timbreo, who loved him as a comrade, went with him, discoursing of various matters, and a few steps brought them to the church where Fenicia's monument stood. There come, Girondo bade his serving-men await him without and besought Don Timbreo to lay the like commandment on his; the which he straightway did. The two gentlemen, then, alone entered the church, where they found no one, and Girondo carried[3] Timbreo to the chapel where was the pretended tomb. There he fell on his knees before the tomb and unsheathing a poniard which he had by his side, gave it naked into the hand of Don Timbreo, who waited, all full of wonderment, to know what this might mean, more by token that he had not yet observed whose tomb it was before which his friend knelt. Then, in a voice broken with sobs and tears, Girondo thus bespoke him, saying, "Magnanimous and noble knight, having, as I judge, done thee infinite wrong, I am not come hither to crave thee of pardon, for that my default is such as meriteth it not. Wherefore, if ever thou look to do aught worthy of thy valour, if thou think to act knightly, if thou desire to do a deed to God acceptable and grateful to the world, plant that steel which thou hast in hand in this wicked and traitorous breast and make of my vicious and abominable blood a befitting sacrifice unto these most sacred ashes of the innocent and ill-starred Fenicia, who was late entombed in this sepulchre; for that of her unmerited and untimely death I of my malice was the sole cause. Nay, if thou, more compassionate of me than I of myself, deny me this, I will with mine own hands wreak that uttermost vengeance on myself which shall be possible unto me. But, if thou be that true and loyal knight thou has been till now,

---

[1] dagger
[2] follow closely
[3] led

who would never brook the least shadow of a stain, thou wilt forthright take due vengeance both for thyself and for the ill-fated Fenicia."

Don Timbreo, seeing himself before the resting-place of the fair Fenicia's body and hearing that which Girondo said to him, was well-nigh beside himself and could nowise[1] conceive what this might be. However, moved by I know not what, he fell to weeping bitterly and besought Girondo to rise to his feet and more plainly to discover the matter. Therewith he cast the poniard far from him and after did and said to such purpose that Girondo arose, weeping the while, and thus replied to him, saying, "Know, then, my lord, that Fenicia was most ardently beloved of me and on such wise° that, should I live an hundred lives, I might nevermore hope to find comfort or consolation, since my love was to the hapless maid the occasion of a most bitter death; for that, seeing I might never have of her a kind look nor a least token conformable unto my desires and hearing that she was promised to thee for wife, I, being blinded by my unbridled appetite, conceived that, so but I found a means of preventing her from becoming thy wife, I might after, demanding her in marriage of her father, have espoused her. Wherefore, unable to devise another remedy for my most fervent love, without farther consideration I hatched the blackest treason was ever plotted and caused thee by practice see one go up by night into her house, who was none other than one of my servants; moreover, he who came to speak with thee and who gave thee to understand that Fenicia had bestowed her love upon another was lessoned and set on[2] by me to the errand which he did thee. Accordingly, Fenicia was on the ensuing day repudiated by thee and through that repudiation the ill-fortuned maid died and is here buried. Wherefore, I having been the butcher, the hangman and the barbarous assassin who hath so cruelly wronged both thee and her, I beseech thee with clasped hands," and here he fell to his knees anew, "that thou wilt e'en take due vengeance for the wickedness committed of me; for that, when I think of the dire calamity whereof I have been the cause, I hold life in horror."

Don Timbreo, hearing these things, wept passing[3] bitterly and knowing that the error, once committed, was irreparable and that Fenicia, being dead, might no more return to life, determined not to seek to avenge himself upon Girondo, but, by pardoning him his every default, to procure Fenicia's fair fame to be vindicated and that honour restored to her, whereof she had without cause been so shamefully bereaved.[4] Accordingly, he bade Girondo rise to his feet and after many heavy sighs, mingled with most bitter tears,

---

[1] in no way (*wise*: see glossary)
[2] taught and commissioned
[3] very
[4] robbed (see glossary)

bespoke him on this wise,° saying, "How far better were it for me, brother mine, that I had never been born or that, if I must needs come into the world, I had been born deaf, so I might never have heard a thing so hurtful and so grievous to me and by reason whereof I shall never again live happy, considering that I, of my over-credulity, have slain her, whose love and the singular and surpassing virtues and qualities wherewith the King of Heaven had endowed her merited of me anothergates guerdon[1] than so shameful a defamement and so untimely a death! But, since God hath so permitted it, against whose will there stirreth not a leaf upon a tree, and since things past may eather[2] be blamed than amended, I purpose not to take of thee any manner of vengeance, for that to lose friend upon friend were to add dolour unto dolour, nor withal[3] would Fenicia's blessed soul return to her most chaste body, which hath accomplished its course. Of one thing I will e'en rebuke thee, so thou mayst never more fall into a like error, and that is that thou discoveredst not to me thy love, knowing that I was enamoured of her and knew nothing of thy passion; for that, ere I caused demand her of her father, I would in this amorous emprise have yielded place unto thee and overcoming myself, as magnanimous and generous spirits use to do,[4] would have preferred our friendship before my appetite; nay, maybe thou, hearing my reasonings, wouldst have desisted from this thine undertaking and so this scandal had not ensued. However, the thing is done and there is no means of procuring it to be undone; but in one thing I would fain have thee complease[5] me and do that which I shall bid thee." Quoth Girondo, "Command me, my lord, for that I will do all without exception." "I wish then," rejoined Don Timbreo, "that, Fenicia having been of us twain wrongfully impeached for a strumpet, we, in so far as we may, restore her her fair fame and render her due honour, first in the eyes of the disconsolate parents and after of all the Messinese; for, that which I let say to her having gotten wind,[6] the whole city might lightly[7] believe that she was a harlot. Else meseemeth I should without cease have her angry shade before mine eyes, still crying sore to God for vengeance against me."

To this, still weeping, Girondo straightway answered, "To thee, sir, it pertaineth to command and to me to obey. I was before bounden unto thee by friendship and now, through the wrong which I have done thee and which

---

[1] a different kind of reward (guerdon)
[2] more easily
[3] nor by it (an act of vengeance)
[4] usually or habitually do
[5] gratify
[6] what I permitted myself to say, having circulated around
[7] easily

thou, like an over-pitiful and loyal knight, so generously pardonest unto me, base and perfidious wretch that I am, I am for ever become thy servant and thy slave." These words said, both, weeping bitterly, fell on their knees before the sepulchre and with clasped hands humbly besought pardon of Fenicia and of God, the one of the wickedness committed and the other of his own credulousness; then, their eyes dried, Timbreo would have Girondo go with him to Messer Lionato's house. Accordingly, they repaired thither and found Messer Lionato, who had dined in company with sundry of his kinsfolk, in act to[1] rise from table. When he heard that the two gentlemen would fain speak with him, he came to meet them, all full of wonderment, and bade them welcome; whilst they, seeing him and his wife clad in black, fell a-weeping for the cruel remembrance of Fenicia's death and could scarce speak. Then, two stools being brought and all having seated themselves, Don Timbreo, with many sighs and sobs, recounted, in the presence of as many as were there, the woeful story of the cause of Fenicia's (as he believed) most cruel and untimely death and cast himself, he and Signor Girondo, on the ground, craving her father and mother pardon of the wickedness committed. Messer Lionato, weeping for joy and tenderness, lovingly embraced them both and pardoned them their every wrong, thanking God that his daughter was acknowledged innocent.

Then Don Timbreo, after much talk, turning to Messer Lionato, said to him, "Sir and father, since ill fortune hath willed that I should not become your son-in-law, as was my supreme desire, I pray you, nay, as most I may, I require you that you will still avail yourself of me and mine, as if the intended alliance had indeed ensued between us, for that I will still have you in such reverence and obedience as a loving and obedient son should have for his father. And if you will deign to command me, you shall find my deeds conformable to my words, for that certes[2] I know nothing in the world, how difficult soever it may be, but I would do it for you." For this the good old man lovingly thanked him and finally said to him, "Since you have so freely made me such courteous proffers and since adverse fortune hath deemed me unworthy of your alliance, I will make bold to crave you of one thing, the which will be eath[3] for you to do; to wit, I pray you, by that loyalty which reigneth in you and by what love soever you bore the unfortunate Fenicia, that, whenas you have a mind to marry, you will vouchsafe to give me to know thereof and that, if I proffer you a lady who shall please you, you will take her to wife." Don Timbreo, himseeming the disconsolate old man asked a little thing in requital of such a loss as that which he had

---

[1] about to
[2] certainly
[3] easy

suffered, proffered him his hand and kissing him on the mouth, replied to him thus, "Sir father, since you ask so slight a thing of me, I being bounden to you for a far greater and wishing to show you how much I desire to do you a pleasure, not only will I take no wife without your knowledge, but her alone will I marry whom you shall counsel me and give me; and this I promise you upon my faith, in the presence of all these noble gentlemen." Signor Girondo on like wise° bespoke Messer Lionato with fair and goodly words, avouching himself still most apt unto his pleasures; which done, the two gentlemen went to dinner. The thing was presently bruited abroad[1] in Messina, so that it was manifest unto all that Fenicia had been unjustly impeached, and on like wise she herself was that same day advised by her father, through an especial messenger, of that which had betided;° whereat she was mightily rejoiced and returned thanks to God for her recovered honour.

Fenicia had now abidden about a year's space in the country, where all went so well that none knew her to be alive, and meantime Don Timbreo held strait intercourse[2] with Messer Lionato, who, having advised his daughter of that which he thought to do, applied himself to the ordinance[3] of the things which pertained unto his purpose. Now in this space of time the damsel was waxen[4] fair beyond belief and having accomplished her seventeenth year, was grown on such wise° that whoso saw her had never known her for Fenicia, especially as they held the latter to be dead. Her sister, Belfiore by name, who abode° with her and was some fifteen years old, appeared in very truth a most fair flower and showed little less beauty than her elder sister; which Messer Lionato, who went often to visit them, seeing, he determined to tarry no longer of carrying his design into effect. Wherefore, being one day in company with the two gentlemen, he said, smiling, to Don Timbreo, "It is time, my lord, that I should acquit you of[5] the obligation which you, of your favour, have undertaken towards me. Methinketh I have found you a very fair and charming young lady to wife, with whom, when you have seen her, you will, to my thinking, be content. And if belike she be not taken of you with so much love as that wherewith you were to espouse Fenicia, of this I can e'en certify you that you will have in her no less beauty, no less nobility and no less gentilesse.[6] With most engaging manners and other womanly charms, she is, Godamercy,

---

[1] rumoured, talked about
[2] private conversation
[3] ordering
[4] grown
[5] release you from
[6] gentility

abundantly provided and adorned; but you shall see her and it shall after be in your discretion to do that which shall seem to you most to your advantage. On Sunday morning I will come to your lodging, with a chosen company of kinsfolk and friends, and do you and Signor Girondo be in readiness, for that it behoveth us go some three miles without[1] Messina to a village where we shall hear mass, after which you shall see the damsel of whom I have bespoken you and we will dine in company."

Timbreo accepted the invitation and the ordinance appointed and on Sunday made ready betimes° to take horse with Signor Girondo. Presently Messer Lionato arrived with a troop of gentlemen, having let make[2] honourable provision at his country-house of everything necessary, and Don Timbreo, being advised of his coming, mounted to horse with Signor Girondo and their servants. Then, good day given and taken, they all in company rode forth of Messina and devising, as it happeneth on such occasions, of various things, they came presently, without perceiving it, to the house, where they were honourably received. They heard mass at a neighbouring church; which ended, they all betook themselves into a saloon, magnificently arrayed with Alexandrian[3] arras and carpets. All being assembled, there came many gentlewomen out of a chamber and amongst them Belfiore and Fenicia, which latter showed as she were the very moon, whenas she most shineth in the serene heavens among the stars. The two knights and the other gentlemen received them with a respectful greeting, as every gentleman should still do with ladies; then Messer Lionato, taking Don Timbreo by the hand and carrying him to Fenicia, who had still, since her bringing into the country, been called Lucilla, "Here, Sir knight," said he, "is Signora Lucilla, whom I have chosen to give you to wife, if it so please you. If you will be ruled by me, you will make her your spouse; nevertheless, you are at liberty to take her or leave her."

Don Timbreo, seeing the damsel, who was in truth most fair, was at first sight marvellously pleased with her and being already determined to content Messer Lionato, bethought himself a little and answered, "Sir father, not only do I accept this damsel, whom you now present to me and who seemeth to me a right noble young lady, nay, but I would on like wise° have accepted any other who had been proffered me of you. And so you may see how desirous I am to content you and may know that the promise I made you is no vain one, this damsel and none other do I take to my lawful spouse, so but her will be conformable unto mine." Whereupon the damsel made answer and said, "Sir knight, I am ready to do all that which shall be bidden

---

[1] beyond
[2] ordered, arranged
[3] made in Alexandria, Egypt

me of Messer Lionato." "And I, fair damsel," rejoined Messer Lionato, "exhort you to take Don Timbreo to husband"; wherefore, to make no further delay with the matter, sign was made to an ecclesiastic, who was there present, that he should pronounce the accustomed words, according to the use of Holy Church; the which he discreetly doing, Don Timbreo by word of mouth[1] then and there espoused his Fenicia, thinking to espouse one Lucilla. Now, whenas he first saw the damsel come forth of the chamber, he felt at heart a certain I know not what, himseeming he discovered in her countenance features of his Fenicia, and could not take his fill of looking upon her; nay, all the love which he had borne Fenicia he felt turn to his new damsel.

The espousals made, water was forthright given to the hands and the company sat down to table, at the head whereof was set the bride, with Don Timbreo on her right hand; overagainst[2] whom sat Belfiore and next after her Signor Girondo, and so in turn a gentleman and a lady side by side. Then came the viands, delicate and in the goodliest ordinance,[3] and all the banquet was sumptuous and fair and softly served; nor lacked there of discourse and witty sallies[4] and a thousand other diversions. Ultimately, fruits being set on such as the season afforded, Fenicia's aunt, who had abidden with her the greater part of the year in the country and who was seated at table beside Don Timbreo, seeing the dinner draw to an end, said merrily to the latter, as if she had heard nothing of the things occurred, "Sir bridegroom, had you never a wife?" At this question, he felt his eyes fill with tears, which fell before he could reply; however, overcoming natural emotion, he replied to her on this wise,° saying, "Mistress aunt, your most affable enquiry bringeth me back to mind a thing which I have ever at heart and through which methinketh I shall early end my days; for that, albeit I am most content with Signora Lucilla here, nevertheless, for another lady, whom I loved and whom, dead as she is, I love more than myself, I feel a worm of dolour at my heart, which still goeth fretting me little by little and tormenteth me sore without cease, more by token that I, against all right, was the sole occasion of her most cruel death." Signor Girondo would fain have replied to these words, but was hindered with a thousand sobs and with the abundance of the tears which fell in streams from his eyes; however, at last, with half-broken speech, "Nay, sir," said he, "it was I; I, disloyal traitor that I was, was e'en the butcher and minister of the death of that most hapless damsel,

---

[1] verbally
[2] beside
[3] order
[4] conversation (literally, military manoeuvres)

who was worthy, for her rare qualities, to live longer than she did, and thou wast nowise° to blame therefor, seeing all the fault was mine."

At this discourse the bride's eyes also began to fill with tearful rain, for the cruel remembrance of the past heartbreak which she had so bitterly suffered; what while her aunt followed on and said to her new-made nephew, "Prithee, sir knight, of your courtesy, now there is nought else whereof to discourse, tell me how this circumstance befell, whereat you and this other gentleman yet weep so piteously." "Alack, madam aunt," replied he, "you would have me renew the cruellest and most despairful dolour was ever suffered of me, the thought whereof alone unmanneth and consumeth me; but, to pleasure you, I will tell you all, to my eternal affliction and little honour; for that I was overcredulous." Accordingly, he began and not without burning tears and the exceeding pity and wonderment of the listeners, recounted all the piteous story from beginning to end; whereupon quoth the matron, "Sir knight, you tell me a strange and cruel case, whereof perchance the like never befell in this world. But tell me, so God aid you; if, before this damsel here had been given you to wife, you might have availed to recall your beloved to life, what would you have done to have her alive again?" Don Timbreo, still weeping, answered, "I swear to God, mistress mine, that I am right well pleased with this my bride and I hope daily for yet better content from her; but, might I before have availed to buy back the dead, I would have given the half of my years to have her again, over and above the treasure I would have expended to that end; for that in truth I loved her as much as woman can be loved of man, and were I to live thousands and thousands of years, dead as she is, I should still love her and for love of her should still have as many as are here of her kinsfolk in reverence." Whereupon, Fenicia's rejoiced father, unable longer to conceal the gladness which possessed him, turned to his son-in-law, weeping for excess of contentment and tenderness of heart, and said to him, "Marry,[1] sir son and son-in-law, for so must I call you, you do ill approve with your acts that which you say with your mouth, inasmuch as, having espoused your much-loved Fenicia and abidden all the morning beside her, you have not yet recognised her. Whither is this your so fervent love gone? Hath she so changed favour, are her fashions so altered that, having her by your side, you know her not?"

These words suddenly opened the eyes of the enamoured knight and he cast himself on his Fenicia's neck, kissing her a thousand times and viewing her with fixed eyes, fulfilled with joy without end. And still the while he wept softly, without availing to utter a word, inwardly calling himself blind;

---

[1] by the Virgin Mary (a mild profanity)

and it being presently recounted of Messer Lionato how the case had betided,° they all abode° full of extreme wonderment and to boot exceeding rejoiced. Signor Girondo, then, rising from the table, cast himself, weeping sore, at Fenicia's feet and humbly besought her of pardon. She received him kindly and with affectionate speech remitted unto[1] him the wrongs he had done her; then, turning to her husband, who still accused himself of the default committed, she prayed him with sweetest words nevermore to bespeak her of the matter, for that, he not having erred, it nowise° behoved him crave pardon of her; and so, kissing and weeping for joy, they drank each other's hot tears, all full of extreme contentment.

Then, what while all abode in the utmost gladness and it[2] was preparing to dance and make merry, Girondo, accosting Messer Lionato, who was so full of joyance that himseemed he touched the sky with his fingers, besought him to vouchsafe him a very great favour, which would, he said, be to him a cause of marvellous contentment. Messer Lionato bade him ask what he would, for that, were it a thing unto which he might avail, he would very gladly and willingly do it. "Then," said Girondo, "I ask you, Signor Lionato, to father-in-law and father, Signora Fenicia and Signor Timbreo to sister and brother-in-law and Signora Belfiore here to my lawful and loving consort." The good father, seeing new joyance heaped on him and well-nigh beside himself for such an unhoped happiness, knew not if he dreamed or if that were indeed true which he heard and saw; but, himseeming he slept not, he thanked God with all his heart, who guerdoned him so magnificently, past his desert,[3] and turning to Signor Girondo, courteously avouched himself content with that which pleased him. Then, calling Belfiore to him, "Thou seest, daughter," quoth he, "how the thing goeth. This knightly gentleman seeketh thee to wife; if thou wilt have him to husband, it will greatly content me and thou hast every reason to do it; so tell us freely thy mind thereof." The fair maid, all trembling, in a low voice shamefastly[4] replied to her father that she was ready to do whatsoever he wished; and so, to make no delay about the matter, Signor Girondo, with the consent of all their kinsfolk, gave the fair Belfiore the ring with due ceremony of accustomed words; whereat infinite was the contentment of Messer Lionato and all his family. Moreover, for that Don Timbreo had espoused his dear Fenicia under the name of Lucilla, he then and there formally espoused her anew under her true name; and so all the day was spent in dancing and delight.

---

[1] pardoned
[2] the collective "all" that lived (abode) in utmost gladness
[3] rewarded him so magnificently, past his deserving
[4] modestly

The fair and lovesomest[1] Fenicia was clad in a robe of the finest damask, white as virgin snow, and was tired[2] with a certain headdress which was wonder-goodly to behold. She was fairly tall for her age and well enough in flesh, algates[3] still waxing, for that she was but a youngling maid. Her bosom, under its thin and costly kerchief of the finest silk, showed somewhat upraised, jutted out in the shape of two round apples, duly parted from one another. Whoso beheld the winsome colour of her countenance saw a pure and pleasing whiteness, overspread with modest and maidenly red, the which not art, but the master-hand of nature suffused more or less with purple, according to the various chances and occasions which betided° her. The swelling breast appeared a very mould of white and polished alabaster, under the round little throat which seemed of snow. But whoso saw her sweetest mouth open and shut, as it gave utterance to her dulcet speech, might certes[4] say that he had seen an inestimable treasury, enchased[5] with the finest rubies and full of the richest and goodliest orient pearls were ever sent us of the odorous East.[6] Moreover, if thou sawest those her two lovely eyes or rather two shining stars, nay, rather two flashing suns, what while she winsomely turned them hither and thither, thou mightest e'en swear that Love harboured in those serenest lights and edged his piercing shafts in their most lucent[7] splendour. How fairly showed her curled and frolic tresses, which, strayed over the pure and straying forehead, seemed very threads of clear and lucent gold, as they wantoned it[8] to the dulcet breathing of the gentle breeze! Her arms were of just proportion, with two loveliest hands so exquisitely wrought that envy itself had found nothing wherein to amend them; and in fine[9] all her shape was lovesome and slender and so graciously fashioned of nature that there lacked nothing unto her. Moreover, she moved now part, now all of her person so timely and so sprightly, according as the occasion required, that her every act, every sign and every movement was full of infinite grace and it seemed she needs must ravish the hearts of the beholders by main force. Wherefore who named her Fenicia nowise° departed from the truth, for that she was indeed a phoenix who far excelled all other damsels in beauty. Nor yet did Belfiore show less

---

[1] most beautiful
[2] attired
[3] albeit, although
[4] certainly
[5] encased
[6] the East was proverbially a place of rich perfumes
[7] light-filled
[8] moved gently
[9] in sum

goodly of presence, save that, being more a child, she had not such majesty and grace in her movements and gestures as her sister.

They abode° all that day in joy and merriment and the two bridegrooms could not take their fill of viewing their mistresses and enjoying them by way of speech. But Don Timbreo especially was beyond measure rejoiced and could scarce bring himself to believe that he was where he was, misdoubting him he dreamed or that belike[1] this was some enchantment wrought by magic art. On the morrow, they made ready to return to Messina and there celebrate the nuptials with such solemnity as pertained unto the rank of the two gentlemen, who had first by post[2] advised a friend of theirs, mighty inward[3] with the king, of that which had betided° them and had committed unto him that which they would fain have done. Accordingly, he that same day went to do obeisance[4] to King Pedro in the name of the two knights and to him recounted the history of the latters' loves and all that had passed from beginning to end; whereat the king discovered no little gladness and sending for his consort, would have the courtier once more tell the whole history in her presence; the which he punctually performed, to the great satisfaction and no small wonderment of the queen, who, hearing the woeful chance that had befallen Fenicia, was constrained to weep for very pity of the damsel. Then, for that in those days of King Pedro, more than in those of all other princes, there reigned a frank and generous courtesy and he it was who best knew how to reward whosoever deserved it and his queen was also very gracious and debonair, he opened his mind to her and told that which he had in mind to do. The queen, hearing so magnificent a resolve, mightily commended the intent and pleasure of her lord and husband; wherefore, letting diligently order all the court and invite[5] all the gentlemen and gentlewomen of the city, the king bade all the most worshipful barons of the realm to go forth to Messina, with an innumerable company of knights and gentlemen, under the care and governance of the Infant[6] Don Giacomo Dongiavo, his first-born son, and meet the two sister-brides.

Accordingly, all being executed after the goodliest fashion, they fared forth the city and had not ridden a mile when they met the two brides, who with their husbands and many other persons came pricking[7] merrily towards Messina. When they drew near, the Infant Don Giacomo caused the knights,

---

[1] perhaps
[2] in haste
[3] very close to
[4] pay formal respects
[5] giving the order to invite
[6] prince (from the Spanish)
[7] riding their horses

who had dismounted to do him reverence, take horse again and courteously
giving them and fair sisters joy of their espousals in his father's name, was
himself received of all the utmost reverence. The greetings of all the
courtiers and of the others of the company who came from Messina to the
two bridegrooms and their brides were no less debonair than welcome, and
so the two knights and their ladies courteously thanked them all; but above
all they rendered unto the Infant Don Giacomo such most thanks as might
be given of them. Then they fared on in company towards the city, devising
and making merry, as is usual at such joyous seasons,[1] whilst Don Giacomo
entertained now Signora Fenicia and now Signora Belfiore with pleasant
discourse. The king, being punctually advised of all that had passed,
mounted to horse, whenas it seemed to him time, with the queen and a
worshipful train of gentlemen and ladies and met the goodly coming
company at the entering in of the city; whereupon all dismounted to do
obeisance to the two princes and were graciously received. The king then
commanded that all should remount and posted himself between Messer
Lionato and Don Timbreo, whilst the queen set the fair Fenicia on her right
hand and Belfiore on her left and the Infant Don Giacomo joined himself
unto Signor Girondo. On like wise° did all the gentlemen and ladies,
following all in succession after the goodliest ordinance, and all, at the
king's bidding, made for the royal palace. There they dined sumptuously
and after dinner, Don Timbreo, by commandment of the king, recounted, in
the presence of all the company, the whole history of his loves; which done,
they fell to dancing and the king kept open court all that week, ordaining
that all comers should eat in the royal palace for that space of time.

The festivities ended, the king called Messer Lionato to him and asked
him what dowry he had promised his daughters and what means he had of
giving it. Messer Lionato answered that nothing had been spoken of the
dowries, but that he would give them such honourable portions[2] as his
means permitted; whereupon quoth the king, "It is our pleasure to give your
daughters that dowry which shall seem to us behoving unto them and unto
my knights, and we will not anywise[3] have them be of more expense to you
in the future." And so this most munificent king, with the singular approof,[4]
not only of all the Sicilians, but of whoso heard it, calling to him the two
bridegrooms and their ladies, would have them all formally renounce all
claim to any share of Messer Lionato's substance and published a royal
ordinance to that effect, confirming every such act of renunciation; then,

---

[1] times
[2] dowries
[3] in any way
[4] approval

immediately thereafterward, he most honourably endowed the two brides, not as a citizen's daughters, but well-nigh as his own, and increased unto the two husbands the entertainment[1] which they had of him. The queen, no less magnificent, generous and liberal than her consort, would have the two brides ladies of her household; wherefore she assigned them a rich yearly provision out of certain of her revenues and still held them dear; and they, who were, in very deed, most debonair, comported themselves on such wise° that in a brief space of time they had gotten the goodwill of all at court. Moreover the king gave Messer Lionato a very honourable office in Messina, wherefrom he drew no little profit; but, feeling himself advanced in years, he procured his said office to be confirmed unto a son of his.[2]

Thus, then, did it betide° Don Timbreo of his most honourable love, whilst the ill that Signor Girondo sought to do was converted unto him for good, and both long after enjoyed their mistresses, living in the utmost peace and oftentimes recalling with pleasure the mischances happened to the fair Fenicia. This same Don Timbreo was the first who founded in Sicily the most noble family of the lords of the house of Cardona, whereof there be nowadays both in Sicily and in the kingdom of Naples many men of no small account. In Spain, on like wise,° the same most noble stock of Cardona flourisheth, producing men no whit unworthy, whether in arms or in matters civil, of their forbears. But what shall I say to you of the two most noble brothers, Don Pietro and Don Giovanni di Cardona, valiant in truth and excellent gentlemen and soldiers? I see some of you here present who have known Signor Don Pietro, Count of Colisano, Lord High Constable and Admiral of Sicily, whom Signor Prosper Colonna, a man without compare, honoured and whose sage counsel he prized. And certes the Count of Colisano was a man of singular merit. He fell at the battle of La Bicocca, to the general grief of all Lombardy; whilst Don Giovanni, his brother, Marquess of La Palude, was slain a great while before, fighting valiantly under the walls of Ravenna, in the battle which there befell[3] between the French and the Spaniards. But I, without perceiving it, have suffered myself, in lieu of story-telling, to digress into panegyric.

Translated by John Payne

---

[1] provision or maintenance (as of a servant)
[2] He arranged for his profitable position (office) to be given to one of his sons.
[3] occurred

Questions

1. Class consciousness and class differences are a major thematic thread in "Sir Timbreo and Fenicia." Why?

2. Compare Lady Fenicia in this story to Hero in *Much Ado About Nothing*: which character do we know better, and why?

3. This story was immensely popular in the sixteenth century. Why, do you think? What elements in the story seem particularly designed to please readers?

4. What should we take from the words of Fenicia's epitaph, which was written by her family?

5. Unlike in *Much Ado About Nothing*, there is no Don John character, no henchmen, and no officers of the watch in this story. What difference do these characters make to the tone of the two stories?

SER GIOVANNI FIORENTINO, FROM *IL PECORONE* (1558)

THE MERCHANT OF VENICE

A wealthy Florentine father who disinherits his favourite son and sends him off to Venice to seek his fortune, a young man who finds a doting surrogate father and then squanders the good man's wealth to gratify his own libidinous passions, an intransigent Jew who foregoes a ten-fold return on his investment of ten thousand ducats in order to have just a pound of a Christian merchant's flesh, and a strangely bewitching widowed lady who confiscates all the worldly goods of her would-be lovers after they fail to perform sexually: these are some of the key elements of the fourteenth-century tale that we traditionally call *Il Pecorone*, the title signifying "the dunce," "the simpleton," or "the dolt'—literally, "the big sheep."

The plot of *The Merchant of Venice* owes its principal debt to this tale by Ser Giovanni Fiorentino, an Italian author about whom very little is known. His name means simply "Sir John of Florence," but his family name might have been Giovanni Antonio degli Antonii. The *Ser* of his pen name (short for *Messer*, the same used for his character Ansaldo) indicates that he was a man of some station and probably wealth, perhaps a notary. However, we should not imagine that he was a knight in shining armour who participated in the kind of lavish jousts and tournaments that his story describes.

We are on more solid ground when we consider the genre in which our author was working and the audience for whom he was writing. The literate and educated urban classes of the Renaissance Italian city-states enjoyed stories that mixed the routine features of their own lives—such as familial and financial arrangements around wills, loans, bonds of surety, the buying and selling of merchandise, and the setting-up of one's children safely and securely in life—with the traditional escapist fictions of heroic and exotic tales characteristic of an older romance tradition. *Il Pecorone* is a notable example of just such a hybrid: the story has elements of what we might call, with some anachronism, medieval middle-class realism, but these elements coexist side by side with the kind of hyperbolic, larger-than-life situations and deeds more commonly found in epic and romance literature. For example, the situation of the protagonist Giannetto, left penniless by his father's will, was a frequent enough condition for Renaissance Europe's mercantile classes. Subject to many significant risks as they ventured for profit or place, they could at any time find themselves financially reduced or even destitute by being cut out of an inheritance. However, the character of Ansaldo, a surrogate father of nearly infinite largesse, derives from an older tradition quite at odds with realism. The Lady of Belmonte's situation as a widow probably gestures toward the hard reality of medieval Europe's mortality rates and the necessary practice of serial marriages, but the strange bedchamber test she imposes on her suitors is certainly the stuff of romance fiction, as is her clever legal solution to block the Jew from obtaining his suit.

Although stories like *Il Pecorone* circulated in manuscript copies during the late Middle Ages, it was the spread of Gutenberg's technology of moveable-type printing beginning in the last half of the fifteenth century that accounts for the popularity of tales of this genre among Europe's readers. The class for whom authors like Ser Giovanni Fiorentino was writing could spend money on popular literature if they chose to do so, but manuscript books took longer to produce and were much more expensive than printed ones. The technological innovation of moveable type meant more stories, more editions, and more readers. This phenomenon was particularly apparent in the sixteenth century, when the efficiency of Europe's paper-making and printing industries increased, driving the price of printed books lower and lower, thereby expanding Europe's library of popular reading material. More books meant more readers, more readers meant more demand for books, more books meant more literacy—a classic chicken-and-egg phenomenon.

How did Shakespeare come to know *Il Pecorone*? If only scholars could be sure. Since the late eighteenth century, when the Shakespeare editor Edward Capell first established the connection, scholars have generally agreed that this story provided Shakespeare with the basic plot of *The Merchant of Venice*, from Bassanio's love quest which opens act 1, scene 1, to the ring trick which closes the final scene. But neither Capell nor any subsequent critic has been able to offer an explanation of Shakespeare's access to the story that everyone can agree upon: did Shakespeare read it in its original Italian because he knew how to read Italian? Did he have someone help him read the original? Did he read it in an English edition that is now lost without a single surviving copy, as many sixteenth century editions are? Or was there once a manuscript translation, likewise now lost or still undiscovered in an archive somewhere? We may never know, in part because we cannot be sure that Shakespeare could read Italian, even the relatively simple Italian of this story.

Or he may have taken the plot not directly from Ser Giovanni but from a lost play called *The Jew*, alluded to by the English writer Stephen Gosson in his 1579 anti-theatrical polemic *The Schoole of Abuse*. Gosson briefly sketches out a play whose plot points seem to match closely with some of those of *The Merchant of Venice*, leading critics since the middle of the eighteenth century to speculate that the lost play may have been based upon *Il Pecorone* and Shakespeare's play upon the lost play. Since the lost play is no longer extant, there is little any modern scholar can do to prove or disprove the suggestion Gosson hints at because we have no text to compare to Shakespeare's. To complicate matters further, an undated printed ballad entitled "A new Song shewing the crueltie of GERNUTUS, a JEWE, who lending to a merchant an hundred crownes, would have a pound of his fleshe, because he could not pay him at the time appointed" may have been derived from this lost source, or it may have been based upon Shakespeare's play.

We can be more certain that other elements of Shakespeare's plot came from different published works of the period: the test of the three caskets, which differs significantly from the three bedchamber tests to which Giannetto must submit in *Il Pecorone*, was probably derived from a 1595 English translation of a much older medieval collection of tales entitled the *Gesta Romanorum*, while details like Shylock's biblical defence of usury in act 1, scene 3 may have come from a collection of six sermons published that same year, Miles Mosse's *The Arraignment and Conviction of Usurie*. The Jessica-Lorenzo plot line, absent from Ser Giovanni's story, may have come from another Italian novella of the fifteenth century written by Masuccio Salernitano, or it may have been partly inspired by Christopher Marlowe's *The Jew of Malta*, which features a daughter who forsakes her father and her religion. Or both. Certainly, as I describe below, Marlowe was an influence on the play in several other ways, both specific and general.

The plot of *Il Pecorone* feels like a folk-tale because, underneath it all, it is one. The author draws on several very familiar folk and romance conventions, perhaps most obviously in the story's several cycles of three, a frequent element of folk stories. The story features three contracts or bargains—the will of Giannetto's father that opens the story, the wager he enters into with the Lady of Belmonte, and the deal that Ansaldo enters into with the Jew of nearby Mestre for 10,000 ducats. There are three episodes in which Giannetto loads up a ship at Ansaldo's expense and seeks his fortune overseas. Three times he returns from Belmonte, each time with a horse and money (his brothers also send him forth with a horse and some money for his expenses). Additionally, with his two brothers he forms a family unit of three, and with his two Venetian sailing companions another trio—a modest flotilla of three ships.

Perhaps somewhat contrary to our expectation of fairy tales, his brothers are not like the wicked siblings of the Cinderella tradition or the greedy Oliver in *As You Like It*, but generous to the point of being willing to defy their deceased father's wishes in order to give their youngest brother his due share of their patrimony. So are his sailing companions, who load up their ships a second and even third time with the intention of giving their proceeds to Giannetto. But these acts of extreme courtesy and generosity are central to the story's spirit: the author wants to emphasize that Giannetto is never abused, never abandoned, and never forsaken by anyone. He and he alone is responsible for his errors and his failings. What's more, the author emphasizes that he does nothing proactive to earn the reprieve that saves his benefactor's life; on the contrary, he entirely forgets the poor man's only request, which is to see Giannetto once before he dies at the hands of the Jew. Indeed, the narrator reveals that Giannetto cruelly forgets his patron and the precarious situation he caused him; the young man is reminded of him only by the chance occurrence of seeing a procession of guildsmen on San Giovanni's Day. Only then does he hasten back to Venice to try to rescue his benefactor, the magnanimous Ansaldo, who is eventually saved only by the ingenuity and legal manoeuvring of the disguised Lady of Belmonte.

Throughout this story, Giannetto receives much but deserves little. What does his obsessive desire to sleep with the widow and his ethically questionable behaviour toward his adopted father and his Venetian friends suggest about the story that Ser Giovanni Fiorentino was attempting to tell? First and most important, although several narrative details show us Giannetto's failings, the characters in the story seem to see only a young man of outward talents and accomplishments. The nobility of both Venice and Belmonte exalt him as a model of courtesy and a man of accomplishment. The Venetians celebrate Giannetto's open-handed generosity as soon as he enters their society—though we know that his largesse is all funded by Ansaldo—while the lords and ladies of Belmonte are immediately delighted with his social graces and pleasant conversation. They ardently wish him to be their lord each time he arrives and they rejoice when he finally wins his pact with the widow lady to become their lord.

These characters' attitudes may suggest that the tale has a conservative social purpose. For them, nobility consists in social graces and pleasant conversation. They are willing and indeed happy to accept Giannetto as their ruler; he subdues or reincorporates (the text allows both readings) the Lady of Belmonte, who operates outside the mercantile system of exchange of the period and also challenges traditional gender roles. The action of the story draws her back into predictable, stable patriarchal structures by providing her with a husband, while at the same time ensuring that the land of Belmonte settles back to patriarchal rule under a new lord. In this regard, Giannetto is an agent of the story's conservative resolution: a clever, perhaps menacing female with uncanny power is brought under the socially sanctioned domination of a male who can take her to bed and delight her. The magical realm of Belmonte is restored by his success. The population's rejoicing, tournaments, and celebrations seem quite earnest and they are treated by the author without irony.

The celebrations last only so long, however, because the third and final pact of the story redirects our attention from the court of Belmonte to a courtroom back in Venice. The legal triumph of the Lady of Belmonte, now Giannetto's wife, clearly fascinated Shakespeare. He retained many details from this phase of the story, four in particular: the legal manoeuvring around flesh and blood that prevents a gruesome murder, the verdict that the Jew will take away nothing but his humiliation for having attempted to gain a pound of Christian flesh, the salvation of the generous Ansaldo, and the final ring trick the Lady of Belmonte plays on her new husband. Shakespeare seems to have taken particular inspiration from these elements as he crafted the comic resolution of his play.

But even with so many obvious plot points in common, *Il Pecorone* does not tell the full story of Shakespeare's borrowing. When we analyze the sources of *The Merchant of Venice*, we must also consider the indisputable influence of Christopher Marlowe's *The Jew of Malta*, performed by The Lord Admiral's Men, the rival company to Shakespeare's own, in the early 1590s, just at the time that a young William Shakespeare arrived in London and began his career in theatre. Even if the plot of *Il Pecorone* is clearly much closer to that of Shakespeare's play, *The Jew of Malta* seems to have provided several important elements, both conceptual and narrative. Marlowe's immensely popular play put the Jew Barabas (the name, that of a biblical criminal, alone tells us something important about the playwright's theme) at the centre of his story. Probably with a significant nod to Marlowe, Shakespeare turns Ser Giovanni's insistent but largely mysterious "Jew of Mestre" into a central character, giving Shylock a much wider range of passions, much greater psychological depth, a daughter, and perhaps most notably a recollected past as a husband. In act 3, scene 1, for example, he woefully recalls his apparently deceased or departed wife Leah. The inspiration for these changes seems to have come from Marlowe: his play features a similarly apostate daughter named Abigail who abandons her Jewish faith, embraces Christianity, and violently squares off against her father over her choices. But the resemblances do not stop there: like Marlowe's Barabas, Shakespeare's Shylock explicitly understands that his religious faith and his ethnic identity are central to who he is. Starting with his first appearance in act 1, he draws attention to both again and again, unlike Ser Giovanni's prototype, who appears only at the end of the story as part of its last major episode. Like Barabas, Shylock pursues revenge, in part, on behalf of "his tribe" against the hypocrisy and the ill treatment of his Christian tormenters. While *Il Pecorone* makes clear that religious and ethnic difference are motives for the Jew of Mestre (he says simply, and only once, that he wants a pound of the richest Christian merchant's flesh), it is never clear whether his motive is based more on religious difference or on social class resentment. Marlowe appears to be the clear inspiration for Shylock's much more thoroughly and passionately articulated contempt for Antonio and his fellow Christians.

Il Pecorone poses two questions well worth considering in detail. First, what does the title mean? Who is the dunce or simpleton of this tale? Is it the Jew of Mestre for attempting an impossible revenge and ending up so publicly and shamefully thwarted? He who thinks he is trapping birds is soon caught in his own trap, the story tells us. Or is it Giannetto, for being so stupid as to lose two shiploads of precious merchandise in his quest to obtain the sexual favours of an unknown lady? Or is it Ansaldo, for being so silly as to back the ventures of an ungrateful and irrepressible surrogate son who nearly let him die while he was revelling in the arms of a faraway woman? Or could it be Bindo, for making such a poor parenting decision at the very start of the story? Second, why are there no consequences for the bad behaviour of Giannetto? Ansaldo forgives him, the communities of Venice and Belmonte consistently adore him, and the Lady of Belmonte overlooks the fact that he cheated at her game to win her love. Should we be so generous?

A Note on the Text

Ser Giovanni Fiorentino's *Il Pecorone* was originally published in Lucca, Italy in 1554 and was reprinted many times. It appears here in a new translation by Marinella Garatti and Thomas G. Olsen. Unlike previous translators, who took considerable liberties with the language of the original text and made the story more sophisticated, we attempted to preserve the distinctively plain style of Ser Giovanni. In particular, the author was quite basic in the verbs used to introduce speech, using only simple terms such as "said," "replied," and "added," and he often repeated simple narrative formulas in ways we usually associate with folk tales.

Il Pecorone by Ser Giovanni Fiorentino

In Florence there once lived, in the house of the Scali, a merchant whose name was Bindo. He had been many a-times to Tana and Alexandria, and on all those long voyages that are made with merchandise.

This Bindo was quite rich and had three beloved grown sons. And nearing death, he called the eldest and the middle one, and in their presence made his last will. He left them both heirs of all his worldly possessions, and to his youngest son left nothing.

Once the will was made, the youngest son, whose name was Giannetto, hearing of this, went to visit him at his bedside and said, "My dear father, I am really quite surprised by what you have done, not remembering me in your will." The father replied, "My dear Giannetto, there is no living creature I love more than you and so I do not want you to stay here after my death—instead, as soon as I am dead I want you to go to Venice to a godfather of yours by the name of Messer Ansaldo.[1] He has no sons and has written to me several times to send you to him. I heard that he is the richest merchant of all among the Christians today. And so when I am dead I want you to leave and go to him and bring him this letter. And if you handle things right, you will end up a rich man." The son said, "My dear father, I am ready to do what you bid me."

At this, the father gave him his blessing and within a few days died. And all the sons grieved deeply and they gave their father's body all due honours. And then after a few days the two brothers called Giannetto and told him this: "Dear brother, it is true that our father made his will and left us as heirs and made no mention of you. Nonetheless, you are still our brother. Until the time comes that we are all in need, you shall not want for anything." Giannetto replied, "My dear brothers, I thank you for your offer, but as for

---

[1] Throughout the Italian text Ansaldo and Giannetto are called *Messer*, as are some characters in the story "Sir Timbreo and Fenicia," above. Cognate with French *monsieur* and the English *mister*, the Italian *messer(e)* has no exact modern equivalent. In the sixteenth century it was used in a more respectful way than the modern English *mister*, but it was a lesser salutation than *signor* (used for lords or powerful magnates). Its cultural effect would not be well conveyed by calling these characters "Sir Ansaldo" or "Sir Giannetto"—titles which for modern English readers inevitably conjure up visions of medieval knights. Faced with these options, we felt that retaining *Messer* came closest to giving the feeling of the original: the term implied the kind of recognition that would be given to rich, respected merchants of the period, but without the more powerful implication of *signor* or the more fanciful associations of *sir*. This said, we translated *Messer(e)* as *Sir* when the term is used as direct address, as in "Sir Judge."

me, my desire is to go seek my fortune elsewhere and I am resolved to do
so. You shall have the inheritance that was given to you by right and with
our father's blessing."

Seeing his resolve, the brothers gave him a horse and some money for
expenses. Giannetto took leave of them and went on to Venice. He arrived
at the counting-house of Messer Ansaldo and gave him the letter that his
father had given him before dying. As Messer Ansaldo was reading this
letter, he realised that this was the dear son of his beloved Bindo, and as
soon as he finished reading it, he immediately hugged him, saying
"Welcome to the dear godson I have so greatly wished for." And he
immediately asked about Bindo, at which Giannetto replied that he had died.
At this, with many tears, he embraced and kissed him and said, "How the
death of Bindo pains me, for he helped me gain a large part of what I have—
but such is the joy that I now have in you that it eases my pain." And he had
him brought home and he commanded his attendants, household, grooms,
servants, and all who were in his home that Giannetto was to be obeyed and
served better than he himself. And to start, he gave him the keys to all his
cash and said to him, "My dear son, what there is, spend it, and buy yourself
clothing and shoes, just as you wish, and keep open table, and let people get
to know you. For I leave you with this thought: the more you get them to
love you, the better I will love you."

And so Giannetto began to associate with the gentlemen of Venice, to
hold and pay court, give and attend dinners, bestow gifts and livery, buy
good horses, joust, and revel as if he were someone accustomed to it; he was
magnanimous and courteous in everything, and he knew well how to show
honour and courtesy where it is due, and always honoured Messer Ansaldo,
more than if he were a hundred times his father. And he knew how to
conduct himself so wisely with all sorts of people that almost the whole of
Venice loved him, seeing him so wise and agreeable and courteous beyond
measure. For this, all women and men seemed to be enamoured of him and
Messer Ansaldo had eyes only for him, so pleased was he with his ways and
manners. Nor was there hardly a party in Venice to which this Giannetto
was not invited, so beloved was he by everyone.

Then it happened that two of his dear friends wanted to go to Alexandria
with their merchandise, with two ships, as they were accustomed to do each
year. They said to Giannetto, "You should come enjoy the pleasures of the
sea with us, to see the world, and especially Damascus and the lands out
there." Giannetto responded, "In good faith, I would very willingly go there
if my father Messer Ansaldo were to give me permission." They said, "We
will make sure he does, and he will be happy." And immediately they went
to Messer Ansaldo and said, "We would like to beseech you to agree to give

your permission to Giannetto to come with us this spring to Alexandria, and that you furnish him with some vessel or ship so that he can see a bit of the world." Messer Ansaldo said, "I am content if it pleases him." They replied, "Sir, he is content."

With that, Messer Ansaldo immediately had him furnished with a beautiful ship and had it filled with a lot of merchandise and decorated with flags and as many arms as were needed. And after it was provisioned, Messer Ansaldo commanded the captain and the others of the crew that they were to do what Giannetto told them and that they were to take good care of him, "for I do not send him," he said, "for any profits that I want him to earn, but for him to see the world as he pleases."

And when Giannetto was about to board the ship all Venice came out to see him because it had been a very long time since such a beautiful and well-furnished ship had left Venice. Everyone was sorry to see his departure, and so he took leave of Messer Ansaldo and all his friends, and they put out to sea, hoisted the sails, and set course for Alexandria in the name of God and good fortune.

Then, while the three friends in their three ships had been sailing for several days, it happened that one morning at the break of day Giannetto saw a bay with a beautiful harbour, and he asked the captain the name of the harbour. He replied, "Sir, that place belongs to a widowed lady who has imperilled many a gentleman." Giannetto said, "How so?" He answered, "Sir, she is both beautiful and enchanting, and she holds to this law: whoever arrives must sleep with her, and if he should succeed, he must take her to wife and be lord of the harbour and all of the country. And if he fails with her, he loses everything he has."

Giannetto thought to himself for a moment and then said, "Use every means you have and bring me to this harbour." The captain said, "Sir, watch what you say because many men have gone there and were left with nothing." Giannetto said, "Do not concern yourself with anything else. Do what I am telling you." And so it was done: they turned the ship around so quickly and slipped into the harbour in such a way that his friends in the other ships did not notice anything.

The next morning the news spread that this beautiful ship had arrived in the harbour, so that all the people went out to see it. And this was immediately reported to the lady. So she sent for Giannetto, who eagerly went to her and greeted her with great respect. She took him by the hand and enquired who he was and from where he came and whether he knew the country's custom.

Giannetto replied that he did, and that he had come there for nothing else. And she said, "You are a hundred times welcome." And so she paid him the greatest honour all that day, and had many barons and counts and knights at her service invited so that they could keep him company. All the barons loved the manners of Giannetto, his politeness, his pleasantness, and his conversation, so that nearly everyone fell in love with him. And all that day they danced and sang and made merry throughout the court for the love of Giannetto. Each one would have been content for him to be their lord.

Then as evening was coming on, the lady took him by the hand and led him to her bedchamber and said, "I think it is now time to go to bed." Giannetto replied, "My lady, I am yours." And immediately two young ladies-in-waiting entered, one bringing wine and the other some delicacies. The lady said, "I know you must be very thirsty, so drink." Giannetto took some delicacies and drank some of the wine, which was laced in order to make one sleep—which he did not know, and drank a half cup because it seemed good to him, and immediately he undressed and went to rest. And as he reached the bed he immediately fell asleep. The lady lay down by his side, and he was not heard from until morning after the third had passed.[1]

So when morning came, the lady arose and ordered the ship emptied, which she found filled with rich and good merchandise. Since the third had passed, the lady's maidservants went to Giannetto's bed and had him get up and told him to go with God because he had lost his ship and all that was in it. He was ashamed about this and felt that he had done poorly. The lady had a horse and some money for expenses given to him. And off he went, sad and heartbroken. He took off toward Venice, where, as he arrived, he did not want to go home for shame. Instead, at night he went to the home of one of his friends, who was very surprised and said to him, "Oh, Giannetto, what happened?" And he replied, "One night my ship hit a rock, broke apart, and everything got shattered. And everyone went this way and that. I clung to a piece of timber that cast me on the shore, and so I came by land. And here I am."

Giannetto stayed several days in the house of this friend, who one day paid a visit to Messer Ansaldo and found him very depressed. Messer Ansaldo said, "I have such great fear that my dear son may be dead or that the sea might bring him harm that I can find no place to rest or good to give me comfort, such is my love for him." The young man said, "I can tell you some news: he was wrecked at sea and lost every last thing, save that he survived." Messer Ansaldo said, "Praised be the Lord! As long as he survived, I am content. I do not care about the goods that got lost. Where is he?" The young man responded, "He is in my house," and immediately

---

[1] The Italian reads *che era passata terza* (until after the third had passed), which refers to the third hour of the day, or 9:00 a.m.

Messer Ansaldo got up and wanted to go see him. And as soon as he saw him, he immediately ran to him and hugged him and said, "My dear son, you have no reason to be ashamed before me, for it is common for ships to wreck at sea. And so, my dear son, do not be dismayed. Since you were not hurt, I am content." And he led him home, comforting him all the while.

The news spread all over Venice and everyone was sorry for Giannetto's losses. Then it happened that a short time later Giannetto's friends returned from Alexandria, and very rich. As soon as they returned they asked about Giannetto and all was told to them. At that they immediately ran to embrace him, saying "How did you get separated and where did you go that we could never find out anything about you? We came back around all that day, but we were never able to see you, nor know where you went. And we were so pained by this that for the whole voyage we could never be happy again, believing that you were dead."

Giannetto replied, "Such a contrary wind arose in an elbow of the sea that led my ship to wreck on a rock near land, that I barely survived and everything turned upside-down." And this is the excuse that Giannetto gave so as not to reveal his fault. And together they had a great celebration, thanking God that he survived and saying "Next spring, by the grace of God, we will win back everything you lost this time, but for now let's think about being merry, without melancholy." And so they gave themselves over to pleasure and happy times, just as they used to do.

Even so, Giannetto could do nothing but think of how he might be able to return to the lady, imagining it and saying, "Surely, I must have her for my wife or else I will die." And he could hardly raise his spirits, which is why Messer Ansaldo told him many times, "Don't be melancholy, for we have plenty and will be able to live very well."

Giannetto replied, "My lord, I will never be content unless I attempt this journey again." At that, seeing his determination, when the time came Messer Ansaldo furnished him with another ship, which had more merchandise than the first one, and of more value, such that he put in it the greater part of all his worldly wealth.

The friends, after furnishing their own ships with everything required, took to the sea along with Giannetto, hoisting their sails and setting off on their journey. And sailing day after day, Giannetto remained constantly alert to spot the harbour of the lady, which was called the Port of the Lady of Belmonte. And reaching the mouth of this harbour one night, which was in a little elbow of the sea, Giannetto immediately recognised it and had the sails and the rudder turned, and he slipped into it in such a way that his friends in the other ships once again would not notice.

The lady, arising the next morning and looking down into the harbour, saw the flags of this ship waving, immediately recognised them, and called one of her serving women and said, "Do you know those flags?" The serving woman said, "My lady, it looks like the ship of the young man who arrived here a year ago today, who brought us such riches with his merchandise." The lady said, "You certainly speak the truth: surely, he must really be in love with me, for I have never seen anyone ever return more than once." The serving woman said, "I never saw a more courteous or gracious man than he."

The lady sent him many young courtiers and squires, who paid him visits with great celebrations; and he made merry and celebrated with everyone, and so he came up to the castle and in the presence of the lady. And when she saw him, she embraced him with great celebration and joy, and with great reverence he embraced her. And in this way they spent that whole day in celebration and in joy, for the lady invited many barons and ladies, who came to the court to celebrate for the love of Giannetto. And almost all the barons felt sorrow and willingly would have had him as their lord because of his pleasing demeanour and graciousness. And almost all the ladies were in love with him, seeing with what measure he led a dance and how his countenance was ever joyous, so that everyone figured that he must be the beloved son of some great *signore*.[1] And seeing that it was time to go to bed, the lady took Giannetto by the hand and said, "Let us go lie down," and they went to the bedchamber and after they sat down, there came two young ladies-in-waiting with wines and delicacies, and they drank and ate, and then went to bed. And as soon as he was in bed he fell straight asleep. The lady undressed and lay down beside him and—in brief—he was not heard from all night.

And when the morning came the lady arose and immediately had his ship emptied. After the third passed, Giannetto came back to his senses, looked for the lady, but did not find her. He lifted his head and saw that it was well into the morning. He got up and began to feel ashamed. And so he was given a horse and some money to spend, and was told "Be gone." And with shame, he immediately departed, sad and melancholy.

And for many days he did not rest until he reached Venice, and by night he went back to the house of his same friend, who, when he saw him, felt the greatest surprise in the world, and said, "Oh my, what happened?" Giannetto answered, "All's bad for me—cursed be my fortune that ever I arrived in that country." His friend said, "You can certainly curse it, for you

---

[1] magnate: a wealthy, powerful man

have ruined poor Messer Ansaldo, who was the greatest and the richest merchant of all the Christians. Greater is the shame than the damage."

Giannetto remained hidden several days in the house of his friend and did not know what to do or say, and he almost wanted to return to Florence without saying a word to Messer Ansaldo. And then he resolved still to go to him, and so he did. When Messer Ansaldo saw him, he stood straight up and ran to embrace him, and said, "Welcome, my dear son!" And, weeping, Giannetto embraced him. Once he had heard everything, Messer Ansaldo said, "Do you know what, Giannetto, don't give yourself any reason for melancholy. Since I have you back, I am content. We still have enough that we can manage to live simply. It is the way of the sea to give to some and take from others."

The news spread across Venice and everyone was talking about Messer Ansaldo, deeply sorry for the losses he had sustained. It was necesssary for Messer Ansaldo to sell many possessions to pay for the merchandise that his creditors had given him.

It happened that Giannetto's friends returned from Alexandria very rich and once they reached Venice they were told how Giannetto had come back and how he had wrecked and lost everything. They marvelled at this, saying "This is the most extraordinary thing ever seen," and they went to Messer Ansaldo and Giannetto, and with great cheer said, "Sir, don't be dismayed, for next year we intend to go out and gain riches for you, because we were partly the cause of your loss since we were the ones who first induced Giannetto to come with us. So have no fear, and as long as we have means, use them as if they were your own." Messer Ansaldo thanked them and said that he still had enough for them to live on.

Then it happened that Giannetto, mulling over his thoughts day and night, could not find happiness. And Messer Ansaldo asked him what troubled him, and he replied, "I will never be content unless I gain back what I lost." Messer Ansaldo said, "My dear son, I do not wish you to go again because it is best that we live simply with the little that we have, rather than you venture it again." Giannetto responded, "I am resolved to do all that I can, for I would hold myself in the greatest shame if I were to stay like this." Seeing his resolve, Messer Ansaldo readied himself to sell everything he had in the world in order to furnish him with another ship. And he did just that, so that nothing at all remained, and he outfitted a most beautiful ship filled with merchandise. And because he was ten thousand ducats short, he went to a Jew in Mestre[1] and obtained them with these terms and conditions: if he were not to repay them by San Giovanni's Day next

---

[1] Mestre is a town near Venice. Ducats were an Italian currency.

June, the Jew could remove one pound of flesh from whatever part of his
body he wanted.

And so Messer Ansaldo was content and the Jew had legal papers drawn
up, with witnesses and the usual necessary precautions and formalities, and
then he counted out ten thousand ducats of gold and with this money Messer
Ansaldo supplied whatever the ship was lacking. And if the first two were
beautiful, the third one was much richer and better furnished. And so his
friends furnished their own two with the intention that everything they
earned would be Giannetto's. And when it came time to go, at the point of
leaving, Messer Ansaldo said to Giannetto, "My dear son, go, but see in
what debt I remain. I beg of you one favour: even if you should meet with
misfortune, may it please you to come and see me so that I might see you
before I die, I will go contentedly." Giannetto answered him, "Messer
Ansaldo, I will do everything that I believe will please you." Messer
Ansaldo gave him his blessing, and thus they took leave and began their
voyage.

All this while his two friends paid careful attention to Giannetto's ship.
And Giannetto went on, ever alert and ready to slip into the Port of
Belmonte, so much that one night he got one of his helmsmen to steer the
ship into the harbour of the gentle lady. When morning lit up the day the
friends who were on the other two ships wondered, not seeing Giannetto's
ship anywhere, and said to each other, "Certainly this is his ill fate." They
resolved to continue on their way, greatly surprised at this.

Once the ship reached the harbour the whole castle came out to watch,
hearing that Giannetto had returned. And marvelling greatly about this, they
said, "He must be the son of some great man, for each year he comes with
so much merchandise and in such beautiful vessels, may God wish him to
be our lord." And so he was visited by all the most prominent people and
by the barons and knights of that land, and the lady was told how Giannetto
had returned to the harbour. And so she came to the windows of the palace
and saw this beautiful ship and recognised the flags, and at this she crossed
herself, saying "Certainly, this is really something extraordinary: this is the
man who has brought wealth to this country." And she sent for him.

Giannetto went to her. With many embraces, they greeted each other and
paid each other all due courtesies. All the day was spent making merry and
celebrating, and for the love of Giannetto a beautiful tournament was held
and many barons and knights jousted that day. And Giannetto too wanted
to joust; and he did wonders that day, so at ease was he in armour and on
horseback. And his manners were so pleasing to all the barons that each one
wanted him for their lord.

Then it happened that at evening, being time to go to bed, the lady took Giannetto by the hand and said, "Let us go lie down." And as they came to the door of the bedchamber a servant woman of the lady who felt sorry for Giannetto leaned down to his ear and said softly, "Pretend to drink, but do not drink tonight." Giannetto understood her words. He entered the bedchamber and the lady said, "I know that you are very thirsty and so I want you to drink before you go to sleep." And immediately there appeared two young ladies-in-waiting who looked like two angels, with wine and delicacies in the usual way, and they started to serve his drink. Giannetto said, "Who would refrain from drinking, seeing two such lovely maidens?" At this the lady laughed. And Giannetto took the cup and made a show of drinking and poured it down his breast. And the lady believed that he had drunk and said in her heart, "You will bring us another ship, for you have lost this one." Giannetto went to bed and felt clear-headed and full of good will, and it seemed like a thousand years for the lady to come to bed, and he said to himself, "I have surely got her—two can play at this game."[1] And so that the lady would come to bed sooner he began to pretend to snore and sleep. At this the lady said, "All's well," and immediately she undressed and lay beside Giannetto, who did not wait a moment, but as the lady came under the covers, he turned toward her, embraced her, and said, "Now I have that which I have so much desired," and with this he gave her the peace of holy matrimony. And all night long she never left his arms.

The lady was more than content with this and she rose before the day broke and sent for all the barons and knights and many other citizens, and told them, "Giannetto is your lord, so prepare to celebrate." Immediately the sound of cheering arose from the land, "Long live our lord! Long live our lord!" and of bells and instruments playing in celebration. And many barons and counts beyond the castle were summoned with the words, "Come see your lord," and then a great and splendid celebration was begun.

And when Giannetto left the bed chamber he was dubbed a knight and placed on the throne, a sceptre was put in his hand, and with great triumph and glory he was named lord. And as soon as all the barons and ladies had come to court, he married the gentle lady with such great celebration and joy as could not be told or imagined. All the barons and all the lords of the land came to the feast, to make merry, to joust, to show their skill at arms, to dance, to sing and play music, with everything that comes with celebrating.

---

[1] The Italian proverb *sì ch'é ne pensa il ghiotto, e un'altra tavernaio* of the original means "as soon as the glutton thinks of a shrewd manoeuvre, the host thinks of another."

Like a magnanimous lord, Messer Giannetto began to give silk cloths and other riches that he had brought; he became strong and formidable, upholding reason and justice for every sort of person. And so he continued in such celebration and happiness, neither caring about nor remembering poor Messer Ansaldo, who remained bound for ten thousand ducats to the Jew.

Then one day, while Messer Giannetto was with his lady at the window of the palace, he saw a group of men with processional candles in their hands crossing the *piazza*,[1] going to make an offering. Messer Giannetto said, "What does this mean?" The lady replied, "That's a group of artisans who are going to the church of San Giovanni to make an offering because today is his feast day." Messer Giannetto then remembered about Messer Ansaldo. He rose from the window, sighed deeply, and his whole face changed. He paced the room up and down several times, thinking about this fact. The lady asked him what was wrong and Messer Giannetto replied, "nothing." At that, the lady began to press him, saying "Certainly, there is something and you don't want to say it." And she persisted so much that he told her how Messer Ansaldo remained bound for ten thousand ducats, "and today," he said, "the bond is due and so I feel great pain that my father may die for me, for if he does not repay the money today he must lose a pound of his own flesh." The lady said, "Sir, mount a horse at once and go across by land, which will be faster than by sea. And bring with you any companions you like, and bring one hundred thousand ducats, and never rest until you are in Venice. If he is not dead, bring him here." With that, he ordered the trumpet sounded and he mounted a horse with a company of twenty men, took plenty of money, and headed for Venice.

Then it happened that, with the term expired, the Jew had Messer Ansaldo arrested and wanted to remove a pound of flesh from him. Messer Ansaldo was begging the Jew that he might agree to delay his death for a few days so that if his Giannetto were to come, at least he could see him. The Jew said, "I am content to give you what you want as far as the delay, but even if he were to come a hundred times, I intend to remove a pound of flesh from your body, as the papers say." Messer Ansaldo replied that he was content.

All of Venice spoke of this, and everyone was sorry about it, and many merchants gathered, wanting to pay the ducats, but the Jew never agreed—to the contrary, he wanted to commit this murder in order to be able to say that he had killed the greatest merchant that ever lived among the Christians.

---

[1] public square, plaza

And then it happened that as Messer Giannetto was coming with all speed his lady followed right behind, dressed like a judge, with two attendants. Reaching Venice, Messer Giannetto went to the home of the Jew and with great joy embraced Messer Ansaldo and then told the Jew that he wanted to give him his ducats and anything more he might want. The Jew replied that he did not want any ducats, because he did not get them in time, but wanted to take a pound of flesh from his body. And here began the great controversy: everyone felt the Jew was in the wrong, but since Venice was considered a land of laws and the Jew had his reasons in full and legal form, no one dared tell him the contrary. They just pleaded with him.

So all the merchants of Venice went up to plead with this Jew, but he was firmer than ever. At that, Messer Giannetto wanted to give him twenty thousand ducats, but he would not accept; then he went to thirty thousand, and then to forty thousand, and then to fifty thousand, and so he went all the way to one hundred thousand ducats. At that the Jew said, "You know what? If you were to give me more ducats than this city is worth, I would not be content to keep them. Instead, I am going to do exactly what my papers say."

And while they were in midst of this quandary, there came to Venice the lady dressed like a judge. She got off her horse at an inn, and the innkeeper asked one of the assistants, "Who is this gentleman?" The assistant, who was already instructed by the lady on what to say, replied, "This is a gentleman judge who comes from his studies in Bologna and is going back home." Hearing this, the innkeeper welcomed him with great honour. And while at the table, the judge said to the innkeeper, "How is this city of yours being governed?" The host replied, "Sir, too much by law." The judge said, "How so?" The host continued, "How, sir? I will tell you. There was a young man who came from Florence, whose name was Giannetto; he came here to some grandfather or other of his, whose name is Messer Ansaldo. And he has been so gracious and polite that the gentlemen and ladies of this land were in love with him. Never did anyone as well-mannered as he come to this city. Now, this grandfather—three times he furnished him with three ships which were of the greatest value. And each time he met with calamity, so that by the last ship he was out of ducats. Therefore, Messer Ansaldo borrowed ten thousand ducats from a Jew, with these rules: that if he were not to repay them by San Giovanni's Day of the next June to come, the said Jew could take a pound of his flesh from wherever on his body he wished. Now this blessed youth has returned, and for these ten thousand ducats he wanted to give him one hundred thousand, but the perfidious Jew does not want to accept. And all the honest men of this land have gone to plead with him, but nothing comes of it."

The judge replied, "This matter is an easy one to examine." The host said, "If you would like to trouble yourself to bring it to a conclusion so that this good man does not die, you will gain the thanks and the love of the most virtuous youth that ever was born, as well as all the men of this land." At that, the judge sent a proclamation across the land that anyone wishing to resolve this question should come to him. Then Messer Giannetto was told how a judge from Bologna had come and would settle all questions, so Messer Giannetto told the Jew, "Let us go to this judge." The Jew said, "Let us go, but come who may, I have the right to do what the paper says."

And once they came into the presence of the judge and paid him all due respect, the judge recognised Messer Giannetto, but Messer Giannetto did not recognise her as the judge because with certain herbs she had disguised her face. Messer Giannetto and the Jew each told their own reason and duly presented the question before the judge, who took the papers and read them, and then said to the Jew, "I want you to take these one hundred thousand ducats and set free this good man, who will always be beholden to you." The Jew replied, "I will do none of it." The judge said, "That is your best course." But the Jew wanted none of it.

By agreement, they went to the court appointed for cases like these and the judge spoke for Messer Ansaldo and said, "Have this man come forth," and when he did, the judge said, "Now, take a pound of flesh from wherever you want, and do what you must do." At that, the Jew had him strip naked and he held in his hand a razor, which he had had made for this very purpose. And Messer Giannetto turned to the judge and said, "Sir, this is not what I was I pleading for." The judge responded, "Stay calm, for he has not yet taken a pound of flesh." Meanwhile, the Jew was moving towards him. The judge said, "Be careful what you do, for if you should remove more or less than one pound, I will have your head taken off. And I tell you more, that if even one droplet of blood leaves his body, I will have you killed. For your papers make no mention of shedding blood. Instead, they say you must remove a pound of flesh and say neither more nor less. And so, if you are wise, use any means you believe will best help you."

So he immediately had the executioner summoned, and the chopping block and axe brought to him, and said, "The moment I see one droplet of blood shed, I will have your head." The Jew began to be afraid and Messer Giannetto to rejoice. And after many arguments the Jew said, "Sir Judge, you have been more knowledgeable than I. Just let me have those one hundred thousand ducats and I am content." The judge said, "I want you to remove a pound of flesh, as your papers say, because I will not give you one penny. You should have taken the ducats when I wanted them given to you."

The Jew came down to ninety thousand, then eighty thousand, but the judge was all the more resolute. Messer Giannetto said to the judge, "Give him what he wants, as long as he hands him back." The judge replied, "I tell you to let me handle it." At that point the Jew said, "Give me fifty thousand." The judge replied, "I wouldn't give you the most miserable penny you have ever had." The Jew continued, "Give me at least my ten thousand ducats—air and earth be damned!" The judge said, "Do you not understand me? I am not giving you any money: if you want to take his flesh, you take it this way. If not, I will have your papers contested and annulled."

At that, each and everyone who was there rejoiced and all mocked this Jew, saying "He who thinks he's trapping birds is the one trapped." And so the Jew, seeing that he could not do what he had wanted, took his papers and in frustration cut them all up. And so Messer Ansaldo was freed. And with great celebration Messer Giannetto brought him back home and then immediately took those one hundred thousand ducats and went to the judge. He found him in the room as he was preparing to leave. Then Messer Giannetto said to him, "Sir, you have done me the greatest service that ever was done to me and so I want you to bring this money home, for you have well earned it."

The judge replied, "My dear Messer Giannetto, many thanks to you, but I have no need for it. Take it with you so that your lady cannot say that you managed your household affairs badly." Messer Giannetto said, "On my faith, she is so magnanimous, so courteous, and so honourable that even if I were to spend four times as much as this, she would be content, for she wanted me to bring much more money than this." The judge added, "How happy are you with her?" Messer Giannetto replied, "There is no creature on earth whom I love more than her, for she is so wise and so beautiful that nature could not have done more. And if you would do me such honour to come and meet her, you would marvel at how she will honour you, and you will see for yourself whether she is what I say, or even more."

The judge answered, "I do not want to go with you because I have other business, but since you say that she is so honourable, when you see her, pay her my respects." Messer Giannetto said, "It will be done, but I want you to take this money." And while he was saying these words the judge saw a ring on his finger and said to him, "I want this ring and I want no other money." Messer Giannetto replied, "I am content, but I give it very unwillingly, for my lady gave it to me and she told me that I should always wear it for love of her; and if she does not see me with it she will believe that I might have given it to another woman and so will be cross with me and believe that I have fallen in love. And I love her more than I love myself." The judge said,

"It seems certain to me that she loves you so much that she would believe what you say, and you will tell her that you gave it to me as a gift. But perhaps you wanted to offer it to one of your old mistresses here?"

Messer Giannetto replied, "So great is the love and the faith that I have for her that there is no lady in the world I would change for her, so perfectly beautiful is she in everything." And with that he took the ring from his finger and gave it to the judge, then they embraced each other and paid each other all due courtesies. The judge said, "Grant me one favour." Messer Giannetto answered, "Ask." The judge said, "That you not stay here—go seek your lady right away." Messer Giannetto said, "It feels like a hundred thousand years until I see her again." And with that they parted.

The judge embarked by boat and went with God. And Messer Giannetto offered lavish dinners and lunches, and gave gifts of horses and money to his friends, and like this he kept celebrating and held court, and then took leave of all the Venetians. He took Messer Ansaldo with him and many of his former friends went along, and out of tender affection for him nearly all the men and ladies wept at his departure, so pleasingly had he conducted himself with everyone during the time he was in Venice. And so he left and returned to Belmonte.

And so it happened that his lady had arrived a few days before him. And she pretended that she had been at the baths: she dressed again in women's clothing and ordered great preparations, had all the streets adorned with silk cloth, and had many brigades of soldiers outfitted. And when Messer Giannetto and Messer Ansaldo arrived, all the barons and the court went out to meet them, shouting "Long live our lord! Long live our lord!" And as soon as they arrived, the lady ran to embrace Messer Ansaldo and pretended to be a bit cross with Messer Giannetto, whom she loved more than herself.

A great celebration took place, with jousting, feats of arms, dancing, and singing for all the barons, ladies, and ladies-in-waiting who were present. Messer Giannetto, seeing that his wife did not appear as pleased to see him as she used to be, left and went to the bedchamber. He called her and said, "What's wrong?" and wanted to embrace her. The lady said, "No need for such tenderness, since I know well that in Venice you found your old mistresses again."

Messer Giannetto began to defend himself. The lady said, "Where is the ring that I gave you?" Messer Giannetto replied, "This is just what I thought would happen, and I said correctly that you would take this badly. But I swear to you by my faith in God and you that that ring—I gave it to the judge who decided the case in my favour." Said the lady, "I swear by the faith that I have in God and you that you gave it to a woman. And I know it—and you are not ashamed of swearing falsely."

Messer Giannetto added, "I pray God to take me from this world if I do not speak the truth, and what's more, I talked about this with the judge when he asked me for it." The lady said, "You might as well have stayed there and sent Messer Ansaldo here, so that you could revel with your mistresses, who I hear all wept when you left."

Messer Giannetto began to weep and become quite upset, saying "You make a sacrament of what is not and could not be true." With that the lady, seeing him weep, looked like a knife had been thrust into her heart, and immediately she ran to embrace him, roaring with the greatest laughter in the world. She showed him the ring and told him everything: the way he had talked to the judge, how she had been that very judge, and in what manner he gave the ring to him. Hearing this, Messer Giannetto felt the greatest surprise in the world and realising that it was really true, he started to rejoice. After he left the chamber, he told this to some of his barons and friends, and for this, the love between the two of them grew and multiplied. After that Messer Giannetto called for the serving woman who that night had taught him not to drink and he gave her as wife to Messer Ansaldo. And they lived in joy and celebration the rest of their lives.

Translated by Marinella Garatti and Thomas G. Olsen

Questions

1. Why is Ansaldo so consistently generous and forgiving toward Giannetto? How does he compare to Giannetto's father Bindo?

2. How do you think a character like the Lady of Belmonte would have been interpreted by readers in Renaissance Italy? Could her qualities or circumstances suggest something about the values of the society that produced this story?

3. How much does the story permit us to know about the motives of the Jew of Mestre? Why is this narrative detail important?

4. *Il Pecorone*, the title of Ser Giovanni's collection means "simpleton" or "dunce" or "dolt'—but does this story clearly identify who is intended by the title?

5. This story contains no equivalent characters to Shakespeare's Jessica and Lorenzo, the lovers who cross religious lines to marry. What did Shakespeare add to Ser Giovanni's story when he added this plot element?

6. The maidservant of the Lady of Belmonte is wily and clever, and she is partly responsible for Giannetto's success. What does Shakespeare make of this role in *The Merchant of Venice*? Why?

ARTHUR BROOKE,
THE TRAGICALL HISTORYE
OF ROMEUS AND JULIET (1562)

ROMEO AND JULIET

In deciding to write a play about the characters Romeo and Juliet, Shakespeare contributed to a literary tradition that reaches back to at least fifteenth-century Italy, when Masuccio Salernitano's *Cinquante Novelle* ("Fifty Stories") appeared in print. The core story is even older, with elements like the young lovers' opposition to their feuding families and the unintended effects of a sleeping potion extending back into the shadowy reaches of an unrecoverable oral tradition. The story of Romeo and Juliet crossed several linguistic and cultural borders between the time of Salernitano's first printed text of 1476 and late sixteenth-century Europe, when it appeared in multiple Italian, French, and English versions.

One way to understand Shakespeare's decision to turn to this story in about 1595 or 1596, relatively early in his career as a playwright and half a decade before he would begin an almost ten-year intensive experiment in writing tragedy, is to surmise that he was betting on the success of a famous and beloved story—one that had already proved very popular across Europe for over one hundred years. To the up-and-coming playwright, its combination of archetypal themes, celebration of youthful love, and tragic storyline must have seemed a sure winner in the lottery of late Elizabethan theatrical taste.

He was right. The play proved popular almost immediately and has remained so ever since. It may be his most performed play, and with over 60 cinematic versions, it is his most frequently filmed. It might also be his most frequently adapted and parodied play, with full-length operas and ballets, a beloved Broadway musical, many pop songs, television spoofs, memes, cartoons, and advertising pitches complementing a seemingly endless series of live performances and films of the play itself. And although "cultural impact" is a very hard thing to gauge, *Romeo and Juliet* certainly has a claim to being among Shakespeare's most influential plays worldwide, largely because the protagonists are so convincingly drawn and seem to touch with such authority and sympathy deep human universals related to youth, family, fate, love, and loss. A "Romeo" is a Romeo and a "Romeo and Juliet story" is a Romeo and Juliet story in nearly every culture.

It is not clear whether Shakespeare consulted any of the early printed Italian or French versions of the story. He may not have needed to: his immediate source was Arthur Brooke's verse translation *The Tragicall Historye of Romeus and Juliet*, published in 1562, and again in 1567; and it was probably reprinted twenty years later. At 3020 lines, the poem is only about 150 lines shorter than Shakespeare's five-act dramatization. Brooke's version was based on a 1559 French prose story by Pierre Boaistuau, which itself was translated from an Italian version published five years before. That Italian version, by Matteo Bandello, was in turn based upon a previous Italian *novella* by Luigi da Porto (published in 1530 and also reprinted later in the century). Da Porto derived his story in part from that of Salernitano, but also seems to have settled on the feuding families' names because he recalled a passing reference to them in Dante's early fourteenth-century verse epic *Inferno*. The pattern of cultural and literary recycling which is described in the general introduction to this volume can have no better illustration than the Romeo and Juliet story's amazing history of circulation in late medieval and early modern Europe.

Tales like these came to be called *novelle* in Italian, meaning something akin to "short stories" or "little novels." They were often recycled from oral tradition or from previously published versions, and as we see in the case of the Romeo and Juliet story, they travelled across national and linguistic borders with remarkable regularity and speed. Several *novelle* also crossed from prose into drama, inspiring Shakespeare and other early modern playwrights by providing the basis of what became classic works of the early modern theatre: *Othello*, *The Duchess of Malfi*, *Much Ado About Nothing*, and *The Merchant of Venice*, to name a few. The plots of *novelle* tended to feature characters and situations close to the lives of their merchant-class and semi-noble readers, but not to the exclusion of magical and paranormal elements to spice up the lives of more or less average people. The Romeo and Juliet story conforms to this pattern: the families—whatever the particular version calls them—are always noble and lofty in some respects, but their lives and activities also resemble the lives of the story's readers in many ways.

Arthur Brooke's translation was not the only English one available to Shakespeare, either. In William Painter's *The Palace of Pleasure* (1567) the tale of "Rhomeo and Julietta" appears alongside other racy short prose narratives that featured love, sex, jealousy, violence, and various other forms of impetuous human behaviour among noble and middling classes of people. Painter's version follows Brooke's in nearly every particular, but lacks some of Brooke's flair for description. An earlier English version, *The Tragicall and True Historie which Happened between Two Lovers*, by a certain B. G. (later identified by scholars as the poet and religious controversialist Bernard Garter) appeared in 1565. It is another deliberate knock-off of Brooke's poem and, remarkably, it was even published by Brooke's own publisher, Richard Tottell. It does not appear that Shakespeare consulted either of these post-Brooke tales, however.

Not a great deal is known about Arthur Brooke, and it is probably safe to say that if his translation of the story of Romeo and Juliet had not caught the attention of Shakespeare, his name would be completely obscure to us today. However, in his own day he moved in literary circles in London, where he was admitted to the Inner Temple—essentially a combination of law school and professional society, but also a hub of amateur literary and dramatic activity during the Elizabethan period—on the recommendation of Thomas Sackville and Thomas Norton, co-authors of one of the most important early Elizabethan tragedies, *Gorboduc* (1561). Records of the Inner Temple suggest that Brooke was involved in the production of plays and masques there. But his life was soon cut short: in March of 1563 he died in a shipwreck en route to France, apparently while in some form of service to the crown.

Except for the Argument, which (as in Shakespeare's play) is a sonnet in pentameter, Brooke uses a poetic form known as poulter's measure, in which lines of 12 syllables (sometimes called Alexandrines) alternate and rhyme with lines of 14 syllables (called fourteeners). Not uncommonly, each long line was split into two, making each rhymed pair a unit of four lines. Here is an example from the conclusion to the poem, given in its original form:

> That with their emptied tears,
>   their choler and their rage
> Was emptied quite; and they,
>   whose wrath no wisdom could assuage,
> Nor threat'ning of the prince,
>   ne mind of murthers done,
> At length, so mighty Jove it would,
>   by pity they are won.
> And lest that length of time
>   might from our minds remove
> The memory of so perfect, sound,
>   and so approvèd love,

The bodies dead, removed
    from the vault where they did lie,
In stately tomb, on pillars great,
    of marble, raise they high.
On every side above
    were set, and eke beneath,
Great store of cunning epitaphs,
    in honour of their death.
And even at this day
    the tomb is to be seen;
So that among the monuments
    that in Verona been,
There is no monument
    more worthy of the sight,
Than is the tomb of Juliet
    and Romeus her knight. (3013-3020)

Poulter's measure—the term refers to the tradition of merchants giving an extra egg or two to customers who bought a dozen—has never been particularly popular in English letters, despite various attempts to use it over the years. Compared to the more energetic 10-syllable line favoured by Shakespeare and most other English authors since, poulter's measure can seem affected, sing-songy, and even tedious—the extra syllables in each line notably slowing the pace of the poem. However, even though this experiment did not take hold in English poetry, when the 14-syllable lines are broken after the fourth iamb, they produce lines of four and three iambs familiar to students of English and American literature as the "common meter" found in, for example, traditional English hymns and the poems of Emily Dickinson.

Brooke's version of the story tells us something important about sixteenth-century reading tastes. His preface announces a conventionally pious moral purpose to the work—avoiding sin, keeping the passions in check, obeying one's parents—and it adopts a deliberately archaic poetic language that draws heavily from medieval forms. These antiquated usages and tropes suggest a story drawn from the ages, a timeless tale with a timeless message. Individual word choices, archaic or regional or both, suggest the heroic language of the past: *hight* for "called" or "named," *eyne* for "eyes," *eke* for "also," *trow* and *ween* for "guess" or "know," *withouten* for "without," *ne* for "nor," "not," or "no," and so on. Past and occasionally present participles are sometimes indicated with a *y*, as in *y-planted, y-graved, y-kept*, and so on—a form that reaches back to Anglo-Saxon grammar, but which was on the decline even in the time of Chaucer, who nonetheless employed it for effect. (Years later Edmund Spenser would make frequent use of *y*-verbs in *The Faerie Queen*, published in 1590 and 1596, to create a similarly fanciful, antiquarian picture of England's chivalric past.) Of particular thematic relevance is Brooke's frequent use of the words *hap* (fortune) and *ware* (caution) and their derivatives: the terms are employed literally dozens of times in the poem to signal the effects of fortune and the need for caution as the characters try to beat fate.

Brooke also consistently invokes classical thought in the poem, if in rather basic ways. He often summons up the image of Fortuna with her wheel of fortune, invokes the three Fates, and makes other apt allusions to the thought and figures of ancient Greece and ancient Rome. But none of these make the poem especially pedantic or arcane; passing references to Helen of Troy, or to Mars, Cupid, and Venus are precisely the kind with which middling readers with some level of education and cultural sophistication would have been familiar. They probably felt rewarded for recognising them as they made their way through the poem.

The poem presents some interesting thematic contradictions and questions. Brooke's opening gesture is curiously at odds with the rest of his story. In his preface he asserts the conservative, didactic purposes of a conventional sixteenth-century cautionary tale: "to describe unto thee a couple of unfortunate lovers, thralling themselves to unhonest desire, neglecting the authority and advice of parents and friends . . . abusing the honourable name of lawful marriage . . . finally, by all means of unhonest life, hasting to most unhappy death." But the story itself scarcely condemns the behaviour of the youthful lovers, and indeed in many ways it offers a sympathetic view of their actions, even when they violate social conventions and the wishes of their parents.

There is something beautiful and timeless about the tragedy Brooke narrates, even if it sometimes feels plodding or ponderous to modern ears. Clearly his subject matter fired something in Shakespeare's own fertile imagination. For although Shakespeare closely followed Brooke's storyline and benefitted a great deal from the high concentration of dialogue already in his source, he also made many significant changes to it. Perhaps most notably, he compresses the poem's time frame and speeds up its action. As you read Brooke's poem, which opens with a Christmas feast, you might notice specific time markers indicating how long the story is to supposed have taken. These differ significantly in Shakespeare's version, and so his story suggests a very different pace of events from that of Brooke's tale. Likewise, the young playwright altered his source's characters. Mercutio, one of Shakespeare's great comic-tragic inventions, bears the same name as one of Brooke's characters, but his place in and significance to the story are changed in Shakespeare's version. What does Shakespeare seem to want to achieve by making this change? And while you consider that topic, ask yourself whether he does anything in particular with other roles or plot points in the story. What about the ending of the poem compared to that of the play? Does there seem to be a clear artistic reason for Shakespeare's changes as the story wraps up? And as always, what changes did Shakespeare make concerning the psychological motives of his tragic protagonists?

Finally, let us not forget a basic principle as we think about Shakespeare's debt to Brooke. Although he took the general outline and many details from Brooke, Shakespeare also went well beyond Brooke's story in crafting his version, drawing discrete elements from other sources and mixing them into the general plot outline that Brooke and others before him created. He drew freely upon English oral folk traditions in introducing the tale of Queen Mab, for example, and he endowed his characters with psychological complexity that neither Brooke nor earlier authors cared to dwell upon. Determining the artistic motives for such profound changes to the received story is a question for lengthy and robust discussion about how a work of art inspires another one. And that question takes us to the very heart of how Shakespeare used a single story line as a basis and transformed it by seeing old material in a new way and adding to what he found.

A Note on the Text

This text of *The Tragicall Historye of Romeus and Juliet* is based on Arthur Brooke's first edition (London: Richard Tottel, 1562). I have added notes and glosses, modernised the original spelling, and brought Brooke's punctuation into conformity with modern standards wherever possible. In addition, I inserted verse paragraph breaks into the original text, which runs well over 3,000 lines without breaks. I silently corrected a few obvious misprints and collapsed the poem's split poulter's measure lines into couplets (see introduction, above). Frequently repeated archaic words are footnoted on their first occurrence and thereafter noted with °, which refers readers to the glossary at the end of this volume.

Arthur Brooke, *The Tragical History of Romeus and Juliet* (1562)

To the Reader

The God of all Glory created, universally, all creatures to set forth His praise; both those which we esteem profitable in use and pleasure, and also those which we accompt noisome[1] and loathsome. But principally He hath appointed man the chiefest instrument of His honour, not only for ministering matter thereof in man himself, but as well in gathering out of other the occasions of publishing[2] God's goodness, wisdom, and power. And in like sort,[3] every doing of man hath, by God's dispensation, something whereby God may and ought to be honoured. So the good doings of the good and the evil acts of the wicked, the happy success of the blessed and the woeful proceedings of the miserable, do in divers sort[4] sound one praise of God. And as each flower yieldeth honey to the bee, so every example ministereth good lessons to the well-disposed mind. The glorious triumph of the continent man upon the lusts[5] of wanton flesh, encourageth men to honest restraint of wild affections; the shameful and wretched ends of such as have yielded their liberty thrall[6] to foul desires teach men to withhold themselves from the headlong fall of loose dishonesty. So, to like effect, by sundry means the good man's example biddeth men to be good, and the evil man's mischief warneth men not to be evil. To this good end serve all ill ends of ill beginnings. And to this end, good Reader, is this tragical matter written, to describe unto thee a couple of unfortunate lovers, thralling themselves to unhonest desire; neglecting the authority and advice of parents and friends; conferring their principal counsels with drunken gossips and superstitious friars (the naturally fit instruments of unchastity); attempting all adventures of peril for th' attaining of their wished lust; using auricular confession,[7] the key of whoredom and treason, for furtherance of their purpose; abusing the honourable name of lawful marriage to cloak the

---

[1] consider disgusting
[2] make publicly known
[3] a similar way (see glossary)
[4] in various ways (see glossary)
[5] continent: restrained, temperate; lust: either sexual desire or desire more generally, and used in both senses in the poem (see glossary)
[6] slave (see glossary)
[7] confession made to a priest, a topic of significant religious controversy in newly Protestant England in 1562

shame of stolen contracts;[1] finally by all means of unhonest life hasting to most unhappy death.

This precedent, good Reader, shall be to thee, as the slaves of Lacedaemon,[2] oppressed with excess of drink, deformed and altered from likeness of men both in mind and use of body, were to the freeborn children, so shewed[3] to them by their parents, to th' intent to raise in them an hateful loathing of so filthy beastliness. Hereunto, if you apply it, ye shall deliver my doing from offence and profit yourselves. Though I saw the same argument lately set forth on stage[4] with more commendation than I can look for—being there much better set forth than I have or can do—yet the same matter penned as it is may serve to like good effect, if the readers do bring with them like good minds to consider it, which hath the more encouraged me to publish it, such as it is.

The Argument
Love hath inflamèd twain by sudden sight,
And both do grant the thing that both desire.
They wed in shrift[5] by counsel of a friar.
Young Romeus climbs fair Juliet's bower by night.
Three months he doth enjoy his chief delight.
By Tybalt's rage provokèd unto ire,
He payeth death to Tybalt for his hire.[6]
A banished man he 'scapes by secret flight.
New marriage is offered to his wife.
She drinks a drink that seems to reave[7] her breath:
They bury her that sleeping yet hath life.
Her husband hears the tidings of her death.
He drinks his bane. And she with Romeus' knife,
When she awakes, herself, alas! she slay'th.[8]

---

[1] extramarital affairs

[2] According to the historian Plutarch (46-c. 119 CE), the slaves of the ancient Greek city-state of Lacedaemon (Sparta) were periodically made drunk so that their masters could show their sons what a contemptible example they made, negative examples of behaviour ("so filthy beastliness"), as detailed in the rest of the sentence.

[3] showed (see glossary)

[4] If Brooke is correct that there was a previous stage version of the story, the play is now lost.

[5] after confession and absolution

[6] reward, due (see glossary)

[7] take or steal away (see glossary)

[8] The argument is in the form of an Italian sonnet. Shakespeare opens his play with a sonnet as well, but changes the form to an English rhyme scheme.

Romeus and Juliet
There is beyond the Alps a town of ancient fame
Whose bright renown yet shineth clear: Verona men it name;
Built in a happy time, built on a fertile soil,
Maintained by the heavenly fates, and by the townish toil,
The fruitful hills above, the pleasant vales below,
The silver stream with channel deep that thro' the town doth flow,
The store of springs that serve for use and eke[1] for ease,
And other more commodities which profit may and please—
Eke many certain signs of things betid[2] of old
To fill the hungry eyes of those that curiously behold
Do make this town to be preferred above the rest
Of Lombard[3] towns, or at the least compared with the best.
In which while Escalus as prince alone did reign,
To reach reward unto the good, to pay the lewd with pain,
Alas, I rue to think, an heavy hap befell,[4]
Which Boccace[5] scant, not my rude tongue, were able forth to tell.
Within my trembling hand my pen doth shake for fear
And on my cold amazèd head upright doth stand my hair.
But sith[6] she doth command, whose hest[7] I must obey,
In mourning verse a woeful chance to tell I will assay.[8]
Help, learnèd Pallas; help, ye Muses with your art;
Help, all ye damnèd fiends to tell of joys returned to smart.[9]
Help eke, ye sisters three, my skilless pen t'indite:
For you it caused which I, alas, unable am to write.

There were two ancient stocks which Fortune high did place
Above the rest, indued[10] with wealth and nobler of their race,

---

[1] also (see introduction and glossary)
[2] that occurred (see glossary)
[3] of Lombardy, a region of northern Italy
[4] A heavy fate (*hap*: see introduction and glossary) occurred
[5] Giovanni Boccaccio (1313-1375), a widely influential Italian poet and humanist thinker, can barely (scant) tell this story.
[6] Since she whose command I must obey: the poet first invokes Pallas Athena, the ancient Greek goddess of wisdom, inspiration, and other positive attributes as his muse; he then invokes the three (often nine) Muses.
[7] command (see glossary)
[8] attempt (see glossary)
[9] pain, injury (see glossary)
[10] endowed

Loved of the common sort,[1] loved of the prince alike,
And like unhappy were they both when Fortune list[2] to strike,
Whose praise, with equal blast, Fame in her trumpet blew:
The one was clepèd[3] Capulet, and th'other Montague.
A wonted[4] use it is that men of likely sort°
(I wot[5] not by what fury forced) envy each other's port.[6]
So these, whose egall[7] state bred envy pale of hue
And then, of grudging envy's root, black hate and rancour grew
As of a little spark oft riseth mighty fire,
So of a kindled spark of grudge in flames flash out their ire:
And then their deadly food, first hatched of trifling strife,
Did bathe in blood of smarting° wounds; it reavèd[8] breath and life.

No legend lie[9] I tell, scarce yet their eyes be dry
That did behold the grisly sight with wet and weeping eye,
But when the prudent prince who there the sceptre held
So great a new disorder in his commonweal[10] beheld
By gentle mean[11] he sought their choler to assuage
And by persuasion to appease their blameful furious rage.
But both his words and time the prince hath spent in vain:
So rooted was the inward hate he lost his busy[12] pain.
When friendly sage advice ne[13] gentle words avail,
By thund'ring threats and princely power their courage 'gan he quail
In hope that when he had the wasting flame supprest
In time he should quite quench the sparks that burned within their breast.

Now whilst these kindreds do remain in this estate
And each with outward friendly show doth hide his inward hate
One Romeus, who was of race a Montague,

---

[1] the common people
[2] was pleased (see glossary)
[3] named (see introduction and glossary)
[4] usual, habitual (see glossary)
[5] know (see introduction and glossary)
[6] station in life
[7] equal
[8] took away (see glossary)
[9] false tale
[10] commonwealth (see glossary)
[11] means (see glossary)
[12] anxious (see glossary)
[13] nor (see introduction and glossary)

Upon whose tender chin as yet no manlike beard there grew,
Whose beauty and whose shape so far the rest did stain
That from the chief of Verone youth he greatest fame did gain,
Hath found a maid so fair (he found so foul his hap°),
Whose beauty, shape, and comely grace did so his heart entrap
That from his own affairs his thought she did remove;
Only he sought to honour her, to serve her, and to love.
To her he writeth oft, oft messengers are sent;
At length, in hope of better speed,[1] himself the lover went
Present to plead for grace, which absent was not found,
And to discover to her eye his new receivèd wound.
But she that from her youth was fostered evermore
With virtue's food and taught in school of wisdom's skilful lore[2]
By answer did cut off th'affections of his love,
That he no more occasion had so vain a suit to move.
So stern she was of cheer, for all the pain he took,
That in reward of toil she would not give a friendly look.
And yet how much she did with constant mind retire,
So much the more his fervent mind was pricked forth by desire.

But when he many months, hopeless of his recure,[3]
Had servèd her who forced[4] not what pains he did endure,
At length he thought to leave Verona and to prove
If change of place might change away his ill-bestowèd love;
And speaking to himself, thus 'gan he make his moan:
"What booteth me[5] to love and serve a fell,[6] unthankful one,
Sith° that my humble suit and labour sowed in vain
Can reap none other fruit at all but scorn and proud disdain?
What way she seeks to go, the same I seek to run,
But she the path wherein I tread with speedy flight doth shun.
I cannot live except[7] that near to her I be;
She is aye[8] best content when she is farthest off from me.

---

[1] success (see glossary)
[2] knowledge (see glossary)
[3] recovery (from lovesickness)
[4] cared, worried
[5] what does it gain or profit me (see glossary)
[6] cruel in love
[7] unless (see glossary)
[8] ever, always (see introduction and glossary)

Wherefore[1] henceforth I will far from her take my flight;
Perhaps mine eye, once banished by absence from her sight,
This fire of mine that by her pleasant eyne[2] is fed
Shall little and little wear away and quite at last be dead."

But whilst he did decree this purpose still to keep,
A contrary, repugnant thought sank in his breast so deep
That doubtful is he now which of the twain is best:
In sighs, in tears, in plaint, in care, in sorrow and unrest
He moans the day, he wakes[3] the long and weary night;
So deep hath love with piercing hand, y-graved[4] her beauty bright
Within his breast and hath so mastered quite his heart
That he of force must yield as thrall°—no way is left to start.
He cannot stay[5] his step, but forth still must he run;
He languisheth and melts away, as snow against the sun.
His kindred and allies do wonder what he ails
And each of them in friendly wise[6] his heavy hap° bewails.

But one among the rest, the trustiest of his feres,[7]
Far more than he with counsel filled and riper of his years,
'Gan sharply him rebuke; such love to him he bare[8]
That he was fellow of his smart° and partner of his care.
"What mean'st thou, Romeus," quoth he, "what doting rage
Doth make thee thus consume away the best part of thine age
In seeking her that scorns and hides her from thy sight,
Not forcing all[9] thy great expense, ne yet thy honour bright,
Thy tears, thy wretched life, ne thine unspotted truth,
Which are of force, I ween, to move the hardest heart to ruth?[10]
Now for our friendship's sake, and for thy health, I pray,
That thou henceforth become thine own—Oh, give no more away

---

[1] for that reason (see glossary)

[2] eyes (see introduction and glossary)

[3] stays awake

[4] engraved (see introduction for an explanation of *y*-verbs)

[5] refrain, stop, prevent, (see glossary)

[6] manner, way (see glossary)

[7] fellows, friends (see glossary)

[8] bore (see glossary)

[9] not caring at all

[10] ween: know, believe (see introduction and glossary) ruth: pity, compassionate
   sorrow (see glossary)

Unto a thankless wight[1] thy precious free estate;
In that thou lovest such a one thou seem'st thyself to hate.
For she doth love elsewhere—and then thy time is lorn,[2]
Or else (what booteth° thee to sue?) Love's court she hath forsworn.
Both young thou art of years, and high in Fortune's grace:
What man is better shaped than thou? Who hath a sweeter face?
By painful studies' mean° great learning hast thou won;
Thy parents have none other heir; thou art their only son.
What greater grief, trowst[3] thou, what woeful deadly smart°
Should so be able to distrain thy seely[4] father's heart
As in his age to see thee plungèd deep in vice
When greatest hope he hath to hear thy virtue's fame arise?
What shall thy kinsmen think, thou cause of all their ruth?°
Thy deadly foes do laugh to scorn thy ill-employèd youth.
Wherefore my counsel is that thou henceforth begin
To know and fly the error which too long thou liv'st in.
Remove the veil of love that keeps thine eyes so blind
That thou ne canst the ready path of thy forefathers find.
But if unto thy will so much in thrall° thou art,
Yet in some other place bestow thy witless wand'ring heart.
Choose out some worthy dame; her honour thou and serve,
Who will give ear to thy complaint and pity ere thou sterve.[5]
But sow no more thy pains in such a barren soil
As yields in harvest time no crop in recompense of toil.
Ere long the townish dames together will resort;
Someone of beauty, favour, shape, and of so lovely port,
With so fast fixed eye, perhaps thou mayst behold
That thou shalt quite forget thy love and passions past of old."

The young man's listening ear received the wholesome sound
And reason's truth, y-planted so, within his head had ground
That now with healthy cool y-tempered is the heat
And piecemeal wears away the grief that erst[6] his heart did fret.
To his approved friend a solemn oath he plight,[7]

---

[1] person, creature (see glossary)
[2] lost, wasted
[3] do you believe (see glossary)
[4] innocent, helpless, naïve (see glossary)
[5] before you die (see glossary)
[6] earlier, previously (see glossary)
[7] pledged (see glossary)

At every feast y-kept by day and banquet made by night,
At pardons in the church, at games in open street,
And everywhere he would resort where ladies wont° to meet;
Eke should his savage heart like all indifferently,
For he would view and judge them all with unallurèd eye.
How happy had he been had he not been forsworn,
But twice as happy had he been had he been never born.
For ere the moon could thrice her wasted horns renew,
False Fortune cast for him, poor wretch, a mischief new to brew.

The weary winter nights restore the Christmas games
And now the season doth invite to banquet townish dames.
And first in Capel's house, the chief of all the kin,
Spar'th for no cost the wonted use of banquets[1] to begin.
No lady fair or foul was in Verona town,
No knight or gentleman of high or low renown,
But Capulet himself hath bid unto his feast,
Or by his name in paper sent, appointed as a geast.[2]
Young damsels thither flock, of bachelors a rout,[3]
Not so much for the banquet's sake as beauties to search out.
But not a Montague would enter at his gate,
(For as you heard, the Capulets and they were at debate[4])
Save Romeus, and he in mask with hidden face,
The supper done, with other five did press into the place.

When they had masqued awhile with dames in courtly wise,°
All did unmask, the rest did show them to their ladies' eyes;
But bashful Romeus with shamefast face forsook
The open press[5] and him withdrew into the chamber's nook.
But brighter than the sun the waxen torches shone
That maugre[6] what he could he was espied of everyone.
But of the women chief, their gazing eyes that threw
To wonder at his sightly shape and beauty's spotless hue,
With which the heavens him had and nature so bedecked
That ladies thought the fairest dames were foul in his respect.

---

[1] the usual habit of hosting banquets
[2] guest (see glossary)
[3] crowd (see glossary)
[4] contentious with each other
[5] crowd (see glossary)
[6] despite

And in their head beside another wonder rose,
How he durst[1] put himself in throng among so many foes.
Of courage stout they thought his coming to proceed,
And women love an hardy heart, as I in stories read.
The Capulets disdain the presence of their foe,
Yet they suppress their stirrèd ire, the cause I do not know:
Perhaps t'offend their guests the courteous knights are loth,
Perhaps they stay° from sharp revenge, dreading the prince's wroth.[2]
Perhaps for that they shamed to exercise their rage
Within their house 'gainst one alone, and him of tender age.

They use no taunting talk ne harm him by their deed;
They neither say, "What mak'st thou here?" ne yet they say, "God speed"
So that he freely might the ladies view at ease
And they also beholding him, their change of fancies please,
Which Nature had him taught to do with such a grace
That there was none but joyèd at his being there in place.
With upright beam[3] he weighed the beauty of each dame
And judged who best and who next her was wrought in Nature's frame.
At length he saw a maid right fair, of perfect shape,
Which Theseus or Paris would have chosen to their rape.[4]
Whom erst° he never saw of all she pleased him most;
Within himself he said to her, "Thou justly may'st thee boast
Of perfect shape's renown and beauty's sounding praise,
Whose like ne hath, ne shall be seen, ne liveth in our days."
And whilst he fixed on her his partial piercèd eye,
His former love, for which of late he ready was to die,
Is now as quite forgot as it had never been.
The proverb saith, "Unminded oft are they that are unseen,"
And as out of a plank a nail a nail doth drive,
So novel love out of the mind the ancient love doth rive.[5]
This sudden kindled fire in time is wox[6] so great
That only death and both their bloods might quench the fiery heat.

---

[1] dared (see glossary)
[2] intense anger (see glossary)
[3] uplifted gaze
[4] The author cites two well-known abductions from classical literature: Paris's rape of Helen of Troy and Theseus's forceful seizure of the Amazonian queen Hippolyta.
[5] So new love drives old love out from the mind.
[6] waxed, grown

When Romeus saw himself in this new tempest tossed,
Where both was hope of pleasant port and danger to be lost,
He, doubtful, scarcely knew what countenance to keep;
In Lethe's flood[1] his wonted° flames were quenched and drenched deep.

Yea, he forgets himself, ne is the wretch so bold
To ask her name that without force hath him in bondage fold.
Ne how t'unloose his bonds doth the poor fool devise,
But only seeketh by her sight to feed his hungry eyes:
Through them he swalloweth down love's sweet impoisoned bait.
How surely are the wareless[2] wrapt by those that lie in wait!
So is the poison spread throughout his bones and veins
That in a while, alas, the while, it hasteth deadly pains.
Whilst Juliet, for so this gentle damsel hight,[3]
From side to side on everyone did cast about her sight.
At last her floating eyes were anchored fast on him,
Who for her sake did banish health and freedom from each limb.
He in her sight did seem to pass the rest as far
As Phoebus' shining beams do pass the brightness of a star.
In wait lay warlike Love with golden bow and shaft,
And to his ear with steady hand the bowstring up he raft.[4]
Till now she had escaped his sharp inflaming dart;
Till now he listed° not assault her young and tender heart.
His whetted arrow loosed, so touched her to the quick
That through the eye it strake[5] the heart and there the head did stick.
It booted° not to strive, for why, she wanted[6] strength;
The weaker aye° unto the strong of force must yield, at length.
The pomps[7] now of the feast her heart 'gins to despise
And only joyeth when her eyne° meet with her lover's eyes.
When their new smitten hearts had fed on loving gleams,
Whilst passing to and fro their eyes y-mingled were their beams.
Each of these lovers 'gan by other's looks to know
That friendship in their breast had root and both would have it grow.

---

[1] The waters (flood) of Lethe, the river of forgetfulness, flowed through the Plain of Hades, one of the underworld's five rivers.
[2] unwary
[3] was named (see introduction)
[4] drew
[5] struck
[6] lacked (see glossary)
[7] celebrations

When thus in both their hearts had Cupid made his breach
And each of them had sought the mean° to end the war by speech
Dame Fortune did assent their purpose to advance:
With torch in hand a comely knight did fetch her forth to dance.
She quit[1] herself so well and with so trim[2] a grace
That she the chief praise won that night from all Verona race,
The whilst our Romeus a place had warely[3] won,
Nigh to the seat where she must sit, the dance once being done.

Fair Juliet turned to her chair with pleasant cheer
And glad she was her Romeus approachèd was so near.
At th'one side of her chair her lover Romeo
And on the other side there sat one called Mercutio,
A courtier that each ware was highly had in price,
For he was courteous of his speech and pleasant of device.
Even as a lion would among the lambs be bold,
Such was among the bashful maids Mercutio to behold.
With friendly grip he seized fair Juliet's snowish hand:
A gift he had that Nature gave him in his swathing band,
That frozen mountain ice was never half so cold
As were his hands, though ne'er so near the fire he did them hold.
As soon as had the knight the virgin's right hand raught,[4]
Within his trembling hand her left hath loving Romeus caught.
For he wist well himself for her abode most pain,[5]
And well he wist she loved him best, unless she list° to feign.
Then she with tender hand his tender palm hath pressed,
What joy, trow you, was graffèd[6] so in Romeus' cloven breast
The sudden sweet delight hath stoppèd quite his tongue,
Ne can he claim of her his right, ne crave redress of wrong.
But she espied straightway, by changing of his hue
From pale to red, from red to pale, and so from pale anew,
That veh'ment love was cause why so his tongue did stay,°
And so much more she longed to hear what Love could teach him say.
When she had longèd long and he long held his peace,

---

[1] conducted, behaved
[2] fine
[3] carefully, cautiously (see glossary)
[4] gripped
[5] For he knew (*wist*: see glossary) he endured (*abode*: see glossary) great pain for her
[6] firmly set, grafted

And her desire of hearing him by silence did increase,
At last with trembling voice and shamefast cheer the maid
Unto her Romeus turned herself and thus to him she said:
"O blessed be the time of thy arrival here."
But ere she could speak forth the rest, to her Love drew so near
And so within her mouth her tongue he gluèd fast,
That no one word could 'scape her more than what already passed.

In great contented ease the young man straight is rapt:
"What chance," quoth he, "un'ware to me, O lady mine, is hapt,[1]
That gives you worthy cause my coming here to bliss?"
Fair Juliet was come again unto herself by this:
First ruthfully° she looked, then said with smiling cheer,
"Marvel no whit, my heart's delight, my only knight and fere,°
Mercutio's icy hand had all-to frozen mine
And of thy goodness thou again hast warmed it with thine."
Whereto with stayèd[2] brow 'gan Romeus to reply:
"If so the gods have granted me such favour from the sky,
That by my being here some service I have done
That pleaseth you, I am as glad, as I a realm had won.
O well-bestowed time that hath the happy hire,°
Which I would wish, if I might have, my wished heart's desire.
For I of God would crave, as price of pains forepast,
To serve, obey, and honour you, so long as life shall last;
As proof shall teach you plain, if that you like to try
His faultless truth, that nill for aught[3] unto his lady lie.
But if my touched hand have warmed yours some deal
Assure yourself the heat is cold which in your hand you feel
Compared to such quick sparks and glowing furious glead,[4]
As from your beauty's pleasant eyne, Love causèd to proceed,
Which have so set on fire each feeling part of mine
That, lo, my mind doth melt away, my outward parts do pine.
And but[5] you help, all whole to ashes shall I turn;
Wherefore, alas, have ruth° on him, whom you do force to burn."

Even with his ended tale the torches' dance had end

---

[1] chanced, happened
[2] sober
[3] will not for anything (aught); see glossary
[4] gladness, joy
[5] unless

And Juliet of force must part from her new chosen friend.
His hand she clasped hard and all her parts did shake
When leisureless with whisp'ring voice thus did she answer make:
"You are no more your own, dear friend, than I am yours,
My honour savèd, pressed t'obey your will while life endures."
Lo, here the lucky lot that seld[1] true lovers find,
Each takes away the other's heart, and leaves the own behind.
A happy life is love if God grant from above
That heart with heart by even weight do make exchange of love.

But Romeus gone from her, his heart for care is cold;[2]
He hath forgot to ask her name that hath his heart in hold.
With forgèd careless cheer, of one he seeks to know
Both how she hight[3] and whence she came that him enchanted so.
So hath he learned her name and know'th she is no geast;°
Her father was a Capulet and master of the feast.
Thus hath his foe in choice to give him life or death,
That scarcely can his woeful breast keep in the lively breath.
Wherefore with piteous plaint fierce Fortune doth he blame,
That in his ruth° and wretched plight doth seek her laughing game.
And he reproveth Love, chief cause of his unrest,
Who ease and freedom hath exiled out of his youthful breast.
Twice hath he made him serve, hopeless of his reward;
Of both the ills to choose the less, I ween° the choice were hard.
First to a ruthless one he made him sue for grace
And now with spur he forceth him to run an endless race.
Amid these stormy seas one anchor doth him hold:
He serveth not a cruel one as he had done of old
And therefore is content and chooseth still to serve,
Though hap should swear that guerdonless the wretched wight should
                                                        sterve.[4]
The lot of Tantalus is, Romeus, like to thine:
For want of food amid his food, the miser still doth pine.

---

[1] seldom
[2] his heart is cold with worry
[3] what her name was
[4] Although fortune (hap) should swear that, without reward (guerdon), the poor
    creature (wight) should die (sterve). The author next invokes Tantalus, who was
    condemned to drink from a pool of water that receded from him each time he
    stooped to drink. He became a byword for frustrated hopes.

As careful was the maid what way were best devise
To learn his name that entertained her in so gentle wise,°
Of whom her heart received so deep, so wide a wound.
An ancient dame she called to her, and in her ear 'gan round.[1]
This old dame in her youth had nursed her with her milk,
With slender needle taught her sew, and how to spin with silk.
"What twain are those," quoth she, "which press unto the door,
Whose pages in their hand do bear two torches light before?"
And then as each of them had of his household name,
So she him named yet once again, the young and wily dame.
"And tell me, who is he with visor in his hand
That yonder doth in masquing weed[2] beside the window stand?"
"His name is Romeus," said she, "a Montague,
Whose father's pride first stirred the strife which both your households
                                                    rue."
The word of Montague her joys did overthrow
And straight instead of happy hope despair began to grow.
"What hap° have I," quoth she, "to love my father's foe?
What, am I weary of my weal?[3] What, do I wish my woe?"
But though her grievous pains distrained her tender heart,
Yet with an outward show of joy she cloakèd inward smart;°
And of the courtlike dames her leave so courtly took
That none did guess the sudden change by changing of her look.
Then at her mother's hest° to chamber she her hied;°
So well she feigned, mother ne nurse the hidden harm descried.[4]

But when she should have slept as wont° she was in bed
Not half a wink of quiet sleep could harbour in her head.
For lo, an hugy heap of divers[5] thoughts arise
That rest have banished from her heart and slumber from her eyes.
And now from side to side she tosseth and she turns,
And now for fear she shivereth, and now for love she burns.
And now she likes her choice, and now her choice she blames,
And now each hour within her head a thousand fancies frames.
Sometime[6] in mind to stop amid her course begun,

---

[1] began to whisper
[2] masquerading costume, clothing (see glossary)
[3] well-being (see glossary)
[4] discovered
[5] great quantity of various (see glossary)
[6] sometimes (see glossary)

Sometime she vows, what so betide,[1] th'attempted race to run.
Thus danger's dread and love within the maiden fought:
The fight was fierce, continuing long by their contrary thought.
In turning maze of love she wand'reth to and fro,
Then standeth doubtful what to do, lost, overpressed with woe.
How so her fancies cease, her tears did never blin,[2]
With heavy cheer and wringèd hands thus doth her plaint begin:
"Ah, silly fool," quoth she, "y-caught in subtle snare!
Ah, wretchèd wench, bewrapt in woe! Ah, caitiff[3] clad with care!
Whence come these wand'ring thoughts to thy unconstant breast
By straying thus from reason's law, that reave° thy wonted° rest?
What if his subtle brain to feign have taught his tongue,
And so the snake that lurks in grass thy tender heart hath stung?
What if with friendly speech the traitor lie in wait,
As oft the poisoned hook is hid, wrapt in the pleasant bait?
Oft under cloak of truth hath Falsehood served her lust°
And turned their honour into shame that did so slightly trust.
What, was not Dido so, a crowned queen, defamed?
And eke for such a heinous crime have men not Theseus[4] blamed?
A thousand stories more to teach me to beware
In Boccace and in Ovid's books[5] too plainly written are.
Perhaps the great revenge he cannot work by strength
By subtle sleight, my honour stained, he hopes to work at length.
So shall I seek to find my father's foe his game;
So I, befiled,[6] Report shall take her trump of black defame,
Whence she with puffèd cheek shall blow a blast so shrill
Of my dispraise that with the noise Verona shall she fill.[7]
Then I, a laughing-stock through all the town become,
Shall hide myself but not my shame within an hollow tomb."

---

[1] whatever might happen
[2] cease
[3] wretch
[4] Dido was a legendary queen of Tyre, Theseus the legendary founder of Athens. Theseus was famous for deceiving Ariadne and Dido for being disappointed in love.
[5] The works of Giovanni Boccaccio (see note above) and Publius Ovidius Naso, popularly known as Ovid (43 BCE-c. 17 CE) were widely known, admired, and imitated.
[6] defiled
[7] The personified or allegorical figure Report plays a trump card to destroy Juliet's reputation throughout Verona.

Straight underneath her foot she treadeth in the dust,
Her troublesome thought as wholly vain, y-bred of fond[1] distrust.
"No, no, by God above, I wot° it well," quoth she,
"Although I rashly spake before, in no wise° can it be
That where such perfect shape with pleasant beauty rests,
There crooked craft and treason black should be appointed guests.
Sage writers say the thoughts are dwelling in the eyne;
Then sure I am, as Cupid reigns, that Romeus is mine.
The tongue the messenger eke call they of the mind;
So that I see he loveth me; shall I then be unkind?
His face's rosy hue I saw full oft to seek;
Straight again it flashèd forth, and spread in either cheek.
His fixèd heavenly eyne,° that through me quite did pierce
His thoughts unto my heart, my thought they seemèd to rehearse.[2]
What meant his falt'ring tongue in telling of his tale?
The trembling of his joints and eke his colour waxen pale?
And whilst I talked with him himself he hath exiled
Out of himself, a[3] seemèd me, ne was I sure beguiled.
Those arguments of love Craft wrate[4] not in his face,
But Nature's hand, when all deceit was banished out of place.
What other certain signs seek I of his good will?
These do suffice and steadfast I will love and serve him still
Till Atropos[5] shall cut my fatal thread of life,
So that he mind to make of me his lawful wedded wife.
For so perchance this new alliance may procure
Unto our houses such a peace as ever shall endure."
Oh, how we can persuade ourself to what we like
And how we can dissuade our mind if aught our mind mislike![6]
Weak arguments are strong, our fancies straight to frame
To pleasing things, and eke to shun if we mislike the same.

The maid had scarcely yet ended the weary war,
Kept in her heart by striving thoughts, when every shining star

---

[1] foolish
[2] repeat, echo
[3] he
[4] The allegorical figure of Craft wrote not.
[5] Atropos was the classical Fate (or Moirai, or Parcae) responsible for cutting the
    thread of human life.
[6] How can we dissuade our minds if they dislike anything (aught)?

Had paid his borrowed light and Phoebus spread in skies
His golden rays, which seemed to say now time it is to rise.
And Romeus had by this forsaken his weary bed,
Where restless he a thousand thoughts had forgèd in his head.
And while with ling'ring step by Juliet's house he passed
And upwards to her windows high his greedy eyes did cast,
His love that looked for him there 'gan he straight espy.
With pleasant cheer each greeted is; she followeth with her eye
His parting steps and he oft looketh back again
But not so oft as he desires; warely° he doth refrain.
What life were like to love, if dread of jeopardy
Y-soured not the sweet, if love were free from jealousy!
But she more sure within, unseen of any wight,
When so he comes, looks after him till he be out of sight.
In often passing so, his busy° eyes he threw,
That every pane and tooting hole¹ the wily lover knew.
In happy hour he doth a garden plot espy
From which, except he warely walk, men may his love descry;²
For, lo, it fronted full upon her leaning place,
Where she is wont° to show her heart by cheerful friendly face.
And lest the arbours might their secret love bewray,³
He doth keep back his forward foot from passing there by day;
But when on earth the Night her mantle black hath spread
Well armed he walketh forth alone, ne dreadful foes doth dread.

Whom maketh Love not bold, nay, whom makes he not blind?
He reaveth° danger's dread oft-times out of the lover's mind.
By night he passeth here a week or two in vain
And for the missing of his mark his grief hath him nigh slain.
And Juliet that now doth lack her heart's relief,
Her Romeus' pleasant eyne I mean, is almost dead for grief.
Each day she changeth hours (for lovers keep an hour
When they are sure to see their love in passing by their bower).
Impatient of her woe, she happed° to lean one night
Within her window and anon the moon did shine so bright
That she espied her love: her heart revivèd sprang
And now for joy she claps her hands, which erst° for woe she wrang.
Eke Romeus, when he saw his long desirèd sight,

---

¹ peephole
² unless he walk carefully, people might discover him
³ betray, reveal (see glossary)

His mourning cloak of moan cast off, hath clad him with delight.
Yet dare I say of both that she rejoicèd more:
His care was great, hers twice as great was all the time before;
For whilst she knew not why he did himself absent,
Aye doubting[1] both his health and life, his death she did lament
For love is fearful oft where is no cause of fear
And what love fears, that love laments, as though it chancèd[2] were.
Of greater cause alway° is greater work y-bred;
While he nought doubteth° of her health she dreads lest he be dead.
When only absence is the cause of Romeus' smart,°
By happy hope of sight again he feeds his fainting heart.
What wonder then if he were wrapped in less annoy?
What marvel if by sudden sight she fed of greater joy?
His smaller grief or joy no smaller love do prove;
Ne, for she passed him in both, did she him pass in love:
But each of them alike did burn in equal flame,
The well-beloving knight and eke the well-beloved dame.

Now whilst with bitter tears her eyes as fountains run,
With whispering voice y-broke with sobs thus is her tale begun:
"O Romeus, of your life too lavas[3] sure you are
That in this place and at this time to hazard it you dare.
What if your deadly foes, my kinsmen, saw you here?
Like lions wild, your tender parts asunder would they tear.
In ruth° and in disdain, I weary of my life
With cruel hand my mourning heart would pierce with bloody knife.
For you, mine own, once dead, what joy should I have here?
And eke my honour stained, which I than life do hold more dear."

"Fair lady mine, dame Juliet, my life," quod he,
"Even from my birth committed was to fatal sisters three.[4]
They may in spite of foes draw forth my lively thread
And they also, whoso saith nay, asunder may it shred.
But who to reave° my life, his rage and force would bend,
Perhaps should try unto his pain how I it could defend.
Ne yet I love it so, but always for your sake,
A sacrifice to death I would my wounded corpse betake.

---

[1] ever fearing (see glossary)
[2] fated
[3] careless (lavish)
[4] The classical Fates: see note above.

If my mishap were such that here before your sight
I should restore again to death, of life, my borrowed light,
That part he should before that you by certain trial knew
The love I owe to you, the thrall° I languish in,
And how I dread to lose the gain which I do hope to win;
And how I wish for life, not for my proper[1] ease,
But that in it you might I love, you honour, serve and please,
Till deadly pangs the sprite[2] out of the corpse shall send."
And thereupon he sware[3] an oath, and so his tale had end.

Now love and pity boil in Juliet's ruthful° breast,
In window on her leaning arm her weary head doth rest,
Her bosom bathed in tears to witness inward pain,
With dreary cheer to Romeus thus answered she again:
"Ah, my dear Romeus, keep in these words," quod she,
"For lo, the thought of such mischance already maketh me
For pity and for dread well-nigh to yield up breath;
In even balance peisèd[4] are my life and eke my death.
For so my heart is knit, yea, made one self with yours,
That sure there is no grief so small by which your mind endures,
But as you suffer pain, so I do bear in part,
Although it lessens not your grief, the half of all your smart.°
But these things overpast, if of your health and mine
You have respect or pity aught° my teary, weeping eyne,°
In few unfeigned words your hidden mind unfold
That as I see your pleasant face your heart I may behold.
For if you do intend my honour to defile
In error shall you wander still, as you have done this while;
But if your thought be chaste and have on virtue ground,
If wedlock be the end and mark which your desire hath found,[5]
Obedience set aside unto my parents due,
The quarrel eke that long ago between our households grew,
Both me and mine I will all whole to you betake
And following you whereso you go my father's house forsake.
But if by wanton love and by unlawful suit
You think in ripest years to pluck my maidenhood's dainty fruit

---

[1] own
[2] spirit (see glossary)
[3] swore
[4] weighed
[5] foundation, basis

You are beguiled; and now your Juliet you beseeks
To cease your suit and suffer her to live among her likes."[1]

Then Romeus, whose thought was free from foul desire
And to the top of virtue's height did worthily aspire,
Was filled with greater joy than can my pen express,
Or till they have enjoyed the like, the hearer's heart can guess.
And then with joined hands heaved up into the skies
He thanks the gods and from the heavens for vengeance down he cries
If he have other thought but as his lady spake;
And then his look he turned to her and thus did answer make:
"Since, lady, that you like to honour me so much
As to accept me for your spouse, I yield myself for such.
In true witness whereof, because I must depart,
Till that my deed do prove my word I leave in pawn my heart.
To-morrow eke betimes[2] before the sun arise,
To Friar Laurence will I wend, to learn his sage advice.
He is my ghostly sire[3] and oft he hath me taught
What I should do in things of weight when I his aid have sought.
And at this self-same hour I plight you here my faith
I will be here, if you think good, to tell you what he saith."
She was contented well, else favour found he none
That night at lady Juliet's hand, save pleasant words alone.
You see that Romeus no time or pain doth spare;
Think that the whilst fair Juliet is not devoid of care.

This barefoot friar girt with cord his grayish weed,
For he of Francis' order was, a friar, as I rede.[4]
Not as the most was he, a gross unlearned fool,
But doctor of divinity proceeded he in school.
The secrets eke he knew in Nature's works that lurk;
By magic's art most men supposed that he could wonders work.
Ne doth it ill beseem divines those skills to know
If on no harmful deed they do such skilfulness bestow;
For justly of no art can men condemn the use,
But right and reason's lore° cry out against the lewd abuse.

---

[1] let her live among her own family or kind
[2] early
[3] spiritual father (see glossary)
[4] The narrator guesses that this barefoot friar girded his greyish habit with cord (in the traditional dress of the Franciscan order).

The bounty of the friar and wisdom hath so won
The townsfolks' hearts, that well nigh all to Friar Laurence run
To shrive[1] themselves: the old, the young, the great and small,
Of all he is beloved well and honoured much of all.
And for he did the rest in wisdom far exceed,
The prince by him, his counsel craved, was holp[2] at time of need.
Betwixt the Capulets and him great friendship grew,
A secret and assurèd friend unto the Montague.
Loved of this young man more than any other guest,
The friar eke of Verone youth aye° likèd Romeus best,
For whom he ever hath in time of his distress,
As erst° you heard, by skilful lore° found out his harm's redress.
To him is Romeus gone, ne stay'th he till the morrow;
To him he painteth all his case,[3] his passèd joy and sorrow.
How he hath her espied with other dames in dance,
And how that first to talk with her himself he did advance;
Their talk and change of looks he 'gan to him declare
And how so fast by faith and troth they both y-couplèd are,
That neither hope of life nor dread of cruel death
Shall make him false his faith to her while life shall lend him breath.
And then with weeping eyes he prays his ghostly sire°
To further and accomplish all their honest hearts' desire.

A thousand doubts and mo[4] in th'old man's head arose;
A thousand dangers like to come the old man doth disclose
And from the spousal rites he redeth him refrain:
Perhaps he shall be bet advised[5] within a week or twain.
Advice is banished quite from those that follow love,
Except° advice to what they like their bending mind do move.
As well the father might have counselled him to stay°
That from a mountain's top thrown down is falling half the way
As warn his friend to stop amid his race begun,
Whom Cupid with his smarting° whip enforceth forth to run.
Part won by earnest suit, the friar doth grant at last,
And part because he thinks the storms so lately overpast
Of both the households' wrath this marriage might appease;

---

[1] confess
[2] helped
[3] describes his situation
[4] a thousand fears and more
[5] advised him to refrain because he may consider marriage more clearly

So that they should not rage again, but quite forever cease
The respite of a day he asketh to devise
What way were best, unknown, to end so great an enterprise.
The wounded man that now doth deadly pains endure
Scarce patient tarrieth whilst his leech[1] doth make the salve to cure:
So Romeus hardly grants a short day and a night,
Yet needs he must, else must he want his only heart's delight.
Young Romeus poureth forth his hap° and his mishap
The secrets of her heart. To whom shall she unfold
Her hidden burning love and eke her thought and cares so cold?

The nurse of whom I spake within her chamber lay.
Upon the maid she waiteth still; to her she doth bewray°
Her new receivèd wound and then her aid doth crave:
In her, she saith, it lies to spill;[2] in her, her life to save.
Not easily she made the froward nurse to bow,[3]
But won at length with promised hire° she made a solemn vow.
To do what she commands, as handmaid of her hest;°
Her mistress' secrets hide she will within her covert breast.
To Romeus she goes; of him she doth desire
To know the mean of marriage[4] by counsel of the friar.
"On Saturday," quod he, "if Juliet come to shrift,°
She shall be shrived° and marrièd; how like you, nurse, this drift?"
"Now by my truth," quod she, "God's blessing have your heart,
For yet in all my life I have not heard of such a part.
Lord, how you young men can such crafty wiles devise,
If that you love the daughter well, to blear the mother's eyes.
An easy thing it is with cloak of holiness
To mock the seely° mother that suspecteth nothing less.
But that it pleasèd you to tell me of the case,
For all my many years, perhaps, I should have found it scarce.
Now for the rest let me and Juliet alone;
To get her leave, some feat[5] excuse I will devise anon,
For that her golden locks by sloth have been unkempt,
Or for unwares[6] some wanton dream the youthful damsel dreampt,

---

[1] medical doctor
[2] end, kill
[3] Not easily did she get the headstrong nurse to give in.
[4] way to marry
[5] apt, fitting
[6] unawares

Or for in thoughts of love her idle time she spent,
Or otherwise within her heart deservèd to be shent.[1]
I know her mother will in no case say her nay;
I warrant you, she shall not fail to come on Saturday."
And then she swears to him the mother loves her well;
And how she gave her suck in youth, she leaveth not[2] to tell.
"A pretty babe," quod she, "it was when it was young;
Lord, how it could full prettily have prated with its tongue!
A thousand times and more I laid her on my lap,
And clapped her on the buttock soft, and kissed where I did clap.
And gladder then was I of such a kiss, forsooth,
Than I had been to have a kiss of some old lecher's mouth."

And thus of Juliet's youth began this prating nurse
And of her present state to make a tedious, long discourse.
For though he pleasure took in hearing of his love,
The message's answer seemèd him to be of more behove.[3]
But when these beldames[4] sit at ease upon their tail
The day and eke the candle-light before their talk shall fail.
And part they say is true and part they do devise,
Yet boldly do they chat of both when no man checks their lies.
Then he six crowns of gold out of his pocket drew
And gave them her: "A slight reward," quod he, "and so, adieu."
In seven years twice told she had not bowed so low
Her crooked knees, as now they bow; she swears she will bestow
Her crafty wit, her time, and all her busy° pain
To help him to his hopèd bliss; and, cow'ring down again,
She takes her leave, and home she hies° with speedy pace.
The chamber door she shuts and then she saith with smiling face:
"Good news for thee, my girl, good tidings I thee bring.
Leave off thy wonted° song of care and now of pleasure sing.
For thou may'st hold thyself the happiest under sun
That in so little while, so well, so worthy a knight hast won.
The best y-shaped is he, and hath the fairest face
Of all this town, and there is none hath half so good a grace,
So gentle of his speech, and of his counsel wise,"
And still with many praises more she heaved him to the skies.

---

[1] lost
[2] does not omit
[3] benefit
[4] old women

"Tell me else what," quod she, "This evermore I thought,
But of our marriage, say at once what answer have you brought?"
"Nay, soft," quoth she, "I fear your hurt by sudden joy."
"I list° not play," quod Juliet, "although thou list to toy."
How glad, trow° you, was she when she had heard her say
No farther off than Saturday deferrèd was the day!
Again the ancient nurse doth speak of Romeus:
"And then," said she, "he spake to me, and then I spake him thus."
Nothing was done or said that she hath left untold,
Save only one that she forgot, the taking of the gold.
"There is no loss," quod she, "sweet wench, to loss of time,
Ne in thine age shalt thou repent so much of any crime.
For when I call to mind my former passèd youth
One thing there is which most of all doth cause my endless ruth.°
At sixteen years I first did choose my loving fere,°
And I was fully ripe before, I dare well say, a year.
The pleasure that I lost that year so overpast
A thousand times I have bewept and shall while life doth last.
In faith it were a shame—yea, sin it were, y-wis,[1]
When thou may'st live in happy joy, to set light by thy bliss."

She that this morning could her mistress' mind dissuade
Is now become an oratress, her lady to persuade.
If any man be here whom love hath clad with care,
To him I speak: if thou wilt speed,° thy purse thou must not spare.
Two sorts of men there are seld[2] welcome in at door:
The wealthy sparing niggard[3] and the suitor that is poor.
For glitt'ring gold is wont° by kind to move the heart;
And oftentimes a slight reward doth cause a more desart.[4]
Y-written have I read, I wot° not in what book,
There is no better way to fish than with a golden hook.
Of Romeus these two do sit and chat awhile
And to themself they laugh how they the mother shall beguile.
A feat[5] excuse they find, but sure I know it not,
And leave for her to go to shrift° on Saturday she got.

---

[1] surely (literally, "I know")
[2] seldom
[3] cheapskate
[4] greater reward (*desert*: see glossary)
[5] apt, fitting

So well this Juliet, this wily wench, did know
Her mother's angry hours and eke the true bent of her bow.[1]
The Saturday betimes in sober weed y-clad[2]
She took her leave and forth she went with visage grave and sad.
With her the nurse is sent as bridle of her lust;°
With her the mother sends a maid almost of equal trust.
Betwixt her teeth the bit the jennet[3] now hath caught;
So warely° eke the virgin walks, her maid perceiveth nought.
She gazeth not in church on young men of the town,
Ne wand'reth she from place to place, but straight she kneeleth down
Upon an altar's step, where she devoutly prays,
And there upon her tender knees the weary lady stays;
Whilst she doth send her maid the certain truth to know
If Friar Laurence leisure had to hear her shrift° or no.
Out of his shriving place he comes with pleasant cheer;
The shamefast maid with bashful brow to himward draweth near.
"Some great offence," quoth he, "you have committed late.
Perhaps you have displeased your friend by giving him a mate?"[4]
Then turning to the nurse and to the other maid,
"Go, hear a mass or two," quod he, "which straightway shall be said.
For, her confession heard, I will unto you twain
The charge that I received of you restore to you again."
What, was not Juliet, trow° you, right well apaid
That for this trusty friar hath changed her young mistrusting maid?
I dare well say, there is in all Verona none
But Romeus, with whom she would so gladly be alone.

Thus to the friar's cell they both forth walkèd bin.[5]
He shuts the door as soon as he and Juliet were in,
But Romeus, her friend, was entered in before
And there had waited for his love two hours large and more.
Each minute seemed an hour and every hour a day;
'Twixt hope he livèd and despair of coming or of stay.[6]
Now wavering hope and fear are quite fled out of sight,
For what he hoped he hath at hand, his pleasant, chief delight.

---

[1] Juliet knows her mother's fits of anger and also her true disposition.
[2] early Saturday, clad in sombre clothes
[3] small horse
[4] a checkmate: figuratively, made a move that that displeased him
[5] been walked (i.e., walked in)
[6] remaining

And joyful Juliet is healed of all her smart,°
For now the rest of all her parts have found her straying heart.
Both their confessions first the friar hath heard them make.
And then to her with louder voice thus Friar Laurence spake:
"Fair lady Juliet, my ghostly° daughter dear,
As far as I of Romeus learn, who by you standeth here,
'Twixt you it is agreed that you shall be his wife
And he your spouse in steady truth, till death shall end your life.
Are you both fully bent to keep this great behest?"
And both the lovers said it was their only heart's request.
When he did see their minds in links of love so fast,
When in the praise of wedlock's state some skilful talk was past,
When he had told at length the wife what was her due
His duty eke by ghostly° talk the youthful husband knew,
How that the wife in love must honour and obey,
What love and honour he doth owe and debt that he must pay.
The words pronouncèd were which holy church of old
Appointed hath for marriage, and she a ring of gold
Received of Romeus, and then they both arose.
To whom the friar then said: "Perchance apart you will disclose
Betwixt yourself alone the bottom of your heart;
Say on at once, for time it is that hence you should depart."

Then Romeus said to her, both loth to part so soon,
"Fair lady, send to me again your nurse this afternoon.
Of cord I will bespeak a ladder by that time,[1]
By which this night while others sleep I will your window climb.
Then will we talk of love and of our old despairs,
And then, with longer leisure had, dispose our great affairs."
These said, they kiss, and then part to their fathers' house,
The joyful bride unto her home, to his eke go'th the spouse,
Contented both, and yet both uncontented still
Till Night and Venus' child give leave the wedding to fulfil.
The painful[2] soldier sore y-beat with weary war,
The merchant eke that needful things doth dread to fetch from far,
The ploughman that for doubt° of fierce invading foes
Rather to sit in idle ease than sow his tilt hath chose[3]
Rejoice to hear proclaimed the tidings of the peace,

---

[1] By then I will have arranged a rope ladder.
[2] wracked with pain
[3] has chosen to sit in idle ease rather than cultivate his field

Not pleasured with the sound so much. But when the wars do cease
Then ceased are the harms which cruel war brings forth.
The merchant then may boldly fetch his wares of precious worth;
Dreadless the husbandman doth till his fertile field.
For wealth, her mate, not for herself, is peace so precious held:
So lovers live in care, in dread, and in unrest
And deadly war by striving thoughts they keep within their breast:
But wedlock is the peace whereby is freedom won
To do a thousand pleasant things that should not else be done.

The news of ended war these two have heard with joy
But now they long the fruit of peace with pleasure to enjoy.
In stormy wind and wave, in danger to be lost,
Thy steerless ship, O Romeus, hath been long while betossed.
The seas are now appeased and thou by happy star
Art come in sight of quiet haven, and now the wrackful bar[1]
Is hid with swelling tide; boldly thou may'st resort
Unto thy wedded lady's bed, thy long desirèd port.
God grant no folly's mist so dim thy inward sight
That thou do miss the channel that doth lead to thy delight.
God grant no danger's rock y-lurking in the dark
Before thou win the happy port wrack thy sea-beaten bark.

A servant Romeus had, of word and deed so just
That with his life if need required his master would him trust.
His faithfulness had oft our Romeus proved of old
And therefore all that yet was done unto his man he told,
Who straight, as he was charged, a corden ladder[2] looks,
To which he hath made fast two strong and crooked iron hooks.
The bride to send the nurse at twilight faileth not,
To whom the bridegroom given hath the ladder that he got.
And then to watch for him appointeth her an hour,
For whether Fortune smile on him or if she list to lour[3]
He will not miss to come to his appointed place,
Where wont° he was to take by stealth the view of Juliet's face.
How long these lovers thought the lasting of the day,

---

[1] This image is an important one to the fatalism of poem: even as Romeus safely
    enters the quiet haven or "port" of Juliet's bed, a sandbar lies hidden below the
    waters and rocks lurk in the dark, both ready to wreck him.
[2] rope ladder
[3] would rather scowl

Let other judge that wonted are like passions to assay.[1]
For my part, I do guess each hour seems twenty year,
So that I deem if they might have, as of Alcume we hear,[2]
The sun bound to their will; if they the heavens might guide
Black shade of night and doubled dark should straight all overhide.

Th'appointed hour is come; he, clad in rich array,
Walks toward his desirèd home: good fortune guide his way.
Approaching near the place from whence his heart had life,
So light he wox[3] he leapt the wall and there he spied his wife,
Who in the window watched the coming of her lord;
Where she so surely had made fast the ladder made of cord,
That dangerless her spouse the chamber window climbs,
Where he ere then had wished himself above ten thousand times.
The windows close are shut; else look they for no guest.
To light the waxen quariers[4] the ancient nurse is pressed,
Which Juliet had before prepared to be light,[5]
That she at pleasure might behold her husband's beauty bright.
A kerchief white as snow ware[6] Juliet on her head,
Such as she wonted° was to wear, attire meet[7] for the bed.
As soon as she him spied about his neck she clung
And by her long and slender arms a great while there she hung.
A thousand times she kissed and him unkissed again,
Ne could she speak a word to him though would she ne'er so fain.[8]
And like betwixt his arms to faint his lady is;
She fets[9] a sigh and clappeth close her closèd mouth to his;
And ready then to sownd[10] she lookèd ruthfully,°
That, lo, it made him both at once to live and eke to die.
These piteous painful pangs were haply° overpast,

---

[1] This is an example of the narrator's coyness around matters of love: let others who know these passions try to judge how long the lovers felt the day lasted.

[2] Alcmene, the mother of Hercules, suffered a particularly long and difficult childbirth, as described in Ovid, *Metamorphoses*, Book 9. The author suggests that, like Alcmene, Romeus and Juliet feel that time stands still.

[3] he grew (waxed) so happy

[4] large candles

[5] lit

[6] wore

[7] suitable, fitting (see glossary)

[8] no matter how she wished

[9] fetches, heaves forth

[10] swoon

And she unto herself again returnèd home at last.
Then through her troubled breast, even from the farthest part,
An hollow sigh, a messenger, she sendeth from her heart.
"O Romeus," quoth she, "in whom all virtues shine,
Welcome thou art into this place, where from these eyes of mine
Such teary streams did flow that I suppose well-nigh
The source of all my bitter tears is altogether dry.
Absence so pined my heart, which on thy presence fed,
And of thy safety and thy health so much I stood in dread.
But now what is decreed by fatal destiny
I force it not;[1] let Fortune do, and death, their worst to me.
Full recompensed am I for all my passèd harms,
In that the gods have granted me to clasp thee in mine arms."

The crystal tears began to stand in Romeus' eyes
When he unto his lady's words 'gan answer in this wise:°
"Though cruel Fortune be so much my deadly foe
That I ne can by lively proof cause thee, fair dame, to know
How much I am by love enthrallèd° unto thee,
Ne yet what mighty power thou hast by thy desert[2] on me,
Ne torments that for thee I did ere this endure.
Yet of thus much, ne will I feign, I may thee well assure,
The least of many pains which of thy absence sprung,
More painfully than death itself my tender heart hath wrung.
Ere this one death had reft[3] a thousand deaths away,
But life prolongèd was by hope of this desirèd day,
Which so just tribute pays of all my passèd moan
That I as well contented am as if myself alone
Did from the Ocean reign unto the sea of Ind.[4]
Wherefore now let us wipe away old cares out of our mind.
For as the wretched state is now redressed at last,
So is it skill behind our back the cursèd care to cast.
Since Fortune of her grace hath place and time assigned
Where we with pleasure may content our uncontented mind,
In Lethes[5] hide we deep all grief and all annoy

---

[1] I do not care

[2] deserving (see glossary)

[3] taken, torn

[4] India

[5] The River Lethe, associated with forgetfulness and oblivion, separated Hades from the human world.

Whilst we do bathe in bliss and fill our hungry hearts with joy.
And for the time to come let be our busy° care
So wisely to direct our love, as no wight else beware,
Lest envious foes by force despoil our new delight,
And us throw back from happy state to more unhappy plight."
Fair Juliet began to answer what he said,
But forth in haste the old nurse stepped and so her answer stayed.
"Who takes not time," quoth she, "when time well offered is,
Another time shall seek for time and yet of time shall miss.
And when occasion serves, whoso doth let it slip
Is worthy sure, if I might judge, of lashes with a whip.
Wherefore if each of you hath harmed the other so
And each of you hath been the cause of other's wailèd woe,
Lo here a field"—she showed a field-bed ready dight[1] —
"Where you may, if you list,° in arms revenge yourself by fight."
Whereto these lovers both 'gan easily assent
And to the place of mild revenge with pleasant cheer they went,
Where they were left alone—the nurse is gone to rest —
How can this be? They restless lie, ne yet they feel unrest.

I grant that I envy the bliss they livèd in;
Oh, that I might have found the like; I wish it for no sin,
But that I might as well with pen their joys depaint,[2]
As heretofore I have displayed their secret hidden plaint.[3]
Of shivering care and dread I have felt many a fit,
But Fortune such delight as theirs did never grant me yet.
By proof no certain truth can I unhappy write,
But what I guess by likelihood, that dare I to indite.
The blindfold goddess that with frowning face doth fray,[4]
And from their seat the mighty kings throws down with headlong sway.
Beginneth now to turn to these her smiling face;
Needs must they taste of great delight, so much in Fortune's grace.
If Cupid, god of love, be god of pleasant sport
I think, O Romeus, Mars himself envies thy happy sort.[5]
Ne Venus[6] justly might, as I suppose, repent

---

[1] prepared
[2] depict, describe
[3] complaint, troubles
[4] Fortuna, the Roman goddess of fortune (see lines above), causes strife (fray).
[5] lot, circumstances
[6] Mars and Venus were, respectively, the Roman god of war and goddess of love.

If in thy stead, O Juliet, this pleasant time she spent.

Thus pass they forth the night, in sport, in jolly game;
The hastiness of Phoebus' steeds in great despite they blame.
And now the virgin's fort hath warlike Romeus got,
In which as yet no breach was made by force of cannon shot;
And now in ease he doth possess the hopèd place:
How glad was he, speak you that may your lover's parts embrace.
The marriage thus made up and both the parties pleased,
The nigh approach of day's return these seely° fools dis-eased.
And for they might no while in pleasure pass their time,
Ne leisure had they much to blame the hasty morning's crime,
With friendly kiss in arms of her his leave he takes
And every other night to come a solemn oath he makes,
By one self mean,° and eke to come at one self hour:
And so he doth till Fortune list° to sauce his sweet with sour.
But who is he that can his present state assure
And say unto himself thy joys shall yet a day endure?
So wavering Fortune's wheel; her changes be so strange
And every wight y-thrallèd° is by Fate unto her change,
Who reigns so over all that each man hath his part
(Although not aye,° perchance, alike) of pleasure and of smart.°
For after many joys some feel but little pain
And from that little grief they turn to happy joy again.
But other some there are that living long in woe,
At length they be in quiet ease but long abide not so,
Whose grief is much increased by mirth that went before
Because the sudden change of things doth make it seem the more.
Of this unlucky sort our Romeus is one,
For all his hap° turns to mishap and all his mirth to moan.
And joyful Juliet another leaf must turn,
As wont° she was: her joys bereft, she must begin to mourn.

The summer of their bliss doth last a month or twain,
But winter's blast with speedy foot doth bring the fall again.
Whom glorious Fortune erst° had heaved to the skies,
By envious Fortune overthrown on earth now grovelling lies.
She paid their former grief with pleasure's doubled gain,
But now for pleasure's usury tenfold redoubleth pain.
The prince could never cause those households so agree
But that some sparkles of their wrath as yet remaining be,

Which lie this while raked up in ashes pale and dead
Till time do serve that they again in wasting flame may spread.
At holiest times, men say, most heinous crimes are done;
The morrow after Easter day the mischief new begun.
A band of Capulets did meet—my heart it rues! —
Within the walls, by Purser's gate,[1] a band of Montagues.
The Capulets as chief a young man have chose out
Best exercised in feats of arms and noblest of the rout,°
Our Juliet's uncle's son that clepèd[2] was Tybalt;
He was of body tall and strong, and of his courage halt.[3]
They need no trumpet sound to bid them give the charge,
So loud he cried with strainèd voice and mouth outstretchèd large:
"Now, now," quod he, "my friends, ourself so let us wreak,
That of this day's revenge and us our children's heirs may speak.
Now once for all let us their swelling pride assuage;[4]
Let none of them escape alive." Then he with furious rage,
And they with him, gave charge upon their present foes
And then forthwith a skirmish great upon this fray arose.
For, lo, the Montagues thought shame away to fly
And rather than to live with shame, with praise did choose to die.

The words that Tybalt used to stir his folk to ire
Have in the breasts of Montagues kindled a furious fire.
With lions' hearts they fight, warely° themself defend;
To wound his foe his present wit and force each one doth bend.
This furious fray is long on each side stoutly fought,
That whether[5] part had got the worst, full doubtful were the thought.
The noise hereof anon throughout the town doth fly
And parts are taken on every side; both kindreds thither hie.[6]
Here one doth gasp for breath, his friend bestrideth him;
And he hath lost a hand and he another maimèd limb;
His leg is cut whilst he strikes at another full
And whom he would have thrust quite through hath cleft his cracked skull.
Their valiant hearts forbode their foot to give the ground;
With unappallèd cheer they took full deep and doubtful° wound.

---

[1] probably an area of the city where purses and leather goods are made and sold
[2] named (see introduction and glossary)
[3] endowed with courage
[4] lessen (i.e., let us take them down a notch)
[5] whichever
[6] hasten (see glossary)

Thus foot by foot long while and shield to shield set fast
One he doth make another faint but makes him not aghast.[1]

And whilst this noise is rife in every townsman's ear,
Eke, walking with his friends, the noise doth woeful Romeus hear.
With speedy foot he runs unto the fray apace;
With him those few that were with him he leadeth to the place.
They pity much to see the slaughter made so great,
That wetshod[2] they might stand in blood on either side the street.
"Part, friends," said he, "Part, friends – help, friends, to part the fray,"
And to the rest, "Enough," he cries, "Now time it is to stay.°
God's farther wrath you stir, beside the hurt you feel,
And with this new uproar confound all this our common weal."°
But they so busy are in fight, so eager and fierce,
That through their ears his sage advice no leisure had to pierce.
Then leapt he in the throng to part and bar the blows
As well of those that were his friends, as of his deadly foes.

As soon as Tybalt had our Romeus espied
He threw a thrust at him that would have passed from side to side;
But Romeus ever went, doubting° his foes, well armed
So that the sword kept out by mail[3] hath nothing Romeus harmed.
"Thou dost me wrong," quoth he, "for I but part the fray;
Not dread but other weighty cause my hasty hand doth stay.°
Thou art the chief of thine, the noblest eke thou art,
Wherefore leave off thy malice now and help these folk to part.
Many are hurt, some slain, and some are like to die."
"No, coward, traitor boy," quoth he, "straightway I mind to try
Whether thy sugared talk and tongue so smoothly filed
Against the force of this my sword shall serve thee for a shield."
And then at Romeus' head a blow he strake[4] so hard
That might have clove him to the brain but for his cunning ward.[5]
It was but lent to him that could repay again
And give him death for interest, a well forborne gain.

Right as a forest boar that, lodgèd in the thick,

---

[1] frightened
[2] with wet feet
[3] armour
[4] struck
[5] defensive manoeuvre

Pinchèd with dog, or else with spear y-prickèd to the quick,
His bristles stiff upright upon his back doth set
And in his foamy mouth his sharp and crooked tusks doth whet,
Or as a lion wild that rampeth in his rage,
His whelps bereft, whose fury can no weaker beast assuage,
Such seemèd Romeus in every other's sight
When he him shope,[1] of wrong received, t'avenge himself by fight.
Even as two thunderbolts thrown down out of the sky
That through the air, the massy earth, and seas have power to fly,
So met these two, and while they change a blow or twain
Our Romeus thrust him through the throat and so is Tybalt slain.

Lo, here the end of those that stir a deadly strife:
Who thirsteth after other's death, himself hath lost his life.
The Capulets are quailed[2] by Tybalt's overthrow,
The courage of the Montagues by Romeus' sight doth grow.
The townsmen waxen strong, the prince doth send his force;
The fray hath end. The Capulets do bring the breathless corse[3]
Before the prince and crave that cruel deadly pain
May be the guerdon[4] of his fault that hath their kinsman slain.
The Montagues do plead their Romeus void of fault;
The lookers-on do say the fight begun was by Tybalt.
The prince doth pause and then gives sentence in a while,
That Romeus for slaying him should go into exile.
His foes would have him hanged or sterve° in prison strong;
His friends do think but dare not say that Romeus hath wrong.
Both households straight are charged on pain of losing life,
Their bloody weapons laid aside, to cease the stirrèd strife.
This common plague is spread through all the town anon;
From side to side the town is filled with murmur and with moan,
For Tybalt's hasty death bewailèd was of some,
Both for his skill in feats of arms and for in time to come
He should, had this not chanced, been rich and of great power
To help his friends and serve the state, which hope within an hour
Was wasted quite and he, thus yielding up his breath,
More than he holp[5] the town in life hath harmed it by his death.

---

[1] readied himself (literally, shaped himself)
[2] made feeble or frightened
[3] corpse (see glossary)
[4] reward
[5] helped

And other some bewail, but ladies most of all,
The luckless lot by Fortune's guilt that is so late befall
Without his fault unto the seely° Romeus,
For whilst that he from native land shall live exilèd thus,
From heavenly beauty's light and his well-shapèd parts,
The sight of which was wont,° fair dames, to glad your youthful hearts
Shall you be banished quite, and till he do return
What hope have you to joy, what hope to cease to mourn?

This Romeus was born so much in heaven's grace,
Of Fortune and of Nature so beloved that in his face
Beside the heavenly beauty glist'ring aye° so bright
And seemly grace that wonted° so to glad the seer's sight,
A certain charm was 'graved by Nature's secret art
That virtue had to draw to it the love of many a heart.
So everyone doth wish to bear a part of pain,
That he releasèd of exile might straight return again.

But how doth mourn among the mourners Juliet!
How doth she bathe her breast in tears! What deep sighs doth she fet!¹
How doth she tear her hair! Her weed° how doth she rent!
How fares the lover hearing of her lover's banishment!
How wails she Tybalt's death, whom she had loved so well!
Her hearty grief and piteous plaint, cunning I want to tell.²
For delving deeply now in depth of deep despair,
With wretched sorrow's cruel sound she fills the empty air
And to the lowest hell down falls her heavy cry,
And up unto the heaven's height her piteous plaint doth fly.
The waters and the woods of sighs and sobs resound
And from the hard resounding rocks her sorrows do rebound.
Eke from her teary eyne° down rainèd many a shower
That in the garden where she walked might water herb and flower.
But when at length she saw herself outraged³ so
Unto her chamber straight she hied.° There, overcharged with woe,
Upon her stately bed her painful parts⁴ she threw
And in so wondrous wise° began her sorrows to renew
That sure no heart so hard but it of flint had bin°

---

¹ utter (fetch forth)
² I lack the ability to describe.
³ insulted, injured
⁴ aching limbs

But would have rued the piteous plaint that she did languish in.
Then, rapt out of herself, whilst she on every side
Did cast her restless eye, at length the window she espied
Through which she had with joy seen Romeus many a time,
Which oft the vent'rous knight was wont° for Juliet's sake to climb.
She cried, "O cursed window, accursed be every pane,
Through which, alas, too soon I raught[1] the cause of life and bane;[2]
If by thy mean° I have some slight delight received
Or else such fading pleasure as by Fortune straight was reaved,°
Hast thou not made me pay a tribute rigorous
Of heapèd grief and lasting care and sorrows dolorous
That these my tender parts, which needful strength do lack
To bear so great unwieldy load upon so weak a back,
Oppressed with weight of cares and with these sorrows rife,
At length must open wide to death the gates of loathèd life;
That so my weary sprite° may somewhere else unload
His deadly load and free from thrall° may seek elsewhere abode°
For pleasant, quiet ease and for assurèd rest,
Which I as yet could never find but for my more unrest?
O Romeus, when first we both acquainted were,
When to thy painted[3] promises I lent my list'ning ear,
Which to the brinks you filled with many a solemn oath
And I them judged empty of guile and fraughted full of troth,[4]
I thought you rather would continue our good will
And seek t'appease our fathers' strife, which daily groweth still.
I little weened° you would have sought occasion how
By such an heinous act to break the peace and eke your vow,
Whereby your bright renown all whole y-clipsèd is
And I unhappy, husbandless, of comfort robbed, and bliss.
But if you did so much the blood of Capels thirst
Why have you often sparèd mine—mine might have quenched it first.
Since that so many times and in so secret place,
Where you were wont° with veil of love to hide your hatred's face
My doubtful life hath happed by fatal doom to stand
In mercy of your cruel heart, and of your bloody hand.
What? – seemed the conquest which you got of me so small?
What?—seemed it not enough that I, poor wretch, was made your thrall°

---

[1] grasped, seized
[2] harm
[3] false, deceptive
[4] filled full with truth

But that you must increase it with that kinsman's blood,
Which for his worth and love to me most in my favour stood?
Well, go henceforth elsewhere and seek another while
Some other as unhappy as I by flattery to beguile.
And where I come, see that you shun to show your face,
For your excuse within my heart shall find no resting place.
And I that now too late my former fault repent
Will so the rest of weary life with many tears lament
That soon my joiceless¹corpse shall yield up banished breath
And where on earth it restless lived, in earth seek rest by death."

These said, her tender heart, by pain oppressèd sore,
Restrained her tears and forced her tongue to keep her talk in store;
And then as still she was, as if in sownd² she lay,
And then again, wroth° with herself, with feeble voice 'gan say:
"Ah, cruel murthering tongue, murth'rer of others' fame,
How durst° thou once attempt to touch the honour of his name
Whose deadly foes do yield him due and earnèd praise?
For though his freedom be bereft his honour not decays.
Why blam'st thou Romeus for slaying of Tybalt,
Since he is guiltless quite of all and Tybalt bears the fault?
Whither shall he, alas, poor banished man, now fly?
What place of succour shall he seek beneath the starry sky?
Since she pursueth him and him defames by wrong,
That in distress should be his fort and only rampire³ strong.
Receive the recompense, O Romeus, of thy wife,
Who, for she was unkind herself, doth offer up her life
In flames of ire, in sighs, in sorrow and in ruth,°
So to revenge the crime she did commit against thy truth."

These said, she could no more; her senses all 'gan fail
And deadly pangs began straightway her tender heart assail;
Her limbs she stretchèd forth, she drew no more her breath:
Who had been there might well have seen the signs of present death.
The nurse that knew no cause why she absented her
Did doubt° lest that some sudden grief too much tormented her.
Each where but where she was the careful⁴ beldam sought;

---

¹ lifeless (literally, juiceless)
² in a swoon
³ rampart, fortification
⁴ worried, filled with care (see glossary)

Last, of the chamber where she lay she haply° her bethought,
Where she with piteous eye her nurse-child[1] did behold,
Her limbs stretched out, her outward parts as any marble cold.
The nurse supposed that she had paid to death her debt
And then, as she had lost her wits, she cried to Juliet:
"Ah, my dear heart," quoth she, "how grieveth me thy death!
Alas, what cause hast thou thus soon to yield up living breath?"
But while she handled her and chafèd[2] every part
She knew there was some spark of life by beating of her heart,
So that a thousand times she called upon her name;
There is no way to help a trance but she hath tried the same.
She openeth wide her mouth, she stoppeth close her nose,
She bendeth down her breast, she wrings her fingers and her toes,
And on her bosom cold she layeth clothes[3] hot;
A warmèd and a wholesome juice she poureth down her throat.

At length doth Juliet heave faintly up her eyes,
And then she stretcheth forth her arm, and then her nurse she spies.
But when she was awaked from her unkindly trance,
"Why dost thou trouble me," quoth she, "what drave[4] thee with
                                                        mischance
To come to see my sprite° forsake my breathless corse?°
Go hence, and let me die, if thou have on my smart° remorse.
For who would see her friend to live in deadly pain?
Alas, I see my grief begun forever will remain,
Or who would seek to live, all pleasure being past?
My mirth is done, my mourning moan for aye° is like to last.
Wherefore since that there is none other remedy,
Come, gentle death and rive my heart at once, and let me die."
The nurse with trickling tears to witness inward smart,°
With hollow sigh fetched from the depth of her appallèd heart
Thus spake to Juliet, y-clad with ugly care:
"Good lady mine, I do not know what makes you thus to fare,[5]
Ne yet the cause of your unmeasured heaviness.
But of this one I you assure, for care and sorrow's stress,
This hour large and more I thought, so God me save,

---

[1] the child she is charged with caring for
[2] warmed
[3] cloths
[4] drove
[5] behave (see glossary)

That my dead corpse should wait on yours to your untimely grave."
"Alas, my tender nurse and trusty friend," quoth she,
"Art thou so blind that with thine eye thou canst not easely see
The lawful cause I have to sorrow and to mourn,
Since those the which I held most dear I have at once forlorn."
Her nurse then answered thus: "Methinks it sits you ill
To fall in these extremities that may you guiltless spill.[1]
For when the storms of care and troubles do arise
Then is the time for men to know the foolish from the wise.
You are accounted wise; a fool, am I your nurse,
But I see not how in like case I could behave me worse.
Tybalt your friend is dead; what, ween° you by your tears
To call him back again? Think you that he your crying hears?
You shall perceive the fault, if it be justly tried,
Of his so sudden death was in his rashness and his pride.
Would you that Romeus himself had wrongèd so
To suffer himself causeless to be outraged of his foe,
To whom in no respect he ought a place to give?
Let it suffice to thee, fair dame, that Romeus doth live
And that there is good hope that he within a while
With greater glory shall be called home from his hard exile.
How well y-born he is thyself, I know, canst tell,
By kindred strong and well allied, of all belovèd well.
With patience arm thyself, for though that Fortune's crime,
Without your fault, to both your griefs, depart[2] you for a time
I dare say, for amends of all your present pain
She will restore your own to you within a month or twain
With such contented ease as never erst° you had.
Wherefore[3] rejoice a while in hope and be ne more so sad.
And that I may discharge your heart of heavy care
A certain way I have found out, my pains ne will I spare
To learn his present state and what in time to come
He minds to do; which known by me, you shall know all and some.
But that I dread the whilst your sorrows will you quell,
Straight would I hie° where he doth lurk, to Friar Laurence's cell.
But if you 'gin eftsoons as erst you did to mourn[4]
Whereto go I? You will be dead before I thence return.

---

[1] kill you, despite being innocent
[2] separate
[3] therefore (see glossary)
[4] but if you begin to mourn again as first (erst) you did

So I shall spend in waste my time and busy° pain.
So unto you, your life once lost, good answer comes in vain;
So shall I rid myself with this sharp-pointed knife;
So shall you cause your parents dear wax weary of their life;
So shall your Romeus, despising lively breath,
With hasty foot before his time run to untimely death.
Where, if you can awhile, by reason, rage suppress
I hope at my return to bring the salve of your distress.
Now choose to have me here a partner of your pain
Or promise me to feed on hope till I return again."

Her mistress sends her forth and makes a grave behest
With reason's reign to rule the thoughts that rage within her breast.
When hugy° heaps of harms are heaped before her eyes,
Then vanish they by hope of 'scape; and thus the lady lies
'Twixt well assurèd trust and doubtful lewd despair:
Now black and ugly be her thoughts; now seem they white and fair.
As oft in summer tide black clouds do dim the sun
And straight again in clearest sky his restless steeds do run,
So Juliet's wand'ring mind y-clouded is with woe
And by and by her hasty thought the woes doth overgo.

But now is time to tell, whilst she was tossèd thus,
What winds did drive or haven did hold her lover Romeus.
When he had slain his foe that 'gan this deadly strife
And saw the furious fray had end by ending Tybalt's life
He fled the sharp revenge of those that yet did live;
And doubting° much what penal doom the troubled prince might give,
He sought somewhere unseen to lurk a little space,
And trusty Laurence's secret cell he thought the surest place.
In doubtful hap aye° best a trusty friend is tried;
The friendly friar in this distress doth grant his friend to hide.
A secret place he hath, well sealed round about,
The mouth of which so close is shut that none may find it out;
But room there is to walk and place to sit and rest,
Beside a bed to sleep upon, full soft and trimly drest.
The floor is planked so, with mats it is so warm
That neither wind nor smoky damps have power him aught° to harm.
Where he was wont° in youth his fair friends to bestow,
There now he hideth Romeus, whilst forth he goeth to know
Both what is said and done and what appointed pain

Is publishèd by trumpet's sound; then home he hies° again.
By this, unto his cell the nurse with speedy pace
Was come the nearest way; she sought no idle resting place.
The friar sent home the news of Romeus' certain health,
And promise made, what so befell[1] he should that night by stealth
Come to his wonted° place that they in needful wise°
Of their affairs in time to come might thoroughly devise.
Those joyful news the nurse brought home with merry joy
And now our Juliet joys to think she shall her love enjoy.

The friar shuts fast his door and then to him beneath
That waits to hear the doubtful° news of life or else of death,
"Thy hap," quoth he, "is good. Danger of death is none,
But thou shalt live and do full well in spite of spiteful fone.[2]
This only pain for thee was erst° proclaimed aloud:
A banished man, thou may'st thee not within Verona shroud."[3]
These heavy tidings heard, his golden locks he tare[4]
And like a frantic man hath torn the garments that he ware.[5]
And as the smitten deer in brakes is walt'ring[6] found,
So wal'treth he and with his breast doth beat the trodden ground.
He rises eft[7] and strikes his head against the walls,
He falleth down again and loud for hasty death he calls:
"Come speedy death," quoth he, "the readiest leech° in love;
Since nought can else beneath the sun the ground of grief remove,
Of loathsome life break down the hated, staggering stays;
Destroy, destroy at once the life that faintly yet decays.
But you, fair dame, in whom dame Nature did devise
With cunning hand to work that might seem wondrous in our eyes,
For you I pray the gods your pleasures to increase
And all mishap with this my death forevermore to cease.
And mighty Jove with speed of justice bring them low,
Whose lofty pride, without our guilt, our bliss doth overblow.
And Cupid grant to those their speedy wrongs' redress
That shall bewail my cruel death and pity her distress."

---

[1] whatever might happen
[2] foes
[3] live in hiding
[4] tore
[5] wore
[6] tossing about in brambles (brakes)
[7] quickly (see glossary)

Therewith a cloud of sighs he breathed into the skies
And two great streams of bitter tears ran from his swollen eyes.

These things the ancient friar with sorrow saw and heard;
Of such beginning, eke the end, the wise man greatly feared.
But, lo, he was so weak, by reason of his age,
That he ne could by force repress the rigour of his rage.
His wise and friendly words he speaketh to the air,
For Romeus so vexèd is with care and with despair
That no advice can pierce his close forestoppèd[1] ears;
So now the friar doth take his part in shedding ruthful° tears.
With colour pale and wan, with arms full hard y-fold,
With woeful cheer his wailing friend he standeth to behold.

And then our Romeus with tender hands y-wrung,
With voice with plaint made hoarse with sobs, and with a falt'ring tongue
Renewed with novel moan[2] the dolours of his heart;
His outward dreary cheer bewrayed° his store of inward smart.°
First Nature did he blame, the author of his life,
In which his joys had been so scant and sorrows aye° so rife;
The time and place of birth he fiercely did reprove;
He cried out with open mouth against the stars above;
The fatal sisters three,[3] he said, had done him wrong,
The thread that should not have been spun they had drawn forth too long.
He wished that he had before this time been born,
Or that as soon as he wan light[4] his life he had forlorn.
His nurse he cursèd and the hand that gave him pap,[5]
The midwife eke with tender grip that held him in her lap;
And then did he complain on Venus' cruel son,[6]
Who led him first unto the rocks which he should warely° shun,
By means whereof he lost both life and liberty,
And died a hundred times a day, and yet could never die.
Love's troubles lasten long, the joys he gives are short;
He forceth not a lover's pain, their earnest is his sport.

---

[1] already closed
[2] with fresh pain
[3] The Fates of classical thought, known as the Moirai in Greek and Parcae in Roman
    mythologies, spun, measured, and cut the thread of human life.
[4] gained light (i.e., was born)
[5] breast milk
[6] Cupid

A thousand things and more I here let pass to write,
Which unto Love this woeful man did speak in great despite.
On Fortune eke he railed; he called her deaf and blind,
Unconstant, fond,° deceitful, rash, unruthful,[1] and unkind.
And to himself he laid a great part of the fault,
For that he slew and was not slain in fighting with Tybalt.
He blamed all the world and all he did defy,
But Juliet for whom he lived, for whom eke would he die.
When after raging fits appeasèd was his rage
And when his passions, poured forth, 'gan partly to assuage
So wisely did the friar unto his tale reply
That he straight cared for his life, that erst° had care to die.

"Art thou," quoth he, "a man? Thy shape saith so thou art;
Thy crying and thy weeping eyes denote a woman's heart.
For manly reason is quite from off thy mind outchased
And in her stead affections lewd and fancies highly placed:
So that I stood in doubt,° this hour, at the least,
If thou a man or woman wert, or else a brutish beast.
A wise man in the midst of troubles and distress
Still stands not wailing present harm, but seeks his harm's redress.

As when the winter flaws with dreadful noise arise
And heave the foamy swelling waves up to the starry skies,
So that the bruisèd bark in cruel seas be-tossed
Despaireth of the happy haven, in danger to be lost,
The pilot bold at helm cries, "Mates, strike now your sail,"
And turns her stem into the waves that strongly her assail;
Then driven hard upon the bare and wrackful shore,
In greater danger to be wracked than he had been before,
He seeth his ship full right against the rock to run,
But yet he doth what lieth in him the perilous rock to shun.
Sometimes the beaten boat, by cunning government,
The anchors lost, the cables broke, and all the tackle spent,
The rudder smitten off, and overboard the mast,
Doth win the long desirèd port, the stormy danger past.
But if the master dread° and overpressed with woe
Begin to wring his hands and lets the guiding rudder go,
The ship rents on the rock or sinketh in the deep,

---

[1] pitiless

And eke the coward drenchèd[1] is. So if thou still beweep
And seek not how to help the changes that do chance,
Thy cause of sorrow shall increase, thou cause of thy mischance.
Other account thee wise, prove not thyself a fool;
Now put in practice lessons learned of old in wisdom's school.
The wise man saith, "Beware thou double not thy pain,
For one perhaps thou may'st abide but hardly suffer twain."
As well we ought to seek things hurtful to decrease
As to endeavour helping things by study to increase.
The praise of true freedom in wisdom's bondage lies;
He winneth blame whose deeds be fond,[2] although his words be wise.
Sickness the body's gaol, grief gaol is of the mind;
If thou canst 'scape from heavy grief true freedom shalt thou find.
Fortune can fill nothing so full of hearty grief,
But in the same a constant mind finds solace and relief.
Virtue is always thrall° to troubles and annoy,
But wisdom in adversity finds cause of quiet joy.
And they most wretched are that know no wretchedness,
And after great extremity mishaps aye° waxen less.
Like as there is no weal° but wastes away sometime,°
So every kind of wailèd woe will wear away in time.
If thou wilt master quite the troubles that thee spill[3]
Endeavour first by reason's help to master witless will.
A sundry[4] med'cine hath each sundry faint disease,
But patience, a common salve, to every wound gives ease.
The world is alway[5] full of chances and of change,
Wherefore the change of chance must not seem to a wise man strange,
For tickle Fortune doth in changing but her kind,[6]
But all her changes cannot change a steady constant mind.
Though wavering Fortune turn from thee her smiling face
And Sorrow seek to set himself in banished Pleasure's place,
Yet may thy marred state be mended in a while
And she eftsoons[7] that frowneth now with pleasant cheer shall smile,
For as her happy state no long while standeth sure,

---

[1] drowned
[2] foolish (see glossary)
[3] destroy, ruin
[4] distinct, separate
[5] always (see glossary)
[6] Inconstant Fortune acts only according to her own nature (kind) in changing.
[7] soon

Even so the heavy plight she brings not always doth endure.

What need so many words to thee that art so wise?
Thou better canst advise thyself than I can thee advise.
Wisdom, I see, is vain if thus in time of need
A wise man's wit unpractisèd doth stand him in no stead.
I know thou hast some cause of sorrow and of care,
But well I wot° thou hast no cause thus franticly to fare.°
Affection's foggy mist thy feebled sight doth blind,
But if that reason's beams again might shine into thy mind,
If thou would'st view thy state with an indifferent[1] eye,
I think thou would'st condemn thy plaint, thy sighing, and thy cry.
With valiant hand thou mad'st thy foe yield up his breath;
Thou hast escaped his sword and eke the laws that threaten death.
By thy escape thy friends are fraughted full of joy
And by his death thy deadly foes are laden with annoy.
Wilt thou with trusty friends of pleasure take some part,
Or else to please thy hateful foes be partner of their smart?°
Why cry'st thou out on love? Why dost thou blame thy fate?
Why dost thou so cry after death? Thy life why dost thou hate?
Dost thou repent the choice that thou so late didst choose?
Love is thy lord; thou ought'st obey and not thy prince accuse.
For thou hast found, thou know'st, great favour in his sight.
He granted thee, at thy request, thy only heart's delight,
So that the gods envied the bliss thou lived'st in;
To give to such unthankful men is folly and a sin.
Methinks I hear thee say the cruel banishment
Is only cause of thy unrest; only thou dost lament
That from thy native land and friends thou must depart,
Enforced to fly from her that hath the keeping of thy heart:
And so oppressed with weight of smart° that thou dost feel
Thou dost complain of Cupid's brand and Fortune's turning wheel.[2]
Unto a valiant heart there is no banishment;
All countries are his native soil beneath the firmament.
As to the fish the sea, as to the fowl the air,
So is like pleasant to the wise each place of his repair.
Though froward[3] Fortune chase thee hence into exile,

---

[1] objective, unbiased
[2] Cupid was conventionally pictured with a burning torch (brand) and Fortune with a wheel, both symbols of their power over human affairs.
[3] boldly assertive

With doubled honour shall she call thee home within a while.
Admit thou should'st abide abroad a year or twain,
Should so short absence cause so long and eke so grievous pain?
Though thou ne may'st thy friends here in Verona see,
They are not banished Mantua, where safely thou may'st be.
Thither they may resort, though thou resort not hither,
And there in surety may you talk of your affairs together.

Yea, but this while, alas, thy Juliet must thou miss,
The only pillar of thy health and anchor of thy bliss.
Thy heart thou leav'st with her when thou dost hence depart
And in thy breast inclosèd bear'st her tender friendly heart.
But if thou rue so much to leave the rest behind
With thought of passèd joys content thy uncontented mind.
So shall the moan decrease wherewith thy mind doth melt,
Compared to the heavenly joys which thou hast often felt.
He is too nice[1] a weakling that shrinketh at a shower
And he unworthy of the sweet that tasteth not the sour.
Call now again to mind thy first consuming flame:
How didst thou vainly burn in love of an unloving dame?
Hadst thou not well nigh wept quite out thy swelling eyne?
Did not thy parts, fordone with pain, languish away and pine?
Those griefs and others like were haply overpast
And thou in height of Fortune's wheel well placèd at the last!
From whence thou art now fall'n, that,[2] raisèd up again,
With greater joy a greater while in pleasure may'st thou reign.
Compare the present while with times y-past before
And think that Fortune hath for thee great pleasure yet in store.
The whilst, this little wrong receive thou patiently
And what of force must needs be done, that do thou willingly.
Folly it is to fear that thou canst not avoid
And madness to desire it much that cannot be enjoyed.
To give to Fortune place, not aye° deserveth blame,
But skill it is according to the times thyself to frame."

Whilst to this skilful lore° he lent his list'ning ears
His sighs are stopped and stoppèd are the conduits of his tears.
As blackest clouds are chased by winter's nimble wind

---

[1] fussy, delicate
[2] who (i.e., Romeus)

So have his reasons chasèd care out of his careful° mind.
As of a morning foul ensues an evening fair,
So banished hope returneth home to banish his despair.
Now is affection's veil removed from his eyes;
He seeth the path that he must walk and reason makes him wise.
For very shame the blood doth flash in both his cheeks;
He thanks the father for his lore° and farther aid he seeks.
He saith that skill-less youth for counsel is unfit
And anger oft with hastiness are joined to want of wit;[1]
But sound advice abounds in heads with hoarish[2] hairs,
For wisdom is by practice won and perfect made by years.
But aye° from this time forth his ready bending will
Shall be in awe and governèd by Friar Laurence's skill.

The governor is now right careful of his charge,
To whom he doth wisely discourse of his affairs at large.
He tells him how he shall depart the town unknown,
Both mindful of his friend's safety and careful of his own;
How he shall guide himself, how he shall seek to win
The friendship of the better sort, how warely° to creep in
The favour of the Mantuan prince, and how he may
Appease the wrath of Escalus and wipe the fault away;
The choler of his foes by gentle means t'assuage,
Or else by force and practices to bridle quite their rage.
And last he chargeth him at his appointed hour
To go with manly, merry cheer unto his lady's bower
And there with wholesome words to salve her sorrow's smart°
And to revive, if need require, her faint and dying heart.

The old man's words have filled with joy our Romeus' breast
And eke the old wife's talk hath set our Juliet's heart at rest.
Whereto may I compare, O lovers, this your day?
Like days the painful mariners are wonted to assay;[3]
For, beat with tempest great, when they at length espy
Some little beam of Phoebus' light that pierceth through the sky
To clear the shadowed earth by clearness of his face,
They hope that dreadless[4] they shall run the remnant of their race.

---

[1] lack of good sense or intelligence
[2] white
[3] used to trying
[4] fearlessly

Yea, they assure themself and quite behind their back
They cast all doubt and thank the gods for scaping of the wrack;
But straight the boisterous winds with greater fury blow,
And overboard the broken mast the stormy blasts do throw;
The heavens large are clad with clouds as dark as hell,
And twice as high the striving waves begin to roar and swell;
With greater dangers dread the men are vexèd more,
In greater peril of their life than they had been before.

The golden sun was gone to lodge him in the west,
The full moon eke in yonder south had sent most men to rest
When restless Romeus and restless Juliet
In wonted sort by wonted mean[1] in Juliet's chamber met.
And from the window's top down had he leapèd scarce,
When she with arms outstretchèd wide so hard did him embrace
That well nigh had the sprite,° not forced by deadly force,
Flown unto death, before the time abandoning the corse.°
Thus mute stood they both the eighth part of an hour
And both would speak, but neither had of speaking any power;
But on his breast her head doth joyless Juliet lay
And on her slender neck his chin doth ruthful° Romeus stay.
Their scalding sighs ascend and by their cheeks down fall
Their trickling tears as crystal clear, but bitterer far than gall.

Then he to end the grief which both they lived in
Did kiss his love and wisely thus his tale he did begin:
"My Juliet, my love, my only hope and care,
To you I purpose not as now with length of word declare
The diverseness and eke the accidents so strange
Of frail unconstant Fortune that delighteth still in change,
Who in a moment heaves her friends up to the height
Of her swift-turning slippery wheel then fleets[2] her friendship straight.
O wondrous change, even with the twinkling of an eye
Whom erst° herself had rashly set in pleasant place so high,
The same in great despite down headlong doth she throw.
And while she treads and spurneth at the lofty state laid low
More sorrow doth she shape within an hour's space
Than pleasure in an hundred years; so geason[3] is her grace.

---

[1] in the usual way, by the usual means
[2] withdraws, makes vanish
[3] rare, extraordinary

The proof whereof in me, alas, too plain appears,
Whom tenderly my careful° friends have fostered with my feres,°
In prosperous high degree, maintainèd so by fate,
That, as yourself did see, my foes envied my noble state.
One thing there was I did above the rest desire,
To which as to the sovereign good by hope I would aspire:
That by our marriage mean[1] we might within a while,
To work our perfect happiness, our parents reconcile,
That safely so we might, not stopped by sturdy[2] strife,
Unto the bounds that God hath set guide forth our pleasant life.
But now, alack, too soon my bliss is overblown
And upside down my purpose and my enterprise are thrown.
And driven from my friends, of strangers must I crave;
Oh, grant it God, from dangers dread that I may surety have.
For lo, henceforth I must wander in lands unknown
(So hard I find the prince's doom), exilèd from mine own.
Which thing I have thought good to set before your eyes
And to exhort you now to prove yourself a woman wise,
That patiently you bear my absent long abode,°
For what above by fatal dooms decreèd is that God"

—And more than this to say, it seemèd, he was bent,
But Juliet in deadly grief, with brackish tears besprent,
Brake off his tale begun and whilst his speech he stayed,[3]
These selfsame words, or like to these, with dreary cheer she said:
"Why, Romeus, can it be thou hast so hard a heart,
So far removed from ruth,° so far from thinking on my smart,°
To leave me thus alone, thou cause of my distress,
Besiegèd with so great a camp of mortal wretchedness
That every hour now and moment in a day
A thousand times Death brags, as he would reave° my life away?
Yet such is my mishap, O cruel destiny,
That still I live and wish for death, but yet can never die;
So that just cause I have to think, as seemeth me,
That froward Fortune did of late with cruel Death agree
To lengthen loathèd life, to pleasure in my pain
And triumph in my harm, as in the greatest hopèd gain.

---

[1] by means of our marriage
[2] reckless
[3] Juliet, in fearful grief and wet with her salty tears, broke off his tale and while he
cut short his speech.

And thou, the instrument of Fortune's cruel will,
Without whose aid she can no way her tyrannous lust fulfil,
Art not a whit ashamed, as far as I can see,
To cast me off when thou hast culled the better part of me.
Whereby, alas, too soon, I, seely° wretch, do prove
That all the ancient sacred laws of friendship and of love
Are quelled and quenchèd quite since he, on whom always
My chief hope and my steady trust was wonted° still to stay,°
For whom I am become unto myself a foe,
Disdaineth me, his steadfast friend, and scorns my friendship so.
Nay, Romeus, nay, thou may'st of two things choose the one,
Either to see thy castaway, as soon as thou art gone,
Headlong to throw herself down from the window's height
And so to break her slender neck with all the body's weight,
Or suffer her to be companion of thy pain
Whereso thou go, Fortune thee guide, till thou return again.
So wholly into thine transformèd is my heart
That even as oft as I do think that thou and I shall part,
So oft, methinks, my life withdraws itself away,
Which I retain to no end else but to the end I may,
In spite of all thy foes, thy present parts enjoy
And in distress to bear with thee the half of thine annoy.
Wherefore, in humble sort,° Romeus, I make request,
If ever tender pity yet were lodged in gentle breast,
Oh, let it now have place to rest within thy heart;
Receive me as thy servant and the fellow of thy smart.°
Thy absence is my death; thy sight shall give me life,
But if perhaps thou stand in dread to lead me as a wife.[1]
Art thou all counsel-less? Canst thou no shift[2] devise?
What letteth but in other weed I may myself disguise?[3]
What, shall I be the first? Hath none done so ere this
To 'scape the bondage of their friends? Thyself can answer yes.
Or dost thou stand in doubt that I thy wife ne can
By service pleasure thee as much as may thy hirèd man?
Or is my loyalty of both accompted° less?
Perhaps thou fear'st lest I for gain forsake thee in distress.
What, hath my beauty now no power at all on you,

---

[1] But perhaps you are afraid to take me along as your wife?
[2] plan
[3] What else may I do but disguise myself in other clothes?

Whose brightness, force, and praise sometime up to the skies you blew?[1]
My tears, my friendship and my pleasures done of old,
Shall they be quite forgot indeed?"

                   When Romeus did behold
The wildness of her look, her colour pale and dead,
The worst of all that might betide° to her, he 'gan to dread;
And once again he did in arms his Juliet take
And kissed her with a loving kiss and thus to her he spake:
"Ah, Juliet," quoth he, "the mistress of my heart,
For whom even now thy servant doth abide in deadly smart,°
Even for the happy days which thou desir'st to see,
And for the fervent friendship's sake that thou dost owe to me,
At once these fancies vain out of thy mind root out,
Except, perhaps, unto thy blame, thou fondly go about
To hasten forth my death and to thine own to run,
Which Nature's law and wisdom's lore° teach every wight to shun.
For but[2] thou change thy mind, I do foretell the end,
Thou shalt undo thyself for aye° and me thy trusty friend.
For why, thy absence known, thy father will be wroth°
And in his rage so narrowly he will pursue us both
That we shall try in vain to 'scape away by flight
And vainly seek a lurking place to hide us from his sight.
Then we, found out and caught, quite void of strong defence,
Shall cruelly be punishèd for thy departure hence,
I as a ravisher, thou as a careless child,
I as a man who doth defile, thou as a maid defiled,
Thinking to lead in ease a long contented life,
Shall short our days by shameful death. But if, my loving wife,
Thou banish from thy mind two foes that counsel hath,
That wont° to hinder sound advice, rash hastiness and wrath;
If thou be bent t'obey the lore° of reason's skill
And wisely by her princely power suppress rebelling will,
If thou our safety seek, more than thine own delight,
Since surety stands in parting, and thy pleasures grow of sight,
Forbear the cause of joy, and suffer for a while,
So shall I safely live abroad and safe turn from exile,
So shall no slander's blot thy spotless life distain,[3]

---

[1] you once declared to the heavens
[2] unless
[3] stain

So shall thy kinsmen be unstirred and I exempt from pain.
And think thou not that aye° the cause of care shall last;
These stormy broils shall overblow, much like a winter's blast.
For Fortune changeth more than fickle fantasy;
In nothing Fortune constant is save in unconstancy.
Her hasty running wheel is of a restless course
That turns the climbers headlong down from better to the worse
And those that are beneath she heaveth up again:
So we shall rise to pleasure's mount out of the pit of pain.
Ere° four months overpass such order will I take
And by my letters and my friends such means I mind to make
That of my wand'ring race ended shall be the toil
And I called home with honour great unto my native soil.
But if I be condemned to wander still in thrall°
I will return to you, mine own, befall what may befall.
And then by strength of friends and with a mighty hand
From Verone will I carry thee into a foreign land,
Not in man's weed° disguised or as one scarcely known,
But as my wife and only fere° in garment of thine own.
Wherefore repress at once the passions of thy heart
And where there is no cause of grief, cause hope to heal thy smart.°
For of this one thing thou may'st well assurèd be,
That nothing else but only death shall sunder me from thee."

The reasons that he made did seem of so great weight
And had with her such force that she to him 'gan answer straight:
"Dear sir, nought else wish I but to obey your will;
But sure whereso you go your heart with me shall tarry still
As sign and certain pledge till here I shall you see,
Of all the power that over you yourself did grant to me;
And in his stead take mine, the gage¹ of my good will.
— One promise crave I at your hand, that grant me to fulfil:
Fail not to let me have, at Friar Laurence's hand,
The tidings of your health and how your doubtful case shall stand.
And all the weary while that you shall spend abroad,
Cause me from time to time to know the place of your abode."
His eyes did gush out tears, a sigh brake° from his breast
When he did grant and with an oath did vow to keep the hest.°

---

¹ pledge, promise

Thus these two lovers pass away the weary night
In pain and plaint, not, as they wont,° in pleasure and delight.
But now, somewhat too soon, in farthest east arose
Fair Lucifer, the golden star that lady Venus chose,
Whose course appointed is with speedy race to run,
A messenger of dawning day and of the rising sun.
Then fresh Aurora with her pale and silver glade
Did clear the skies and from the earth had chasèd ugly shade.
When thou ne lookest wide, ne closely dost thou wink
When Phoebus from our hemisphere in western wave doth sink,
What colour then the heavens do show unto thine eyes,
The same or like saw Romeus in farthest eastern skies.
As yet he saw no day, ne could he call it night
With equal force decreasing dark fought with increasing light.
Then Romeus in arms his lady 'gan to fold
With friendly kiss and ruthfully° she 'gan her knight behold.
With solemn oath they both their sorrowful leave do take;
They swear no stormy troubles shall their steady friendship shake.
Then careful° Romeus again to cell returns
And in her chamber secretly our joyless Juliet mourns.
Now hugy° clouds of care, of sorrow, and of dread
The clearness of their gladsome hearts hath wholly overspread.
When golden-crested Phoebus boasteth him in sky
And under earth to 'scape revenge his deadly foe doth fly,
Then hath these lovers' day an end, their night begun,
For each of them to other is as to the world the sun;
The dawning they shall see, ne summer any more,
But blackfaced night with winter rough, ah, beaten over sore.

The weary watch discharged did hie° them home to sleep,
The warders and the scouts were charged their place and course to keep
And Verone gates awide the porters had set open
When Romeus had of his affairs with Friar Laurence spoken.
Warely° he walked forth, unknown of friend or foe,
Clad like a merchant venturer from top even to the toe.
He spurred apace[1] and came withouten° stop or stay
To Mantua gates, where lighted down, he sent his man away
With words of comfort to his old afflicted sire;
And straight, in mind to sojourn there, a lodging doth he hire,

---

[1] rode quickly

And with the nobler sort he doth himself acquaint
And of his open wrong received the duke doth hear his plaint.
He practiseth[1] by friends for pardon of exile,
The whilst he seeketh every way his sorrows to beguile.
But who forgets the coal that burneth in his breast?
Alas, his cares deny his heart the sweet desirèd rest;
No time finds he of mirth, he finds no place of joy,
But everything occasion gives of sorrow and annoy.
For when in turning skies the heaven's lamps are light,
And from the other hemisphere fair Phoebus chaseth night,
When every man and beast hath rest from painful toil,
Then in the breast of Romeus his passions 'gin to boil.
Then doth he wet with tears the couch whereon he lies
And then his sighs the chamber fill and out aloud he cries
Against the restless stars in rolling skies that range,
Against the fatal sisters three, and Fortune full of change.
Each night a thousand times he calleth for the day;
He thinketh Titan's restless steeds of restiness do stay[2]
Or that at length they have some baiting[3] place found out,
Or, guided ill, have lost their way and wandered far about.
While thus in idle thoughts the weary time he spendeth,
The night hath end, but not with night the plaint of night he endeth.
Is he accompanied? Is he in place alone?
In company he wails his harm; apart he maketh moan,
For if his feres° rejoice what cause hath he to joy,
That wanteth still his chief delight while they their loves enjoy?

But if with heavy cheer they show their inward grief,
He waileth most his wretchedness that is of wretches chief.
When he doth hear abroad the praise of ladies blown,[4]
Within his thought he scorneth them and doth prefer his own.
When pleasant songs he hears, while others do rejoice,
The melody of music doth stir up his mourning voice.
But if in secret place he walk somewhere alone
The place itself and secretness redoubleth all his moan.
Then speaks he to the beasts, to feathered fowls and trees,

---

[1] tries to bring about
[2] Titan's horses (steeds) hesitate: an image to describe his impatience as Romeo
    waits for daybreak.
[3] resting, stopping
[4] spoken about

Unto the earth, the clouds, and to whatso beside he sees.
To them he shew'th° his smart° as though they reason had.
Each thing may cause his heaviness, but nought may make him glad.
And weary of the day, again he calleth night;
The sun he curseth and the hour when first his eyes saw light.
And as the night and day their course do interchange,
So doth our Romeus' nightly cares for cares of day exchange.

In absence of her knight the lady no way could
Keep truce between her griefs and her, though ne'er so fain she would;[1]
And though with greater pain she cloakèd sorrow's smart,°
Yet did her palèd face disclose the passions of her heart.
Her sighing every hour, her weeping everywhere,
Her reckless heed of meat,[2] of sleep, and wearing of her gear
The careful° mother marks. Then of her health afraid,
Because the griefs increasèd still, thus to her child she said:
"Dear daughter, if you should long languish in this sort,°
I stand in doubt° that oversoon your sorrows will make short
Your loving father's life and mine, that love you more
Than our own proper° breath and life. Bridle henceforth therefore
Your grief and pain, yourself on joy your thought to set,
For time it is that now you should our Tybalt's death forget,
Of whom since God hath claimed the life that was but lent
He is in bliss, ne is there cause why you should thus lament.
You cannot call him back with tears and shriekings shrill,
It is a fault thus still to grudge at God's appointed will."

The seely° soul had now no longer power to feign;
No longer could she hide her harm, but answered thus again,
With heavy broken sighs, with visage pale and dead:
"Madam, the last of Tybalt's tears a great while since I shed.
Whose spring hath been ere this so laded out by me
That empty quite and moistureless I guess it now to be.
So that my painèd heart by conduits of the eyne
No more henceforth, as wont° it was, shall gush forth dropping brine."
The woeful mother knew not what her daughter meant
And loath to vex her child by words, her peace she warely hent.[3]
But when from hour to hour, from morrow to the morrow,

[1] no matter how she tried
[2] her reckless avoidance of food of any sort (*meat*: see glossary)
[3] cautiously held her words

Still more and more she saw increased her daughter's wonted° sorrow
All means she sought of her and household folk to know
The certain root whereon her grief and bootless° moan doth grow.
But, lo, she hath in vain her time and labour lore,[1]
Wherefore without all measure is her heart tormented sore.

And sith° herself could not find out the cause of care,
She thought it good to tell the sire how ill his child did fare.
And when she saw her time, thus to her fere° she said:
"Sir, if you mark our daughter well, the countenance of the maid,
And how she fareth since that Tybalt unto death
Before his time, forced by his foe, did yield his living breath,
Her face shall seem so changed, her doings eke so strange,
That you will greatly wonder at so great and sudden change.
Not only she forbears her meat,° her drink, and sleep,
But now she tendeth nothing else but to lament and weep.
No greater joy hath she, nothing contents her heart
So much as in the chamber close to shut herself apart,
Where she doth so torment her poor afflicted mind
That much in danger stands her life, except° some help we find.
But, out, alas, I see not how it may be found,
Unless that first we might find whence her sorrows thus abound.
For though with busy° care I have employed my wit
And used all the ways I knew to learn the truth of it,
Neither extremity ne gentle means could boot;°
She hideth close within her breast her secret sorrow's root.
This was my first conceit,[2] that all her ruth° arose
Out of her cousin Tybalt's death, late slain of deadly foes,
But now my heart doth hold a new repugnant thought:
Some greater thing, not Tybalt's death, this change in her hath wrought.
Herself assurèd me that many days ago
She shed the last of Tybalt's tears, which word amazed me so
That I then could not guess what thing else might her grieve,
But now at length I have bethought me and I do believe
The only crop and root of all my daughter's pain
Is grudging envy's faint disease: perhaps she doth disdain
To see in wedlock yoke the most part of her feres,°
Whilst only she unmarrièd doth lose so many years.

---

[1] lost, lorn
[2] idea, notion

And more perchance she thinks you mind to keep her so;
Wherefore despairing doth she wear herself away with woe.
Therefore, dear sir, in time take on your daughter ruth;°
For why, a brickle thing is glass, and frail is frailless¹ youth.
Join her at once to some in link of marriage,
That may be meet° for our degree, and much about her age:
So shall you banish care out of your daughter's breast,
So we her parents, in our age, shall live in quiet rest."

Whereto 'gan easily her husband to agree,
And to the mother's skilful talk thus straightway answered he:
"Oft have I thought, dear wife, of all these things ere this,
But evermore my mind me gave, it should not be amiss
By farther leisure had a husband to provide;
Scarce saw she yet full sixteen years:² too young to be a bride!
But since her state doth stand on terms so perilous
And that a maiden daughter is a treasure dangerous,³
With so great speed I will endeavour to procure
A husband for our daughter young, her sickness faint to cure;
That you shall rest content, so warely° will I choose
And she recover soon enough the time she seems to lose.
The whilst seek you to learn if she in any part
Already hath, unware to us, fixèd her friendly heart,
Lest we have more respect to honour and to wealth
Than to our daughter's quiet life and to her happy health,
Whom I do hold as dear as th'apple of mine eye
And rather wish in poor estate and daughterless to die
Than leave my goods and her ythralled° to such a one
Whose churlish dealing, I once dead, should be her cause of moan."

This pleasant answer heard, the lady parts again
And Capulet, the maiden's sire, within a day or twain
Conferreth with his friends for marriage of his daughter,
And many gentlemen there were with busy° care that sought her;
Both for the maiden was well shapèd, young, and fair,
As also well brought up, and wise, her father's only heir.
Among the rest was one inflamed with her desire,

---

¹ brittle (i.e., vulnerable); frail or fragile
² Brooke's Juliet is barely sixteen years old: compare her to Shakespeare's Juliet.
³ delicate, vulnerable

Who County Paris clepèd was, an earl he had to sire.[1]
Of all the suitors him the father liketh best
And easily unto the earl he maketh his behest,
Both of his own good will and of his friendly aid,
To win his wife unto his will and to persuade the maid.
The wife did joy to hear the joyful husband say
How happy hap, how meet° a match, he had found out that day.
Ne did she seek to hide her joys within her heart,
But straight she hieth° to Juliet; to her she tells, apart,
What happy talk, by mean° of her, was past no rather
Between the wooing Paris and her careful,° loving father.
The person of the man, the features of his face,
His youthful years, his fairness, and his port and seemly grace
With curious[2] words she paints before her daughter's eyes,
And then with store of virtue's praise she heaves him to the skies.
She vaunts[3] his race and gifts that Fortune did him give,
Whereby, she saith, both she and hers in great delight shall live.

When Juliet conceived her parents' whole intent,
Whereto both love and reason's right forbode her to assent,
Within herself she thought, rather than be forsworn,
With horses wild her tender parts asunder should be torn.
Not now with bashful brow, in wonted wise[4] she spake,
But with unwonted boldness straight into these words she brake:°
"Madam, I marvel much that you so lavas[5] are
Of me your child, your jewel once, your only joy and care,
As thus to yield me up at pleasure of another,
Before you know if I do like or else mislike my lover.
Do what you list,° but yet of this assure you still,
If you do as you say you will, I yield not there until.
For had I choice of twain, far rather would I choose
My part of all your goods and eke my breath and life to lose
Than grant that he possess of me the smallest part;
First, weary of my painful life, my cares shall kill my heart,
Else will I pierce my breast with sharp and bloody knife
And you, my mother, shall become the murd'ress of my life

---

[1] who was named County Paris, and whose father was an earl
[2] carefully chosen
[3] praises
[4] usual way
[5] lavish

In giving me to him whom I ne can, ne may,
Ne ought, to love. Wherefore on knees, dear mother, I you pray
To let me live henceforth as I have lived tofore;
Cease all your troubles for my sake, and care for me no more.
But suffer Fortune fierce to work on me her will;
In her it lieth to do me boot, in her it lieth to spill.[1]
For whilst you for the best desire to place me so,
You haste away my ling'ring death, and double all my woe.
So deep this answer made the sorrows down to sink
Into the mother's breast that she ne knoweth what to think
Of these her daughter's words, but all appalled she stands
And up unto the heavens she throws her wond'ring head and hands.
And, nigh beside herself, her husband hath she sought;
She tells him all; she doth forget ne yet she hideth aught.°

The testy old man, wroth,° disdainful without measure,
Sends forth his folk in haste for her and bids them take no leisure,
Ne on her tears or plaint at all to have remorse
But, if they cannot with her will, to bring the maid perforce.[2]
The message heard, they part to fetch that they must fet[3]
And willingly with them walks forth obedient Juliet.
Arrivèd in the place, when she her father saw,
Of whom, as much as duty would, the daughter stood in awe.
The servants sent away (the mother thought it meet°),
The woeful daughter all bewept fell grovelling at his feet,
Which she doth wash with tears as she thus grovelling lies—
So fast and eke so plenteously distil they from her eyes.
When she to call for grace her mouth doth think to open;
Mute she is—for sighs and sobs her fearful talk have broken.
The sire, whose swelling wrath her tears could not assuage,
With fiery eyne and scarlet cheeks thus spake her in his rage,
Whilst ruthfully° stood by the maiden's mother mild:
"Listen," quoth he, "unthankful and thou disobedient child,
Hast thou so soon let slip out of thy mind the word
That thou so oftentimes hast heard rehearsèd at my board?[4]
How much the Roman youth of parents stood in awe,
And eke what power upon their seed the fathers had by law,

---

[1] Fortune has the power to favour me or kill (spill) me.
[2] by force
[3] to fetch that which they must fetch
[4] repeated at my table

Whom they not only might pledge, alienate, and sell,
Whenso they stood in need; but more, if children did rebel
The parents had the power of life and sudden death.
What if those goodmen should again receive the living breath,
In how strait bonds would they thy stubborn body bind?
What weapons would they seek for thee? What torments would they find
To chasten, if they saw, the lewdness of thy life,
Thy great unthankfulness to me, and shameful sturdy[1] strife?
Such care thy mother had, so dear thou wert to me,
That I with long and earnest suit provided have for thee
One of the greatest lords that wones[2] about this town,
And for his many virtues' sake a man of great renown.
Of whom both thou and I unworthy are too much,
So rich ere long he shall be left, his father's wealth is such,
Such is the nobleness and honour of the race
From whence his father came: and yet, thou playest in this case
The dainty fool, and stubborn girl; for want of skill
Thou dost refuse thy offered weal° and disobey my will.
Even by His strength I swear, that first did give me life
And gave me in my youth the strength to get thee on my wife,
Unless by Wednesday next thou bend as I am bent,
And at our castle called Freetown thou freely do assent
To County Paris' suit and promise to agree
To whatsoever then shall pass 'twixt him, my wife, and me,
Not only will I give all that I have away
From thee to those that shall me love, me honour, and obey,
But also to so close and to so hard a gaol
I shall thee wed for all thy life that sure thou shalt not fail
A thousand times a day to wish for sudden death
And curse the day and hour when first thy lungs did give thee breath.
Advise thee well[3] and say that thou art warnèd now,
And think not that I speak in sport or mind to break my vow.
For were it not that I to County Paris gave
My faith, which I must keep unfalsed my honour so to save,
Ere thou go hence, myself would see thee chastened so,
That thou should'st once for all be taught thy duty how to know
And what revenge of old the angry sires did find
Against their children that rebelled and showed themself unkind."

---

[1] reckless
[2] dwells
[3] reflect carefully

These said, the old man straight is gone in haste away,
Ne for his daughter's answer would the testy father stay.°
And after him his wife doth follow out of door,
And there they leave their chidden[1] child kneeling upon the floor.
Then she that oft had seen the fury of her sire,
Dreading what might come of his rage, nould[2] farther stir his ire.
Unto her chamber she withdrew herself apart,
Where she was wonted° to unload the sorrows of her heart.
There did she not so much busy her eyes in sleeping,
As overpressed with restless thoughts in piteous bootless° weeping.
The fast falling of tears make not her tears decrease,
Ne, by the pouring forth of plaint, the cause of plaint doth cease.
So that to th'end the moan and sorrow may decay,
The best is that she seek some mean° to take the cause away.
Her weary bed betime the woeful wight forsakes
And to Saint Francis' church to mass her way devoutly takes.

The friar forth is called; she prays him hear her shrift;°
Devotion is in so young years a rare and precious gift.
When on her tender knees the dainty lady kneels
In mind to pour forth all the grief that inwardly she feels,
With sighs and salted tears her shriving doth begin,
For she of heapèd sorrows hath to speak, and not of sin.
Her voice with piteous plaint was made already hoarse,
And hasty sobs when she would speak brake° off her words perforce.[3]
But as she may, piece-meal, she poureth in his lap
The marriage news, a mischief new, preparèd by mishap,
Her parents' promise erst° to County Paris past,
Her father's threats she telleth him, and thus concludes at last:
"Once was I wedded well, ne will I wed again;
For since I know I may not be the wedded wife of twain,
For I am bound to have one God, one faith, one make,[4]
My purpose is as soon as I shall hence my journey take,
With these two hands which joined unto the heavens I stretch,
The hasty death which I desire unto myself to reach.
This day, O Romeus, this day thy woeful wife

---

[1] chided, scolded
[2] would not
[3] out of necessity
[4] mate, partner

Will bring the end of all her cares by ending careful° life.
So my departed sprite° shall witness to the sky
And eke my blood unto the earth bear record how that I
Have kept my faith unbroke, steadfast unto my friend."

When this her heavy tale was told, her vow eke at an end,
Her gazing here and there, her fierce and staring look,
Did witness that some lewd attempt her heart had undertook.
Whereat the friar astound, and ghastfully afraid
Lest she by deed perform her word thus much to her he said:
"Ah, Lady Juliet, what need the words you spake?
I pray you, grant me one request for blessèd Mary's sake.
Measure somewhat your grief, hold here awhile your peace
Whilst I bethink me of your case your plaint and sorrows cease.
Such comfort will I give you ere you part from hence,
And for th'assaults of Fortune's ire prepare so sure defence,
So wholesome salve will I for your afflictions find,
That you shall hence depart again with well contented mind."

His words have chasèd straight out of her heart despair;
Her black and ugly dreadful thoughts by hope are waxen fair.
So Friar Laurence now hath left her there alone
And he out of the church in haste is to his chamber gone,
Where sundry thoughts within his careful° head arise.
The old man's foresight divers° doubts hath set before his eyes;
His conscience one while condemns it for a sin
To let her take Paris to spouse since he himself had bin°
The chiefest cause that she unknown to father or mother
Not five months past in that self place was wedded to another.[1]
Anotherwhile an hugy° heap of dangers dread
His restless thought hath heapèd up within his troubled head.
Even of itself th'attempt he judgeth perilous;
The execution eke he deems so much more dangerous,
That to a woman's grace he must himself commit
That young is, simple and unware, for weighty affairs unfit;
For if she fail in aught,° the matter publishèd,[2]
Both she and Romeus were undone, himself eke punishèd.

---

[1] Five months have passed since Juliet's marriage to Romeus.
[2] made known

When to and fro in mind he divers° thoughts had cast,
With tender pity and with ruth° his heart was won at last;
He thought he rather would in hazard set his fame,
Than suffer such adultery. Resolving on the same,
Out of his closet straight he took a little glass
And then with double haste returned where woeful Juliet was,
Whom he hath found well-nigh in trance, scarce drawing breath,
Attending still to hear the news of life or else of death.
Of whom he did enquire of the appointed day:
"On Wednesday next," quod Juliet, "so doth my father say,
I must give my consent, but as I do remember,
The solemn day of marriage is the tenth day of September."
"Dear daughter," quoth the friar, "of good cheer see thou be,
For lo, Saint Francis of his grace hath showed a way to me
By which I may both thee and Romeus together
Out of the bondage which you fear assuredly deliver.
Even from the holy font thy husband have I known
And since he grew in years have kept his counsels as mine own.
For from his youth he would unfold to me his heart
And often have I curèd him of anguish and of smart;°
I know that by desert° his friendship I have won
And I him hold as dear as if he were my proper° son.
Wherefore my friendly heart cannot abide that he
Should wrongfully in aught° be harmed, if that it lay in me
To right or to revenge the wrong by my advice
Or timely to prevent the same in any other wise.°
And sith° thou art his wife, thee am I bound to love
For Romeus' friendship's sake and seek thy anguish to remove
And dreadful torments which thy heart besiegen[1] round;
Wherefore, my daughter, give good ear unto my counsels sound.
Forget not what I say, ne tell it any wight,°
Not to the nurse thou trustest so, as Romeus is thy knight;
For on this thread doth hang thy death and eke thy life,
My fame or shame, his weal° or woe that chose thee to his wife.
Thou art not ignorant—because of such renown
As everywhere is spread of me but chiefly in this town—
That in my youthful days abroad I travellèd
Through every land found out by men, by men inhabited;
So twenty years from home, in lands unknown a guest,

---

[1] besiege

I never gave my weary limbs long time of quiet rest,
But in the desert woods to beasts of cruel kind
Or on the seas to drenching waves at pleasure of the wind
I have committed them to ruth of rover's hand[1]
And to a thousand dangers more by water and by land.

But not in vain, my child, hath all my wand'ring bin;°
Beside the great contentedness my sprite° abideth in
That by the pleasant thought of passèd things doth grow,
One private fruit more have I plucked, which thou shalt shortly know:
What force the stones, the plants, and metals have to work,
And divers° other things that in the bowels of earth do lurk,
With care I have sought out, with pain I did them prove.[2]
With them eke can I help myself at times of my behove[3]—
Although the science be against the laws of men—
When sudden danger forceth me; but yet most chiefly when
The work to do is least displeasing unto God,
Not helping to do any sin that wreakful Jove forbode.
For since in life no hope of long abode° I have,
But now am come unto the brink of my appointed grave
And that my death draws near, whose stripe[4] I may not shun,
But shall be called to make account of all that I have done,
Now ought I from henceforth more deeply print in mind
The judgement of the Lord than when youth's folly made me blind,
When love and fond° desire were boiling in my breast,
Whence hope and dread by striving thoughts had banished friendly rest.
Know therefore, daughter, that with other gifts which I
Have well attainèd to by grace and favour of the sky
Long since I did find out and yet the way I know
Of certain roots and savoury herbs to make a kind of dough
Which bakèd hard and beat into a powder fine
And drunk with conduit water[5] or with any kind of wine,
It doth in half an hour astonne[6] the taker so,
And mast'reth all his senses that he feeleth weal° nor woe:
And so it burieth up the sprite° and living breath

---

[1] to the mercy of a thief or robber
[2] test
[3] choosing
[4] whip or lash mark
[5] spring water
[6] overtake, as in in a trance

That even the skilful leech° would say that he is slain by death.
One virtue more it hath, as marvellous as this:
The taker, by receiving it, at all not grievèd is,
But painless as a man that thinketh nought at all,
Into a sweet and quiet sleep immediately doth fall,
From which, according to the quantity he taketh,
Longer or shorter is the time before the sleeper waketh.
And thence th'effect, once wrought, again it doth restore
Him that received unto the state wherein he was before.

Wherefore, mark well the end of this my tale begun,
And thereby learn what is by thee hereafter to be done.
Cast off from thee at once the weed° of womanish dread;
With manly courage arm thyself from heel unto the head,
For only on the fear or boldness of thy breast
The happy hap° or ill mishap of thy affair doth rest.
Receive this vial small and keep it as thine eye;
And on thy marriage day before the sun do clear the sky
Fill it with water full up to the very brim,
Then drink it off and thou shalt feel throughout each vein and limb
A pleasant slumber slide and quite dispread at length
On all thy parts, from every part reave° all thy kindly strength.
Withouten¹ moving thus thy idle parts shall rest;
No pulse shall go, ne heart once beat within thy hollow breast,
But thou shalt lie as she that dieth in a trance.
Thy kinsmen and thy trusty friends shall wail the sudden chance.²
Thy corpse then will they bring to grave in this churchyard,
Where thy forefathers long ago a costly tomb prepared
Both for themself and eke for those that should come after.
Both deep it is and long and large where thou shalt rest, my daughter,
Till I to Mantua send for Romeus, thy knight;
Out of the tomb both he and I will take thee forth that night.
And when out of thy sleep thou shalt awake again
Then may'st thou go with him from hence; and, healed of thy pain,
In Mantua lead with him unknown a pleasant life.
And yet perhaps in time to come, when cease shall all the strife
And that the peace is made 'twixt Romeus and his foes,
Myself may find so fit a time these secrets to disclose,

---

¹ without
² stroke of fate

Both to my praise and to thy tender parents' joy
That dangerless, without reproach, thou shalt thy love enjoy."

When of his skilful tale the friar had made an end,
To which our Juliet well her ear and wits did bend,
That she hath heard it all and hath forgotten nought,
Her fainting heart was comforted with hope and pleasant thought.
And then to him she said: "Doubt not but that I will
With stout and unappallèd heart your happy hest[1] fulfil.
Yea, if I wist° it were a venomous deadly drink,
Rather would I that through my throat the certain bane should sink
Than I, not drinking it, into his hands should fall
That hath no part of me as yet, ne ought to have at all.
Much more I ought with bold and with a willing heart
To greatest danger yield myself, and to the deadly smart°
To come to him on whom my life doth wholly stay;[2]
That is my only heart's delight, and so he shall be aye."°
"Then go," quoth he, "my child, I pray that God on high
Direct thy foot and by thy hand upon the way thee guie.[3]
God grant He so confirm in thee thy present will,
That no inconstant toy thee let thy promise to fulfil."[4]

A thousand thanks and more our Juliet gave the friar
And homeward to her father's house joyful she doth retire;
And as with stately gait she passèd through the street
She saw her mother in the door, that with her there would meet,
In mind to ask if she her purpose yet did hold,
In mind also, apart 'twixt them, her duty to have told.
Wherefore with pleasant face and with unwonted° cheer,
As soon as she was unto her approachèd somewhat near,
Before the mother spake, thus did she first begin:
"Madam, at Saint Francis' church have I this morning bin,°
Where I did make abode a longer while, percase,[5]
Than duty would; yet have I not been absent from this place
So long a while without a great and just cause why:
This fruit have I receivèd there—my heart, erst° like to die,

---

[1] welcome request
[2] depend
[3] guide
[4] that no idle distraction prevent you from fulfilling your promise
[5] where I stayed a longer while, as it happened (see glossary)

Is now revived again and my afflicted breast
Releasèd from affliction, restorèd is to rest!
For lo, my troubled ghost,[1] alas, too sore dis-eased,
By ghostly° counsel and advice hath Friar Laurence eased,
To whom I did at large discourse my former life
And in confession did I tell of all our passèd strife:
Of County Paris' suit and how my lord, my sire,
By my ungrate and stubborn strife I stirrèd unto ire;
But lo, the holy friar hath by his ghostly lore°
Made me another woman now than I had been before.
By strength of arguments he chargèd so my mind,
That, though I sought, no sure defence my searching thought could find.
So forced I was at length to yield up witless will,
And promised to be ordered by the friar's praisèd skill.
Wherefore, albeit I had rashly long before
The bed and rites of marriage for many years forswore,
Yet mother, now behold your daughter at your will,
Ready if you command her aught° your pleasure to fulfil.
Wherefore in humble wise,° dear madam, I you pray
To go unto my lord and sire withouten° long delay;
Of him first pardon crave of faults already past
And show him, if it pleaseth you, his child is now at last
Obedient to his just and to his skilful hest,°
And that I will, God lending life, on Wednesday next be prest
To wait on him and you unto[2] th'appointed place,
Where I will in your hearing and before my father's face
Unto the County give my faith and whole assent
And take him for my lord and spouse. Thus fully am I bent
And that out of your mind I may remove all doubt
Unto my closet fare° I now to search and to choose out
The bravest[3] garments and the richest jewels there,
Which, better him to please, I mind on Wednesday next to wear.
For if I did excel the famous Grecian rape,[4]
Yet might attire help to amend my beauty and my shape."

The simple mother was rapt into great delight;
Not half a word could she bring forth, but in this joyful plight

---

[1] spirit
[2] at
[3] most noble
[4] Helen of Troy was abducted by Paris, son of King Priam of Troy.

With nimble foot she ran and with unwonted° pace
Unto her pensive husband and to him with pleasant face
She told what she had heard and praiseth much the friar
And joyful tears ran down the cheeks of this gray-bearded sire.
With hands and eyes heaved up he thanks God in his heart
And then he saith: "This is not, wife, the friar's first desert;°
Oft hath he showed to us great friendship heretofore,
By helping us at needful times with wisdom's precious lore.°
In all our commonweal° scarce one is to be found
But is for some good turn unto this holy father bound.
Oh, that the third part of my goods—I do not feign—
But twenty of his passed years might purchase him again!
So much in recompense of friendship would I give,
So much, in faith, his extreme age my friendly heart doth grieve."

These said, the glad old man from home go'th straight abroad
And to the stately palace hieth where Paris made abode,
Whom he desires to be on Wednesday next his geast°
At Freetown, where he minds to make for him a costly feast.
But lo, the earl saith, such feasting were but lost
And counsels him till marriage-time to spare so great a cost,
For then he knoweth well the charges will be great,
The whilst his heart desireth still her sight and not his meat.°
He craves of Capulet that he may straight go see Fair Juliet,
Whereto he doth right willingly agree.
The mother, warned before, her daughter doth prepare;
She warneth and she chargeth her that in no wise° she spare
Her courteous speech, her pleasant looks, and comely grace,
But liberally to give them forth when Paris comes in place,
Which she as cunningly could set forth to the show
As cunning craftsmen to the sale do set their wares on row,
That ere the County did out of her sight depart,
So secretly unwares to him she stale¹ away his heart,
That of his life and death the wily wench had power.
And now his longing heart thinks long for their appointed hour
And with importune suit the parents doth he pray
The wedlock knot to knit soon up and haste the marriage day.
The wooer hath passed forth the first day in this sort°

---

¹ stole

And many other more than this in pleasure and disport.[1]

At length the wishèd time of long hopèd delight,
As Paris thought, drew near; but near approachèd heavy plight.
Against[2] the bridal day the parents did prepare
Such rich attire, such furniture, such store of dainty fare
That they which did behold the same the night before
Did think and say a man could scarcely wish for any more.
Nothing did seem too dear; the dearest things were bought
And as the written story saith indeed there wanted nought[3]
That 'longed to his degree, and honour of his stock:
But Juliet the whilst her thoughts within her breast did lock,
Even from the trusty nurse, whose secretness was tried;
The secret counsel of her heart the nurse-child seeks to hide.
For sith,° to mock her dame she did not stick[4] to lie;
She thought no sin with show of truth to blear her nurse's eye.
In chamber secretly the tale she 'gan renew
That at the door she told her dame, as though it had been true.
The flatt'ring nurse did praise the friar for his skill
And said that she had done right well by wit to order will.[5]
She setteth forth at large the father's furious rage
And eke she praiseth much to her the second marriage;
And County Paris now she praiseth ten times more
By wrong than she herself, by right, had Romeus praised before.
Paris shall dwell there still, Romeus shall not return;
What shall it boot° her life to languish still and mourn?
The pleasures past before she must account as gain;
But if he do return, what then?—for one she shall have twain.
The one shall use her as his lawful wedded wife,
In wanton love with equal joy the other lead his life;
And best shall she be sped of any townish dame,
Of husband and of paramour to find her change of game.[6]
These words and like the nurse did speak in hope to please,

---

[1] diversion and amusement
[2] for
[3] lacked nothing. Brooke refers to an otherwise undefined "written story" as part of his own narrative (see introduction).
[4] hesitate
[5] control (her) desire
[6] She will be more fortunate than the women of the town to have a husband *and* a lover.

But greatly did these wicked words the lady's mind dis-ease;[1]
But aye° she hid her wrath and seemèd well content
When daily did the naughty nurse new arguments invent.

But when the bride perceived her hour approachèd near
She sought the best she could to feign and tempered so her cheer
That by her outward look no living wight° could guess
Her inward woe; and yet anew renewed is her distress.
Unto her chamber doth the pensive wight° repair,
And in her hand a percher light[2] the nurse bears up the stair.
In Juliet's chamber was her wonted use[3] to lie;
Wherefore her mistress, dreading that she should her work descry,[4]
As soon as she began her pallet to unfold,
Thinking to lie that night where she was wont° to lie of old,
Doth gently pray her seek her lodging somewhere else;
And lest she, crafty, should suspect, a ready reason tells.
"Dear friend," quoth she, "you know to-morrow is the day
Of new contract; wherefore, this night my purpose is to pray
Unto the heavenly minds that dwell above the skies
And order all the course of things as they can best devise,
That they so smile upon the doings of to-morrow
That all the remnant of my life may be exempt from sorrow.
Wherefore, I pray you, leave me here alone this night,
But see that you to-morrow come before the dawning light,
For you must curl my hair and set on my attire."
And easily the loving nurse did yield to her desire,
For she within her head did cast before no doubt;
She little knew the close attempt[5] her nurse-child went about.

The nurse departed once, the chamber door shut close
Assurèd that no living wight° her doing might disclose.
She pourèd forth into the vial of the friar
Water out of a silver ewer that on the board stood by her.
The sleepy mixture made, fair Juliet doth it hide
Under her bolster soft and so unto her bed she hied,°
Where divers° novel thoughts arise within her head

---

[1] cause discomfort
[2] large candle
[3] usual habit
[4] discover
[5] secret plan

And she is so environed about with deadly dread
That what before she had resolved undoubtedly
That same she calleth into doubt; and lying doubtfully
Whilst honest love did strive with dread of deadly pain,
With hands y-wrung and weeping eyes thus gan she to complain:
"What, is there anyone beneath the heavens high
So much unfortunate as I? So much past hope as I?
What, am I not myself, of all that yet were born,
The deepest drenchèd in despair and most in Fortune's scorn?
For, lo, the world for me hath nothing else to find
Beside mishap and wretchedness and anguish of the mind
Since that the cruel cause of my unhappiness
Hath put me to this sudden plunge and brought to such distress
As to the end[1] I may my name and conscience save
I must devour the mixèd drink that by me here I have,
Whose working and whose force as yet I do not know."
And of this piteous plaint began another doubt° to grow:
"What do I know," quoth she, "if that this powder shall
Sooner or later than it should or else not work at all?
And then my craft descried as open as the day,
The people's tale and laughing-stock shall I remain for aye."°
"And what know I," quoth she, "if serpents odious
And other beasts and worms that are of nature venomous
That wonted° are to lurk in dark caves underground
And commonly, as I have heard, in dead men's tombs are found
Shall harm me, yea or nay, where I shall lie as dead? —
Or how shall I that alway° have in so fresh air been bred
Endure the lothsome stink of such an heapèd store
Of carcases not yet consumed and bones that long before
Intombèd were, where I my sleeping-place shall have,
Where all my ancestors do rest, my kindred's common grave?
Shall not the friar and my Romeus when they come
Find me, if I awake before, y-stifled in the tomb?"

And whilst she in these thoughts doth dwell somewhat too long,
The force of her imagining anon did wax so strong
That she surmised she saw out of the hollow vault
A grisly thing to look upon, the carcass of Tybalt
Right in the selfsame sort° that she few days before

---

[1] in order that

Had seen him in his blood imbrued,[1] to death eke wounded sore.
And then when she again within herself had weighed
That quick[2] she should be buried there and by his side be laid
All comfortless, for she shall living fere° have none
But many a rotten carcass and full many a naked bone
Her dainty tender parts 'gan shiver all for dread;
Her golden hairs did stand upright upon her chillish[3] head.
Then pressèd with the fear that she there livèd in,
A sweat as cold as mountain ice pierced through her slender skin,
That with the moisture hath wet every part of hers:
And more besides, she vainly thinks, whilst vainly thus she fears,
A thousand bodies dead have compassed her about,
And lest they will dismember her she greatly stands in doubt.°
But when she felt her strength began to wear away
By little and little, and in her heart her fear increasèd aye,°
Dreading that weakness might, or foolish cowardice,
Hinder the execution of the purposed enterprise,
As she had frantic been, in haste the glass she caught,
And up she drank the mixture quite, withouten° farther thought.
Then on her breast she crossed her arms long and small,[4]
And so, her senses failing her, into a trance did fall.

And when that Phoebus bright heaved up his seemly head
And from the East in open skies his glist'ring rays dispread,
The nurse unshut the door, for she the key did keep,
And doubting° she had slept too long, she thought to break her sleep.
First softly did she call, then louder thus did cry:
"Lady, you sleep too long; the earl will raise you by and by."
But, well away, in vain unto the deaf she calls,
She thinks to speak to Juliet, but speaketh to the walls.
If all the dreadful noise that might on earth be found,
Or on the roaring seas, or if the dreadful thunder's sound
Had blown into her ears, I think they could not make
The sleeping wight° before the time by any means awake;
So were the sprites° of life shut up and senses thralled,°
Wherewith the seely° careful° nurse was wondrously appalled.

---

[1] soaked
[2] alive
[3] chilly
[4] slender

She thought to daw[1] her now as she had done of old,
But lo, she found her parts were stiff and more than marble cold:
Neither at mouth nor nose found she recourse of breath;
Two certain arguments were these of her untimely death.

Wherefore, as one distraught, she to her mother ran
With scratchèd face and hair betorn, but no word speak she can.
At last, with much ado, "Dead," quoth she, "is my child!"
"Now, out, alas!" the mother cried, and as a tiger wild
Whose whelps, whilst she is gone out of her den to prey,
The hunter greedy of his game doth kill or carry away,
So raging forth she ran unto her Juliet's bed
And there she found her darling and her only comfort dead.
Then shrieked she out as loud as serve her would her breath
And then, that pity was to hear, thus cried she out on Death:
"Ah cruel Death," quoth she, "that thus against all right
Hast ended my felicity and robbed my heart's delight;
Do now thy worst to me, once wreak thy wrath for all;
Even in despite I cry to thee, thy vengeance let thou fall.
Whereto stay I, alas, since Juliet is gone?
Whereto live I, since she is dead, except to wail and moan?
Alack, dear child, my tears for thee shall never cease;
Even as my days of life increase so shall my plaint[2] increase:
Such store of sorrow shall afflict my tender heart
That deadly pangs when they assail shall not augment my smart."°

Then 'gan she so to sob it seemed her heart would brast;[3]
And while she crieth thus, behold the father at the last,
The County Paris, and of gentlemen a rout,°
And ladies of Verona town and country round about,
Both kindreds and allies, thither apace have preast,[4]
For by their presence there they sought to honour so the feast.
But when the heavy news the bidden guests did hear
So much they mourned that who had seen their count'nance and their
cheer
Might easily have judged by that that they had seen,
That day the day of wrath and eke of pity to have been.

---

[1] awaken
[2] sorrow
[3] burst
[4] pressed, rushed

But more than all the rest the father's heart was so
Smit with the heavy news and so shut up with sudden woe
That he ne had the power his daughter to be-weep,
Ne yet to speak, but long is forced his tears and plaint to keep.[1]
In all the haste he hath for skilful leeches° sent;
And hearing of her passèd life they judge with one assent
The cause of this her death was inward care and thought;
And then with double force again the doubled sorrows wrought.
If ever there hath been a lamentable day,
A day ruthful,° unfortunate, and fatal, then I say
The same was it in which through Verone town was spread
The woeful news how Juliet was stervèd° in her bed.
For so she was bemoaned both of the young and old
That it might seem to him that would the common plaint behold
That all the commonwealth did stand in jeopardy,
So universal was the plaint, so piteous was the cry.
For lo, beside her shape and native beauty's hue,
With which, like as she grew in age, her virtues' praises grew,
She was also so wise, so lowly,[2] and so mild
That even from the hoary head unto the witless[3] child
She wan[4] the hearts of all, so that there was not one
Ne great ne small but did that day her wretched state bemoan.

Whilst Juliet slept and whilst the other weepen thus
Our Friar Laurence hath by this sent one to Romeus,
A friar of his house — there never was a better,
He trusted him even as himself—to whom he gave a letter
In which he written had of everything at length
That passed 'twixt Juliet and him and of the powder's strength.
The next night after that he willeth him to come
To help to take his Juliet out of the hollow tomb,
For by that time the drink, he saith, will cease to work
And for one night his wife and he within his cell shall lurk;
Then shall he carry her to Mantua away—
Till fickle Fortune favour him—disguised in man's array.
This letter closed he sends to Romeus by his brother;
He chargeth him that in no case he give it any other.

---

[1] contain, withhold
[2] humble
[3] lifeless
[4] won

Apace our Friar John to Mantua him hies,°
And for because in Italy it is a wonted guise[1]
That friars in the town should seldom walk alone
But of their convent aye° should be accompanied with one
Of his profession, straight a house he findeth out,
In mind to take some friar with him to walk the town about.
But entered once he might not issue out again,
For that a brother of the house a day before or twain
Died of the plague—a sickness which they greatly fear and hate—
So were the brethren charged to keep within their convent gate,
Barred of their fellowship that in the town do wone.[2]
The townfolk eke commanded are the friar's house to shun
Till they that had the care of health their freedom should renew;
Whereof, as you shall shortly hear, a mischief great there grew.
The friar by this restraint, beset with dread and sorrow,
Not knowing what the letters held, deferred until the morrow
And then he thought in time to send to Romeus.

But whilst at Mantua where he was, these doings framèd thus,
The town of Juliet's birth was wholly busièd
About her obsequies,[3] to see their darling burièd.
Now is the parents' mirth quite changèd into moan
And now to sorrow is returned the joy of everyone;
And now the wedding weeds° for mourning weeds they change,
And Hymen[4] into a dirge—alas! it seemeth strange:
Instead of marriage gloves, now funeral gloves they have
And whom they should see marrièd, they follow to the grave.
The feast that should have been of pleasure and of joy
Hath every dish and cup filled full of sorrow and annoy.

Now throughout Italy this common use they have,
That all the best of every stock are earthèd in one grave:
For every household, if it be of any fame,
Doth build a tomb or dig a vault that bears the household's name,
Wherein if any of that kindred hap° to die

---

[1] usual practice
[2] dwell
[3] funeral arrangements
[4] They change marriage clothing into mourning clothing and wedding songs, or
    hymens, for which the Greek god of marriages Hymen (or Hymenaeus) is
    named, for funeral dirges.

They are bestowed; else in the same no other corpse may lie.
The Capulets her corpse in such a one did lay,
Where Tybalt, slain of Romeus, was laid the other day.
Another use there is, that whosoever dies,
Borne to their church with open face upon the bier he lies,
In wonted° weed° attired, not wrapped in winding sheet.
So as by chance he walked abroad our Romeus' man did meet
His master's wife; the sight with sorrow straight did wound
His honest heart; with tears he saw her lodgèd underground.
And for he had been sent to Verone for a spy
The doings of the Capulets by wisdom to descry[1]
And for he knew her death did touch his master most,
Alas, too soon, with heavy news he hied° away in post
And in his house he found his master Romeus,
Where he, besprent[2] with many tears, began to speak him thus:
"Sire, unto you of late is chanced so great a harm
That sure, except° with constancy you seek yourself to arm,
I fear that straight you will breathe out your latter breath
And I, most wretched wight,° shall be th'occasion of your death.
Know, sir, that yesterday my lady and your wife,
I wot° not by what sudden grief hath made exchange of life
And for because on earth she found nought but unrest,
In heaven hath she sought to find a place of quiet rest
And with these weeping eyes myself have seen her laid
Within the tomb of Capulets. And herewithal he stayed.

This sudden message's sound, sent forth with sighs and tears,
Our Romeus received too soon with open list'ning ears
And thereby hath sunk in such sorrow in his heart
That, lo, his sprite° annoyèd sore with torment and with smart°
Was like to break out of his prison house perforce
And that he might fly after hers, would leave the massy corse.°
But earnest love that will not fail him till his end
This fond° and sudden fantasy into his head did send:
That if near unto her he offered up his breath
That then a hundred thousand parts more glorious were his death.
Eke should his painful heart a great deal more be eased
And more also, he vainly thought, his lady better pleased.

---

[1] discover
[2] sprinkled

Wherefore when he his face hath washed with water clean,
Lest that the stains of drièd tears might on his cheeks be seen
And so his sorrow should of everyone be spied,
Which he with all his care did seek from everyone to hide,
Straight, weary of the house, he walketh forth abroad.
His servant, at the master's hest,° in chamber still abode°
And then fro street to street he wand'reth up and down
To see if he in any place may find in all the town
A salve meet° for his sore, an oil fit for his wound;
And seeking long—alack, too soon!—the thing he sought, he found.
An apothecary sat unbusied at his door,
Whom by his heavy countenance he guessed to be poor.
And in his shop he saw his boxes were but few
And in his window of his wares there was so small a shew;°
Wherefore our Romeus assuredly hath thought
What by no friendship could be got with money should be bought,
For needy lack is like¹ the poor man to compel
To sell that which the city's law forbiddeth him to sell.
Then by the hand he drew the needy man apart,
And with the sight of glitttring gold inflamèd hath his heart:
"Take fifty crowns of gold," quoth he, "I give them thee,
So that before I part from hence thou straight deliver me
Some poison strong that may in less than half an hour
Kill him whose wretched hap° shall be the potion to devour."

The wretch by covetise is won and doth assent
To sell the thing whose sale ere long, too late, he doth repent.
In haste he poison sought, and closely he it bound,
And then began with whispering voice thus in his ear to round:²
"Fair sir," quoth he, "be sure this is the speeding gear³
And more there is than you shall need; for half of that is there
Will serve, I undertake, in less than half an hour
To kill the strongest man alive; such is the poison's power."
Then Romeus, somewhat eased of one part of his care,
Within his bosom putteth up his dear unthrifty ware.
Returning home again, he sent his man away
To Verone town and chargeth him that he without delay
Provide both instruments to open wide the tomb

---

¹ likely
² whisper
³ Be assured that this potion is the right thing to get the job done.

And lights to show him Juliet, and stay till he shall come
Near to the place whereas° his loving wife doth rest,
And chargeth him not to bewray° the dolours of his breast.

Peter, these heard, his leave doth of his master take.
Betime° he comes to town, such haste the painful man did make,
And then with busy° care he seeketh to fulfil
But doth disclose unto no wight° his woeful master's will.
Would God he had herein broken his master's hest!°
Would God that to the friar he had disclosèd all his breast!
But Romeus the while with many a deadly thought
Provokèd much hath caused ink and paper to be brought.
And in few lines he did of all his love discourse,
How by the friar's help and by the knowledge of the nurse
The wedlock knot was knit, and by what mean° that night
And many mo[1] he did enjoy his happy heart's delight;
Where he the poison bought, and how his life should end;
And so his wailful[2] tragedy the wretched man hath penned.
The letters closed and sealed, directed to his sire,
He locketh in his purse and then a post-horse doth he hire.
When he approachèd near he warely lighted down[3]
And even with the shade of night he entered Verone town,
Where he hath found his man, waiting when he should come
With lantern and with instruments to open Juliet's tomb.

"Help, Peter, help," quod he, "help to remove the stone
And straight when I am gone fro thee my Juliet to bemoan
See that thou get thee hence; and on the pain of death
I charge thee that thou come not near while I abide beneath,
Ne seek thou not to let[4] thy master's enterprise
Which he hath fully purposèd to do in any wise.°
Take there a letter, which, as soon as he shall rise,
Present it in the morning to my loving father's eyes;
Which unto him perhaps far pleasanter shall seem
Than either I do mind to say or thy gross head can deem."
Now Peter, that knew not the purpose of his heart,
Obediently a little way withdrew himself apart;

---

[1] more
[2] sorrowful
[3] cautiously dismounted
[4] hinder

And then our Romeus (the vault-stone set upright),
Descended down, and in his hand he bare° the candle light.
And then with piteous eye the body of his wife
He 'gan behold, who surely was the organ of his life,
For whom unhappy now he is, but erst° was blissed,
He watered her with tears and then a hundred times her kissed
And in his folded arms full straitly he her plight,[1]
But no way could his greedy eyes be fillèd with her sight.
His fearful hands he laid upon her stomach cold
And them on divers° parts beside the woeful wight° did hold.

But when he could not find the signs of life he sought
Out of his cursèd box he drew the poison that he bought,
Whereof he greedily devoured the greater part
And then he cried, with deadly sigh fetched from his mourning heart:
"O Juliet, of whom the world unworthy was,
From which for world's unworthiness thy worthy ghost did pass,
What death more pleasant could my heart wish to abide
Than that which here it suff'reth now, so near thy friendly side?
Or else so glorious tomb how could my youth have craved
As in one self-same vault with thee haply to be ingraved?
What epitaph more worth, or half so excellent,
To consecrate my memory could any man invent
As this our mutual and our piteous sacrifice
Of life, set light for love?" But while he talketh in this wise°
And thought as yet awhile his dolours to enforce,[2]
His tender heart began to faint, pressed with the venom's force;
Which little and little 'gan to overcome his heart,
And whilst his busy° eyne° he threw about to every part,
He saw, hard by the corse° of sleeping Juliet,
Bold Tybalt's carcass dead, which was not all consumèd yet
To whom, as having life, in this sort° speaketh he:
"Ah, cousin dear, Tybalt, whereso thy restless sprite° now be
With stretchèd hands to thee for mercy now I cry,
For that before thy kindly hour I forcèd thee to die.
But if with quenchèd life not quenchèd be thine ire,
But with revenging lust° as yet thy heart be set on fire,
What more amends or cruel wreak[3] desirest thou

---

[1] tightly embraced her
[2] contain
[3] punishment, injury as retribution

To see on me than this which here is showed forth to thee now?
Who reft by force of arms from thee thy living breath,
The same with his own hand thou seest doth poison himself to death.
And for he caused thee in tomb too soon to lie,
Too soon also, younger than thou, himself he layeth by."

These said, when he 'gan feel the poison's force prevail
And little and little mastered life for aye° began to fail,
Kneeling upon his knees he said with voice full low—
"Lord Christ, that so to ransom me descendedst long ago
Out of thy Father's bosom and in the Virgin's womb
Didst put on flesh, oh, let my plaint out of this hollow tomb
Pierce through the air and grant my suit may favour find;
Take pity on my sinful and my poor afflicted mind!
For well enough I know this body is but clay,
Nought but a mass of sin, too frail, and subject to decay."
Then pressed with extreme grief he threw with so great force
His overpressèd parts upon his lady's wailèd corse°
That now his weakened heart, weakened with torments past,
Unable to abide this pang, the sharpest and the last,
Remainèd quite deprived of sense and kindly strength,
And so the long imprisoned soul hath freedom won at length.
Ah cruel death, too soon, too soon was this divorce
'Twixt youthful Romeus' heavenly sprite,° and his fair earthy corse!

The friar that knew what time the powder had been taken
Knew eke the very instant when the sleeper should awaken,
But wondering that he could no kind of answer hear
Of letters which to Romeus his fellow friar did bear
Out of Saint Francis' church himself alone did fare°
And for the opening of the tomb meet instruments he bare.[1]
Approaching nigh the place and seeing there the light,
Great horror felt he in his heart by strange and sudden sight
Till Peter, Romeus' man, his coward heart made bold,
When of his master's being there the certain news he told:
"There hath he been," quoth he, "this half hour at the least
And in this time, I dare well say, his plaint hath still increast."
Then both they entered in, where they, alas, did find
The breathless corpse of Romeus, forsaken of the mind:

---

[1] He brought suitable tools to open the tomb.

Where they have made such moan, as they may best conceive
That have with perfect friendship loved, whose friend fierce death did
reave.°

But whilst with piteous plaint they Romeus' fate beweep
An hour too late fair Juliet awakèd out of sleep;
And much amazed to see in tomb so great a light
She wist° not if she saw a dream, or sprite° that walked by night.
But coming to herself she knew them and said thus:
"What, friar Laurence, is it you? Where is my Romeus?"
And then the ancient friar, that greatly stood in fear
Lest if they lingered over long they should be taken there,
In few plain words the whole that was betid° he told
And with his finger showed his corpse outstretchèd, stiff, and cold;
And then persuaded her with patience to abide
This sudden great mischance and saith that he will soon provide
In some religious house for her a quiet place,
Where she may spend the rest of life, and where in time percase°
She may with wisdom's mean° measure her mourning breast
And unto her tormented soul call back exilèd rest.
But lo, as soon as she had cast her ruthful° eye
On Romeus' face that pale and wan fast by her side did lie,
Straightway she did unstop the conduits of her tears
And out they gush—with cruel hand she tare[1] her golden hairs.
But when she neither could her swelling sorrow 'suage
Ne yet her tender heart abide her sickness' furious rage,
Fall'n on his corpse she lay, long panting on his face,
And then with all her force and strength the dead corpse did embrace.
As though with sighs, with sobs, with force, and busy° pain
She would him raise and him restore from death to life again.
A thousand times she kissed his mouth, as cold as stone,
And it unkissed again as oft; then 'gan she thus to moan:
"Ah, pleasant prop of all my thoughts, ah, only ground
Of all the sweet delights that yet in all my life I found,
Did such assurèd trust within thy heart repose
That in this place and at this time thy churchyard thou hast chose
Betwixt the arms of me, thy perfect-loving make,[2]
And thus by means of me to end thy life, and for my sake?

---

[1] tore
[2] mate, partner

Even in the flow'ring of thy youth, when unto thee
Thy life most dear, as to the most and pleasant ought to be,
How could this tender corpse withstand the cruel fight
Of furious Death, that wonts to fray[1] the stoutest with his sight?
How could thy dainty youth agree with willing heart
In this so foul-infected place to dwell, where now thou art?
Where spiteful Fortune hath appointed thee to be
The dainty food of greedy worms, unworthy, sure, of thee.
Alas, alas, alas, what needed now anew
My wonted° sorrows, doubled twice, again thus to renew,
Which both the time and eke my patient long abode°
Should now at length have quenchèd quite and under foot have trode?
Ah, wretch and caitive that I am, even when I thought
To find my painful passion's salve I missed the thing I sought;
And to my mortal harm the fatal knife I ground
That gave to me so deep, so wide, so cruel deadly wound!
Ah thou, most fortunate and most unhappy tomb!
For thou shalt bear, from age to age, witness in time to come
Of the most perfect league betwixt a pair of lovers,
That were the most unfortunate and fortunate of others,
Receive the latter sigh, receive the latter pang,
Of the most cruel of cruel slaves that wrath and death aye wrang."[2]

And when our Juliet would continue still her moan,
The friar and the servant fled and left her there alone,
For they a sudden noise fast by the place did hear
And lest they might be taken there, greatly they stood in fear.
When Juliet saw herself left in the vault alone,
That freely she might work her will, for let or stay° was none,
Then once for all she took the cause of all her harms,
The body dead of Romeus, and clasped it in her arms.
Then she with earnest kiss sufficiently did prove,
That more than by the fear of death, she was attaint[3] by love;
And then past deadly fear, for life ne had she care,
With hasty hand she did draw out the dagger that he ware.[4]
"O welcome Death," quoth she, "end of unhappiness,
That also art beginning of assurèd happiness,

---

[1] habitually bothers or torments
[2] ever wronged
[3] affected by, overcome
[4] wore

Fear not to dart me now, thy stripe no longer stay.°
Prolong no longer now my life; I hate this long delay,
For straight my parting sprite° out of this carcass fled
At ease shall find my Romeus' sprite among so many dead.
And thou my loving lord, Romeus, my trusty fere,°
If knowledge yet do rest in thee, if thou these words dost hear,
Receive thou her whom thou didst love so lawfully,
That caused, alas, thy violent death, although unwillingly;
And therefore willingly offers to thee her ghost,
To th'end that no wight° else but thou might have just cause to boast
Th'enjoying of my love, which aye° I have reserved
Free from the rest, bound unto thee, that hast it well deserved;
That so our parted sprites from light that we see here,
In place of endless light and bliss may ever live yfere."[1]
These said, her ruthless hand through-girt her valiant heart:
Ah, ladies, help with tears to wail the lady's deadly smart!°
She groans, she stretcheth out her limbs, she shuts her eyes,
And from her corpse the sprite doth fly—what should I say—she dies.

The watchmen of the town the whilst are passèd by
And through the gates the candle-light within the tomb they spy,
Whereby they did suppose enchanters to be come,
That with prepared instruments had opened wide the tomb
In purpose to abuse the bodies of the dead,
Which by their science's aid abused, do stand them oft instead.
Their curious hearts desire the truth hereof to know;
Then they by certain steps descend, where they do find below
In claspèd arms y-wrapt the husband and the wife,
In whom as yet they seemed to see some certain marks of life.
But when more curiously with leisure they did view
The certainty of both their deaths assuredly they knew.
Then here and there so long with careful° eye they sought
That at the length hidden they found the murth'rers—so they thought.
In dungeon deep that night they lodged them underground;
The next day do they tell the prince the mischief that they found.

The news was by and by throughout the town dispread,
Both of the taking of the friar and of the two found dead.
Thither might you have seen whole households forth to run,

---

[1] live joined as partners

For to the tomb where they did hear this wonder strange was done
The great, the small, the rich, the poor, the young, the old,
With hasty pace do run to see, but rue when they behold.
And that the murtherers to all men might be known,
Like as the murder's bruit abroad through all the town was blown,[1]
The prince did straight ordain the corses° that were found
Should be set forth upon a stage high raisèd from the ground,
Right in the selfsame form, showed forth to all men's sight
That in the hollow vault they had been found that other night;
And eke that Romeus' man and Friar Laurence should
Be openly examinèd, for else the people would
Have murmurèd or feigned there were some weighty cause
Why openly they were not called and so convict[2] by laws.

The holy friar now, and reverent by his age,
In great reproach set to the show upon the open stage—
A thing that ill beseemed a man of silver hairs—
His beard as white as milk he bathes with great fast-falling tears,
Whom straight the dreadful judge commandeth to declare
Both how this murther had been done and who the murth'rers are,
For that he near the tomb was found at hours unfit
And had with him those iron tools for such a purpose fit.
The friar was of lively sprite° and free of speech;
The judge's words appalled him not, ne were his wits to seech,[3]
But with advised heed a while first did he stay,°
And then with bold assurèd voice aloud thus 'gan he say:
"My lords, there is not one among you, set together,
So that, affection set aside, by wisdom he consider
My former passèd life and this my extreme age,
And eke this heavy sight, the wreak of frantic Fortune's rage,
But that, amazèd much, doth wonder at this change
So great, so suddenly befall'n, unlooked for, and strange.
For I that in the space of sixty years and ten
Since first I did begin, too soon, to lead my life with men
And with the world's vain things myself I did acquaint
Was never yet, in open place, at any time attaint[4]
With any crime in weight as heavy as a rush,

---

[1] A report of the murder was made public through all the town.
[2] tried and convicted
[3] search
[4] accused

Ne is there any stander-by can make me guilty blush,
Although before the face of God I do confess
Myself to be the sinfull'st wretch of all this mighty press.°
When readiest I am and likeliest to make
My great accompt,° which no man else for me shall undertake;
When worms, the earth, and death, do cite me every hour
T'appear before the judgement seat of everlasting power,
And falling ripe I step upon my grave's brink
Even then, am I, most wretched wight,° as each of you doth think,
Through my most heinous deed, with headlong sway thrown down,
In greatest danger of my life and domage of renown.[1]
The spring, whence in your head this new conceit° doth rise
And in your heart increaseth still your vain and wrong surmise,
May be the hugeness of these tears of mine, percase,°
That so abundantly down fall by either side my face;
As though the memory in Scriptures were not kept
That Christ our Saviour himself for ruth° and pity wept.
And more, whoso will read, y-written shall he find
That tears are as true messengers of man's unguilty mind.
Or else, a liker[2] proof that I am in the crime
You say these present irons are, and the suspected time,
As though all hours alike had not been made above!
Did Christ not say the day had twelve[3]—whereby he sought to prove
That no respect of hours ought justly to be had,
But at all times men have the choice of doing good or bad;
Even as the sprite° of God the hearts of men doth guide,
Or as it leaveth them to stray from virtue's path aside.
As for the irons that were taken in my hand,
As now I deem, I need not seek to make ye understand
To what use iron first was made, when it began;
How of itself it helpeth not, ne yet can help a man.
The thing that hurteth is the malice of his will
That such indifferent[4] things is wont° to use and order ill.
Thus much I thought to say to cause you so to know
That neither these my piteous tears, though ne'er so fast they flow,
Ne yet these iron tools, nor the suspected time,
Can justly prove the murther done, or damn me of the crime:

---

[1] harm to reputation
[2] more likely
[3] John 11:9
[4] neutral

No one of these hath power, ne power have all the three
To make me other than I am, how so I seem to be.
But sure my conscience, if so my guilt deserve,
For an appeacher,[1] witness, and a hangman, eke should serve;
For through mine age, whose hairs of long time since were hoar,[2]
And credit great that I was in with you in time tofore,[3]
And eke the sojourn short that I on earth must make,
That every day and hour do look my journey hence to take,
My conscience inwardly should more torment me thrice,
Than all the outward deadly pain that all you could devise.

But, God I praise, I feel no worm that gnaweth me
And from remorse's pricking sting I joy that I am free:
I mean, as touching this, wherewith you troubled are,
Wherewith you should be troubled still if I my speech should spare.
But to the end I may set all your hearts at rest
And pluck out all the scruples that are rooted in your breast,
Which might perhaps henceforth, increasing more and more,
Within your conscience also increase your cureless sore:
I swear by yonder heavens, whither I hope to climb,
And for a witness of my words my heart attesteth Him
Whose mighty hand doth wield them in their violent sway
And on the rolling stormy seas the heavy earth doth stay°
That I will make a short and eke a true discourse
Of this most woeful tragedy and show both th'end and source
Of their unhappy death, which you perchance no less
Will wonder at than they, alas, poor lovers in distress,
Tormented much in mind, not forcing lively breath,
With strong and patient heart did yield themself to cruel death.
Such was the mutual love wherein they burnèd both,
And of their promised friendship's faith so steady was the troth."

And then the ancient friar began to make discourse,
Even from the first, of Romeus' and Juliet's amours:
How first by sudden sight the one the other chose
And 'twixt themself did knit the knot which only death might loose;
And how, within a while, with hotter love oppressed,
Under confession's cloak to him themself they have addressed;

---

[1] accuser
[2] white
[3] prior, before

And how with solemn oaths they have protested both
That they in heart are marrièd by promise and by oath;
And that except° he grant the rites of church to give
They shall be forced by earnest love in sinful state to live,
Which thing when he had weighed, and when he understood
That the agreement 'twixt them twain was lawful, honest, good,
And all things peisèd[1] well, it seemèd meet° to be,
For like they were of nobleness, age, riches, and degree.
Hoping that so, at length, ended might be the strife
Of Montagues and Capulets that led in hate their life,
Thinking to work a work well pleasing in God's sight,
In secret shrift° he wedded them and they the self-same night
Made up the marriage in house of Capulet,
As well doth know, if she be asked, the nurse of Juliet.
He told how Romeus fled for reaving° Tybalt's life,
And how the whilst Paris the earl was offered to his wife,
And how the lady did so great a wrong disdain,
And how to shrift° unto his church she came to him again,
And how she fell flat down before his feet aground,
And how she sware[2] her hand and bloody knife should wound
Her harmless heart except° that he some mean° did find
To disappoint the earl's attempt and, spotless, save her mind.

Wherefore, he doth conclude, although that long before
By thought of death and age he had refused forevermore
The hidden arts which he delighted in in youth—
Yet won by her importuneness and by his inward ruth,°
And fearing lest she would her cruel vow discharge,
His closed conscience he had opened and set at large;
And rather did he choose to suffer for one time
His soul to be spotted somedeal[3] with small and easy crime
Than that the lady should, weary of living breath,
Murther herself and danger much her seely° soul by death.
Wherefore his ancient arts again he puts in ure:[4]
A certain powder gave he her, that made her sleep so sure
That they her held for dead; and how that Friar John
With letters sent to Romeus to Mantua is gone,

---

[1] weighed
[2] swore
[3] somewhat
[4] to use

Of whom he knoweth not as yet what is become;
And how that dead he found his friend within her kindred's tomb.
He thinks with poison strong, for care the young man sterved,°
Supposing Juliet dead; and how that Juliet hath carved,
With Romeus' dagger drawn, her heart, and yielded breath,
Desirous to accompany her lover after death;
And how they could not save her, so they were afeard,
And hid themself, dreading the noise of watchmen that they heard.
And for the proof of this his tale he doth desire
The judge to send forthwith to Mantua for the friar
To learn his cause of stay° and eke to read his letter;
And more beside, to th'end that they might judge his cause the better
He prayeth them depose[1] the nurse of Juliet,
And Romeus' man whom at unwares beside the tomb he met.

Then Peter, not so much erst° as he was, dismayed:
"My lords," quoth he, "too true is all that Friar Laurence said.
And when my master went into my mistress' grave
This letter that I offer you unto me then he gave,
Which he himself did write, as I do understand,
And charged me to offer them unto his father's hand."
The opened packet doth contain in it the same
That erst° the skilful friar said, and eke the wretch's name
That had at his request the deadly poison sold,
The price of it, and why he bought, his letters plain have told.
The case unfolded so and open now it lies,
That they could wish no better proof save seeing it with their eyes;
So orderly all things were told and trièd out[2]
That in the press° there was not one that stood at all in doubt.

The wiser sort, to council called by Escalus,
Have given advice and Escalus sagely decreeth thus:
The nurse of Juliet is banished in her age
Because that from the parents she did hide the marriage,
Which might have wrought much good had it in time been known,
Where now by her concealing it a mischief great is grown.
And Peter, for he did obey his master's hest°
In wonted° freedom had good leave to lead his life in rest.

---

[1] call as witnesses
[2] verified

Th'apothecary high is hangèd by the throat
And for the pains he took with him the hangman had his coat.[1]

But now what shall betide° of this grey-bearded sire?
Of Friar Laurence thus arraigned, that good barefooted friar,
Because that many times he worthily did serve
The commonwealth and in his life was never found to swerve
He was dischargèd quite, and no mark of defame
Did seem to blot or touch at all the honour of his name.
But of himself he went into an hermitage
Two miles from Verone town, where he in prayers passed forth his age
Till that from earth to heaven his heavenly sprite° did fly.
Five years he lived an hermit and an hermit did he die.
The strangeness of the chance, when trièd,° was the truth:
The Montagues and Capulets hath moved so to ruth°
That with their emptied tears their choler and their rage
Was emptied quite; and they, whose wrath no wisdom could assuage,
Nor threat'ning of the prince, ne mind of murthers done
At length, so mighty Jove it would, by pity they are won.
And lest that length of time might from our minds remove
The memory of so perfect, sound, and so approvèd love,
The bodies dead, removed from vault where they did die,
In stately tomb, on pillars great of marble, raise they high.
On every side above were set and eke beneath,
Great store of cunning[2] epitaphs in honour of their death.
And even at this day the tomb is to be seen,
So that among the monuments that in Verona been,
There is no monument more worthy of the sight
Than is the tomb of Juliet and Romeus her knight.

Imprinted at London in
Fleet Street within Temple Bar, at
the sign of the hand and star, by
Richard Tottel the xix day of
November Anno Domini 1562

---

[1] By custom, articles of clothing of those condemned to die by hanging were taken
   by their executioners.
[2] wise, skilful

Questions

1. How is time, especially the passage of time, marked out in Brooke's story? Why is time such a key theme in this tale?

2. Whereas prose stories have a narrator, plays rely on dialogue to develop conflict. How does this narrator describe and develop conflicts?

3. Do you see any ways that Brooke's narrator has a stance or bias toward the characters in the story? How do they speak in their own voices? How does the narrator describe them?

4. What are the effects of Brooke's verse form as you read this story?

5. This story ends differently from Shakespeare's version. Which ending do you think better concludes the events that precede it?

CINTHIO,
FROM *HECATOMMITHI* (1565)

OTHELLO

The story of a Venetian Moor and his wife Disdemona told in Cinthio's *Hecatommithi* presents an excellent opportunity to consider what Shakespeare could do to and with a published source. A short, coherent, well-paced tale that shows Cinthio's crisp, efficient narrative technique to advantage, this story of jealousy, sexual desire, infidelity, and deceit offers a good example of the kind of middle-brow narratives that transfixed Europe's reading population in the sixteenth century. It is also an interesting case of what can happen when a story changes from prose narration to dramatic representation.

As the prices of published books fell and as Europe's literate population grew during the 1500s—the two phenomena are closely related to each other—authors and publishers eagerly met new demands for stories by publishing prose tales like this one, which put people from the middling levels of society such as soldiers, merchants, clerics, and courtiers at the centre of the action. Many were old tales that had enjoyed varying degrees of popularity during the fifteenth century or even before, when the only way a story could be preserved in writing was in a manuscript copy (printing by movable type began in Germany with Gutenberg in the 1450s and spread to Italy by the end of the 1460s). But the sixteenth century was a period of vastly increased technological capacity for spreading information and ideas of all kinds, including a sensational narrative, like this one, about the domestic troubles between a newly married husband and wife.

The Italian author Giovanni Battista Giraldi (1504-73), more commonly known by his academic name Cinthio (also written as Cinzio or Cynthius), was a full participant in this expansion of letters in sixteenth-century Europe, and his collection *Gli Hecatommithi* (meaning "the one hundred tales") is a prime example of what has come to be known as the *novella* genre of prose fiction. Cinthio attended the university in his native city of Ferrara, and before reaching his fortieth year was named to a chair in rhetoric, later in life also teaching in Turin and Pavia. In addition to his teaching, he wrote an epic poem and nine tragedies; in the rich history of

Italian literature he remains an important figure, especially for his innovations in tragic form.

The literary fashion for collections of interwoven tales like the *Hecatommithi* draws upon a tradition dating back to Giovanni Boccaccio's prose *Decameron* (c. 1348-53) and Geoffrey Chaucer's verse *The Canterbury Tales* (c. 1375-1400). As a student of letters, Cinthio enjoyed a privileged position that allowed him both to imitate his predecessors in the accepted fashion of his time and to re-make the genre for the expanding market of readers in the period. His *Hecatommithi,* published in 1565 in Mondovi, near Turin, was popular not only in his native Italy, where it was reprinted multiple times before 1600, but after his death it was translated into French (1583-84) and Spanish (1590). Individual tales from the collection were also translated into English by several of Shakespeare's contemporaries. Cinthio's work is built upon the model of Boccaccio's *Decameron*, with short stories in prose grouped in "decades"—clusters of ten thematically similar short narratives, each of which deals in some way with the general theme of love. The third decade, which includes the tale of the jealous Moor and his wife, is devoted to stories of marital infidelity.

If we compare Shakespeare's play to Cinthio's original and then to Gabriel Chappuys' French translation of Cinthio's tale, we can see how difficult it is to trace a clear line of direct influence. Several turns of phrase suggest that he worked directly from Cinthio's Italian, while others are found only in the French version, not the original. For these reasons, scholars have never come to a consensus around the question of whether Shakespeare read the story in its original Italian or in the French translation, or indeed if there was once an English translation, now lost, that might have been based on both prior versions, and which might resolve the verbal ambiguities we now must contend with when trying to decide which source or sources Shakespeare had at hand when he wrote *Othello*.

Whichever version or versions he used, Shakespeare, like other European readers of the late sixteenth century, was clearly drawn to tales of passionate love gone awry. This same genre of domestic love story forms the basis of his *Romeo and Juliet*, *The Merchant of Venice*, and *Much Ado About Nothing*, to name just a few. He used another tale by Cinthio (though probably via an English translation) for the plot of *Measure for Measure*. His *Othello* (1603-4) is a later work than these, perhaps suggesting that the central problem of jealousy and visual proof that he explores in *Much Ado About Nothing* remained with him until he could work out another story around this question. In fact, he stayed with the theme even longer, returning to it near the end of his playwrighting career in *The Winter's Tale* (1610-11), whose action begins with the destructive sexual jealousy of King

Leontes, who thinks that what he sees is the full and only truth of his wife's and best friend's behaviour together.

"There once lived in Venice a Moor, who was very valiant and of a handsome person." So begins Cinthio's tale. Although the narrative is geographically precise, with specific references to Venice, Cyprus, and Italy, it exists in no specified time period, and its characters, except for Disdemona, are identified only by their position, their ethnicity, or their military rank—and not by their names. What do these features tell us? Part of the story's appeal is precisely its non-specificity, the author's strategic play for universality that encourages the reader's active engagement with the text because it leaves open to the imagination many of the details we have come to expect to see supplied by writers of modern prose fiction. Instead, the story offers up characters that are largely ciphers to be decoded, their actions described by the author, but their motives and their inner thoughts left to be imagined by readers. For example, we learn that like the Moor himself, the Ensign is "a man of handsome figure." But unlike his superior, he is "of the most depraved nature in the world" and "there is "malice lurking in his heart." These are notable details of characterization, but the sources and motives of the Ensign's inner being are withheld from us: the "villainy of his soul" and his skill in making an "outward show" of his bravery are denied to us by the author; we must simply accept him as he's presented to us, just as we must accept that we are not going to learn much about the inner psychology of Disdemona or the Ensign's wife.

This feature of the story may be precisely what drew an experienced poet and playwright like Shakespeare to Cinthio's tale: the plot line is precise and compelling, and in some ways quite remarkable in its efficiency. But the story also leaves open many questions we might like to ask: how does jealousy change a loving husband who "lived in such harmony and peace" with his new wife "that no word ever passed between them that was not affectionate and kind" into a man who goes so far as to commission her murder? Likewise, we want to know how the Ensign, who passionately loved Disdemona and desired her with all his heart, suddenly changes his passion from love to "the bitterest hate." And why does the Ensign's claim that Disdemona "has taken an aversion to your blackness" seem to cut straight to the Moor's heart? We are moved to ask ourselves what kind of prior experience with racism might lie behind his reaction, for indeed the text hints several times that the Moor's blackness, capacity for anger, and barbarism in the eyes of the Venetians are all underlying features of this tale. These and other psychological questions are not the interest of Cinthio, who consistently subordinates the realm of the human psyche to the power of an efficient narrative and refuses to linger over the *whys* that we suppose must lie behind the *whats*. But they were not the interest of other prose writers of the period, either: they also typically created characters whose interior lives seem to hover in a space somewhere between those of individuals and general types.

Enter William Shakespeare. His dramatic mode of storytelling, where characters—who are now given names—speak for themselves in dialogue or in soliloquy, favours interiority and psychology over the sequence of plot points in a narrated story. Indeed, Shakespeare adds very little to Cinthio's story in terms of what happens. Even though Shakespeare's play is considerably longer than his source, he actually cuts off the end of Cinthio's story. *Othello* contains no secondary revenge plot after the murder of Disdemona: Iago never leaves Venice, and he is never arrested and eventually tortured for another, later act of villainy. The playwright shortened the narrative but expanded the story.

One of the more interesting of these changes highlights the differences between prose narrative and dramatic narrative: in Cinthio's story, we learn at the very end of the tale that the Ensign's wife (like others in the story she is never named, but is the basis for Shakespeare's Emilia) was privy to the whole story and was the narrator's source. It was she who remembers and re-tells the story to Cinthio's unnamed third-person narrator, who then tells it to us. Cinthio delivers a fascinating meta-fictional surprise at the end of the story, which may in some general way have suggested to Shakespeare a principle for the tragic story he told in dramatic form, where authority, clarity, and the transmission of information figure so prominently. This kind of reported storytelling at a remove is far more difficult in dramatic form, where action principally occurs in a presentational (or "live") mode. The result is that in drama we as the audience imagine that we see the action occurring before our own eyes, as it is unfolding, rather than in the past and through someone's else's reported experience.

What are the major plot changes that Shakespeare made, and why did he make them? These questions deserve careful consideration, whether you are reflecting upon the two stories side by side on your own or discussing them with classmates or others who have read both. Some examples of the rich questions one might ponder include why Michael Cassio, Shakespeare's version of Cinthio's nameless "Captain of a troop," has no head for drinking and makes it clear to others that he should always avoid liquors. In what ways is that small addition to the story significant to Shakespeare's strategy of adaptation and character development? Or why is Disdemona's father, mentioned very briefly only once in the second paragraph of Cinthio's story, given such a prominent role in the opening of Shakespeare's play? What is gained dramatically and thematically by bringing to life a character who lives only in a brief mention in the source story? And for that matter, why does Shakespeare give his Desdemona an uncle and cousin? Both play significant roles in the changed ending of the story. But perhaps the most compelling question is this: why does Shakespeare change a perfectly logical and believable murder scene, in which the Ensign does the bidding of his captain by beating Disdemona to death with a bag of sand and later wounding her head to simulate an accident, into one in which the grief-stricken husband performs the murder himself, using nothing but his bare hands, with no one else present on stage?

One of the features of Cinthio's story, like many other *novelle* of the sixteenth century, is the author's explicitly expressed trust in divine providence. Disdemona cries out futilely to "the justice of Heaven" just before being struck down by the Ensign's third and final blow. Sadly, providence does not protect her, but in the end the narrator is careful to tell us that the Ensign died "a miserable death" and "Thus did Heaven avenge the innocence of Disdemona." This final narrative detail suddenly places this story of jealousy and gruesome deaths within a tidy moral boundary, suggesting—in the age-old adage that seems to have inspired Shakespeare over his whole career—that the Truth will out, no matter what evils human beings enact upon each other and no matter what motives and reasons circulate within the minds of evil-doers. Whether that same faith in providence operates in Shakespeare's retelling is a question well worth considering in depth.

A Note on the Text

Cinthio's story of a Moorish captain and his wife Disdemona appears here in the translation of John Edward Taylor, *The Moor of Venice: Cinthio's Tale and Shakspere's Tragedy* (London: Chapman and Hall, 1855). I added notes and glosses to Taylor's text, removed several of his notes, and modernised some of his punctuation and spelling. Archaic words are footnoted on their first occurrence and thereafter marked with °, which refers readers to the glossary at the end of this volume.

Cinthio, from *Hecatommithi* (1565)

There once lived in Venice a Moor, who was very valiant and of a handsome person; and having given proofs in war of great skill and prudence, he was highly esteemed by the Signoria[1] of the Republic, who in rewarding deeds of valour advanced the interests of the state.

It happened that a virtuous lady of marvellous beauty, named Disdemona, fell in love with the Moor, moved thereto by his valour; and he, vanquished by the beauty and the noble character of Disdemona, returned her love; and their affection was so mutual that, although the parents of the lady strove all they could to induce her to take another husband, she consented to marry the Moor; and they lived in such harmony and peace in Venice that no word ever passed between them that was not affectionate and kind.

Now it happened at this time that the Signoria of Venice made a change in the troops whom they used to maintain in Cyprus, and they appointed the Moor commander of the soldiers whom they dispatched thither. Joyful as were the Moor at the honour proffered him, such dignity being only conferred on men of noble rank and well-tried faith, and who had displayed bravery in arms—yet his pleasure was lessened when he reflected on the length and dangers of the voyage, fearing that Disdemona would be pained at his absence. But Disdemona, who had no other happiness in the world than the Moor, and who rejoiced to witness the testimony of his valour her husband received[2] from so powerful and noble a republic, was all impatient that he should embark with his troops, and longed to accompany him to so honourable a post. And all the more it vexed her to see the Moor so troubled; and not knowing what could be the reason, one day, when they were at dinner, she said to him, "How is it, O Moor that when so honourable a post has been conferred on you by the Signoria, you are thus melancholy?"

The Moor answered Disdemona, "My pleasure at the honour I have received is disturbed by the love I bear you; for I see that of necessity one of two things must happen—either that I take you to encounter the perils of the sea, or, to save you from this danger, I must leave you here in Venice. The first could not be otherwise than serious to me, for all the toil you would have to bear and every danger that might befall you would cause me extreme anxiety and pain, yet were I to leave you behind me, I should be hateful to myself, since in parting from you I should part from my own life."

Disdemona, on hearing this, replied: "My husband, what thoughts are these that wander through your mind? Why let such things disturb you? I

---

[1] the oligarchy ruling Venice at the time
[2] i.e., the praise and glory her husband received

will accompany you withersoe'er you go, were it to pass through fire, as not to cross the water in a safe and well-provided ship; if indeed there are toils and perils to encounter, I will share them with you. And in truth I should think you loved me little[1] were you to leave me here in Venice, denying me to bear you company, or could believe that I would liefer bide[2] in safety here than share the dangers that await you. Prepare then for the voyage with all the readiness which the dignity of the post you hold deserves."

The Moor, in the fullness of his joy, threw his arms around his wife's neck, and with an affectionate and tender kiss exclaimed, "God keep you long in such love, dear wife!" Then speedily donning his armour, and having prepared everything for his expedition, he embarked on board the galley with his wife and all his troops, and, setting sail, they pursued their voyage, and with a perfectly tranquil sea arrived safely at Cyprus.

Now amongst the soldiery there was an Ensign,[3] a man of handsome figure, but of the most depraved nature in the world. This man was in great favour with the Moor, who had not the slightest idea of his wickedness; for, despite the malice lurking in his heart, he cloaked with proud and valorous speech and with a specious presence the villainy of his soul with such art that he was to all outward show another Hector or Achilles.[4] This man had likewise taken with him his wife to Cyprus, a young, and fair, and virtuous lady; and being of Italian birth she was much loved by Disdemona, who spent the greater part of every day with her.

In the same Company there was a certain Captain of a troop, to whom the Moor was much affectioned. And Disdemona, for this cause, knowing how much her husband valued him, showed him proofs of the greatest kindness, which was all very grateful[5] to the Moor. Now the wicked Ensign, regardless of the faith that he had pledged his wife, no less than of friendship, fidelity and obligation which he owed the Moor, fell passionately in love with Disdemona, and bent all his thoughts to achieve his conquest; yet he dared not to declare his passion openly, fearing that, should the Moor perceive it, he would at once kill him. He therefore sought in various ways, and with secret guile, to betray his passion to the lady. But she, whose every wish was centred in the Moor, had no thought for this Ensign more than any other man, and all the means he tried to gain her love

---

[1] would love me little
[2] prefer to stay
[3] An ensign is a standard-bearer, originally the one charged with carrying the troop's ensign (banner). The position did not imply a particularly high rank or convey any particular honour.
[4] two great classical exemplars of military bravery
[5] gratifying, pleasing

had no more effect that if he had not tried them. But the Ensign imagined that the cause of his ill success was that Disdemona loved the Captain of the troop; and he pondered how to remove him from her sight. The love which he had borne the lady now changed into the bitterest hate, and, having failed in his purposes, he devoted all his thoughts to plot the death of the Captain of the troop and to divert the affection of the Moor from Disdemona. After revolving in his mind various schemes, all alike wicked, he at length resolved to accuse her of unfaithfulness to her husband, and to represent the Captain as her paramour. But knowing the singular love the Moor bore to Disdemona, and the friendship which he had for the Captain, he was well aware that, unless he practiced an artful fraud upon the Moor, it were impossible to make him give ear to either accusation; wherefore[1] he resolved to wait until time and circumstance should open a path for him to engage in his foul project.

Not long afterwards it happened that the Captain, having drawn his sword upon a soldier of the guard and struck him, the Moor deprived him of his rank; whereat Disdemona was deeply grieved, and endeavoured again and again to reconcile her husband to the man. This the Moor told to the wicked Ensign, and how his wife importuned him so much about the Captain that he feared he should be forced at last to receive him back to service. Upon this hint the Ensign resolved to act, and began to work his web of intrigue. "Perchance," said he, "the lady Disdemona may have good reason to look kindly upon him."

"And wherefore?"° said the Moor.

"Nay, I would not step 'twixt man and wife," replied the Ensign, "but let your eyes be witness to themselves."

In vain the Moor went on to question the officer—he would proceed no further; nevertheless, his words left a sharp, stinging thorn in the Moor's heart, who could think of nothing else, trying to guess their meaning and lost in melancholy. And one day, when his wife had been endeavouring to pacify his anger toward the Captain, and praying him not to be unmindful of ancient[2] services and friendship for one small fault, especially since peace had been made between the Captain and the soldier he had struck, the Moor was angered, and exclaimed, "Great cause have you, Disdemona, to care so anxiously about this man! Is he a brother, or your kinsman, that he should be so near your heart?"

The lady, with all gentleness and humility, replied, "Be not angered, my dear lord; I have no other cause to bid me speak than sorrow that I see you

---

[1] for that reason (see glossary)
[2] former, previous

lose so dear a friend as, by your own words, this Captain has been to you; nor has he done so grave a fault that you should bear him so much enmity. Nay, but you Moors are of so hot a nature that every little trifle moves you to anger and revenge."

Still more enraged at these words, the Moor replied, "I could bring proofs—by heaven it mocks belief! But for the wrongs I have endured revenge must satisfy my wrath."

Disdemona, in astonishment and fright, seeing her husband's anger kindled against her, so contrary to his wont,[1] said humbly and with timidness, "None save a good intent has led me thus to speak with you, my lord; but to give cause no longer for offense, I'll never speak a word more on the subject."

The Moor, observing the earnestness with which his wife again pleaded for the Captain, began to guess the meaning of the Ensign's words; and in deep melancholy he went to seek the villain and induce him to speak more openly of what he knew. Then the Ensign, who was bent upon injuring the unhappy lady, after feigning at first great reluctance to say aught[2] that might displease the Moor, at length pretended to yield to his entreaties, and said, "I can't deny it pains me to the soul to be thus forced to say what needs must be more hard to hear than any other grief; but since you will it so, and that the regard I owe your honour compels me to confess the truth, I will no longer refuse to satisfy your questions and my duty. Know, then, that for no other reason is your lady vexed to see the Captain in disfavour than the pleasure that she has in his company whenever he comes to your house, and all the more since she has taken an aversion to your blackness."

These words went straight to the Moor's heart; but in order to hear more (now that he believed true all that the Ensign had told him) he replied, with a fierce glance, "By heavens, I scarce can hold this hand from plucking out that tongue of thine, so bold, which dares to speak such slander of my wife!"

"Captain,"[3] replied the Ensign, "I looked for such reward for these my faithful offices[4]—none else; but since my duty, and the jealous[5] care I bear your honour, have carried me thus far, I do repeat, so stands the truth, as you have heard it from these lips; and if the lady Disdemona hath, with a false show of love for you, blinded your eyes to what you should have seen, this is no argument but that I speak the truth. Nay, this same Captain told it me himself, like one whose happiness is incomplete until he can declare it

---

[1] usual habit
[2] anything
[3] the Moor: the Ensign's commander or captain, not the Captain of the troop
[4] duties
[5] attentive

to another; and, but that I feared your anger, I should have given him, when he told it me, his merited reward and slain him. But since informing you of what concerns you more than any other man brings me so undeserved a recompense, would I had held my peace, since silence might have spared me your displeasure."

Then the Moor, burning with indignation and anguish, said, "Make thou these eyes self-witnesses of what thou tell'st or on thy life I'll make thee wish thou hadst been born without a tongue."

"An easy task it would have been," replied the villain, "when he was used to visit at your house; but now that you have banished him, not for just cause, but for mere frivolous pretext, it will be hard to prove the truth. Still, I do not forgo the hope to make you witness of that which you will not credit my lips."

Thus they parted. The wretched Moor, struck to the heart as by a barbed dart, returned to his home and awaited the day when the Ensign should disclose to him the truth which was to make him miserable to the end of his days. But the evil-minded Ensign was, on his part, not less troubled by the chastity which he knew the lady Disdemona observed inviolate; and it seemed to him impossible to discover a means of making the Moor believe what he had falsely told him; and, turning the matter over in his thoughts in various ways, the villain resolved on a new deed of guilt.

Disdemona often used to go, as I have already said, to visit the Ensign's wife, and remained with her a good part of the day. Now, the Ensign observed that she carried about with her a handkerchief, which he knew the Moor had given her, finely embroidered in the Moorish fashion, and which was precious to Disdemona, nor less so to the Moor. Then he conceived the plan of taking this kerchief from her secretly, and thus laying the snare for her final ruin. The Ensign had a little daughter, a child three years of age, who was much loved by Disdemona; and one day when the unhappy lady had gone to pay a visit at the house of this vile man, he took the little child up in his arms and carried her to Disdemona, who took her and pressed her to her bosom; whilst at the same instant this traitor, who had extreme dexterity of hand, drew the kerchief from her sash so cunningly that she did not notice him, and overjoyed he took his leave of her.

Disdemona, ignorant of what had happened, returned home, and, busy with other thoughts, forgot the handkerchief. But a few days afterwards, looking for it and not finding it, she was in alarm, lest the Moor should ask her for it, as he oft was wont° to do. Meanwhile, the wicked Ensign seizing a fit opportunity, went to the Captain of the troop and with crafty malice left the handkerchief at the head of his bed without his discovering the trick until the following morning, when, on his getting out of bed, the handkerchief fell upon the floor, and he set his foot upon it. And not being able to imagine how it had come into his house, knowing that it belonged to Disdemona, he resolved to give it to her; and waiting until the Moor had gone from home, he went to the back door and knocked. It seemed as if fate conspired with the Ensign to work the death of the unhappy Disdemona. Just at that time the Moor returned home, and hearing a knocking at the back door, he went to the window, and in a rage exclaimed, "Who knocks there?" The Captain, hearing the Moor's voice, and fearing lest he should come downstairs and attack him, took to flight without answering a word. The Moor went down, and opening the door hastened into the street and looked about, but in vain. Then, returning into the house in great anger, he demanded of his wife who it was that had knocked at the door. Disdemona replied, as was true, that she did not know; but the Moor said, "It seemed to me the Captain."

"I know not," answered Disdemona, "whether it was he or another person."

The Moor restrained his fury, great as it was, wishing to do nothing before consulting the Ensign, to whom he hastened instantly, and told him all that had passed, praying him to gather from the Captain all he could respecting the affair. The Ensign, overjoyed at the occurrence, promised the Moor to do as he requested, and one day he took occasion to speak with the Captain when the Moor was so placed that he could see and hear them as they conversed. And whilst talking to him of every other subject than of Disdemona, he kept laughing all the time aloud, and feigning astonishment, he made various movements with his head and hands, as if listening to some tale of marvel. As soon as the Moor saw the Captain depart, he went up to the Ensign to hear what he had said to him. And the Ensign, after long entreaty, at length said, "He has hidden nothing from me and has told me that he has been used to visit your wife whenever you went from home, and that on the last occasion she gave him this handkerchief which you presented to her when you married her."

The Moor thanked the Ensign, and it seemed now clear to him that should he find Disdemona not to have the handkerchief, it was all true that the Ensign had told to him. One day, therefore, after dinner, in conversation with his wife on various subjects, he asked her for the kerchief. The unhappy lady, who had been in great fear of this, grew red as fire at this demand; and to hide the scarlet of her cheeks, which was closely noted by the Moor, she ran to a chest and pretended to seek the handkerchief, and after hunting for it a long time, she said, "I know not how it is—I cannot find it; can you perchance have taken it?"

"If I had taken it," said the Moor, "why should I ask it of you? But you will look better another time."

On leaving the room, the Moor fell to meditating how he should put his wife to death, and likewise the Captain of the troop, so that their deaths should not be laid to his charge. And as he ruminated over this day and night, he could not prevent his wife's observing that he was not the same towards her as he had been wont;° and she said to him again and again, "What is the matter? What troubles you? How comes it that you, who were the most light-hearted man in the world, are now so melancholy?"

The Moor feigned various reasons in reply to his wife's questioning, but she was not satisfied, and, although conscious that she had given the Moor no cause, by act or deed, to be so troubled, yet she feared that he might have grown wearied of her; and she would say to the Ensign's wife, "I know not what to say of the Moor; he used to be all love toward me; but within these few days he has become another man; and much I fear that I shall prove a warning to young girls not to marry against the wishes of their parents, and that the Italian ladies may learn from me not to wed a man whom nature and habitude of life estrange from us. But as I know the Moor is on such terms of friendship with your husband and communicates to him all of his affairs, I pray you, if you have heard from him aught° that you may tell me of, fail not to befriend me." And as she said this, she wept bitterly.

The Ensign's wife, who knew the whole truth (her husband wishing to make use of her to compass[1] the death of Disdemona), but could never consent to such a project, dared not, from fear of her husband, disclose a single circumstance: all she said was, "Beware lest you give any cause of suspicion to your husband, and show to him by every means your fidelity and love."

"Indeed I do so," replied Disdemona, "but it is all of no avail."

Meanwhile the Moor sought in every way to convince himself of what he fain[2] would have found untrue, and he prayed[3] the Ensign to contrive that he might see the handkerchief in the possession of the Captain. This was a difficult matter to the wicked Ensign; nevertheless, he promised to use every means to satisfy the Moor of the truth of what he said.

Now the Captain had a wife at home, who worked the most marvellous embroidery upon lawn.[4] And seeing the handkerchief, which belonged to the Moor's wife, she resolved, before it was returned to her, to work one like it. As she was engaged in this task, the Ensign observed her standing at a window, where she could be seen by all passers-by in the street, and he pointed her out to the Moor, who was now perfectly convinced of his wife's

---

[1] plot
[2] rather
[3] begged
[4] linen

guilt. Then he arranged with the Ensign to slay Disdemona and the Captain of the troop, treating them as it seemed they both deserved. And the Moor prayed the Ensign that he would kill the Captain, promising eternal gratitude to him. But the Ensign at first refused to undertake so dangerous a task, the Captain being a man of equal skill and courage; until at length, after much entreating and being richly paid, the Moor prevailed on him to promise to attempt the deed.

Having formed this resolution, the Ensign, going out one dark night, sword in hand, met the Captain on his way to visit a courtesan,[1] and struck him a blow on his right thigh, which cut off his leg and felled him to the earth. Then the Ensign was on the point of putting an end to his life, when the Captain, who was a courageous man and used to the sight of blood and death, drew his sword and, wounded as he was, kept on his defence, exclaiming with a loud voice, "I'm murdered!" Thereupon the Ensign, hearing the people come running up, with some of the soldiers who were lodged thereabouts, took to his heels to escape being caught; then turning about again, he joined the crowd, pretending to have been attracted by the noise. And when he saw the Captain's leg cut off, he judged that if not already dead, the blow must, at all events, end his life; and whilst in his heart he was rejoiced at this, yet he feigned to compassionate[2] the Captain as he had been his brother.

The next morning the tidings of this affair spread through the whole city, and reached the ears of Disdemona; whereat she, who was kindhearted and little dreamed that any ill would betide° her, evinced the greatest grief at the calamity. This served but to confirm the Moor's suspicions, and he went to seek for the Ensign, and said to him, "Do you know that ass my wife is in such grief at the Captain's accident that she is well nigh gone mad?"

"And what could you expect, seeing he is her very soul?" replied the Ensign.

"Ay, soul forsooth!"[3] exclaimed the Moor; "I'll draw the soul from out her body; call me no man if that I fail to shut the world upon this wretch."

Then they consulted of one means and another—poison and daggers—to kill poor Disdemona, but could resolve on nothing. At length the Ensign said, "A plan comes to my mind, which will give you satisfaction and raise cause for no suspicion. It is this: the house in which you live is very old, and the ceiling of your chamber has many cracks; I propose we take a stocking filled with sand and beat Disdemona with it till she dies; thus will her body bear no signs of violence. When she is dead we can pull down a portion of

---

[1] a mistress or prostitute
[2] show compassion for
[3] indeed, in truth

the ceiling, and thus make it seem as if a rafter falling on her head had killed the lady. Suspicion cannot rest on you, since all men will impute her death to accident."

This cruel counsel pleased the Moor, and he only waited for a fitting time to execute the plot. One night, when he and Disdemona had retired to bed, the Ensign, whom the Moor had concealed in a closet which opened into the chamber, raised a noise in the closet, according to a concerted plan; whereat the Moor said to his wife, "Did you not hear that noise?"

"Indeed I heard it," she replied.

"Rise," said the Moor, "and see what 'tis."

The unhappy Disdemona rose from the bed, and the instant she approached the closet, out rushed the Ensign, and being strong and of stout nerve, he beat her cruelly with the bag of sand across her back; upon which Disdemona fell to the ground, scarce able to draw her breath; but with the little voice she had left, she called upon the Moor for aid. But the Moor, leaping from bed, exclaimed, "Thou wickedest of women, thus has thy falseness found its just reward, the recompense to wives who, counterfeiting love, place horns upon their husbands' brows."[1]

The wretched lady, hearing those words, and feeling that she was near her end (for the Ensign had given her another blow), appealed to the justice of Heaven, since justice here had failed her, in proof of her fidelity and truth; and as she was thus calling Heaven to witness, the wicked Ensign inflicted a third blow, under which she sank lifeless on the floor.

Then the Ensign and the Moor, laying Disdemona on the bed and wounding her head, pulled down part of the ceiling of the chamber, as they had arranged; whereupon the Moor began to call aloud for help, exclaiming that the house was falling. Hearing this uproar, the neighbours all came running up, and there found Disdemona lying dead beneath a rafter—a sight which, from the good life of that poor lady, did fill all hearts with sorrow.

On the following day Disdemona was buried, followed to the grave by the universal grief of the people. But Heaven, the just regarder[2] of all hearts, willed not that so wicked a deed should go unpunished. Ere[3] long the Moor, whom Disdemona had loved more than her own life, began to feel such sorrow at her loss that he went wandering about as one bereft of reason, searching in every part of the house. And reflecting in his thoughts that the Ensign had been the cause that he had lost, with Disdemona, all joy in life, he conceived so deep a hatred to that wicked man he could not bear to set eyes on him, and had it not been for his fear of the inviolable justice of the

---

[1] horns were the traditional sign of a cuckolded man
[2] watcher, guardian
[3] before (see glossary)

Signoria of Venice, he would have slain him openly. But being unable to do this with safety, he deprived him of his rank, and would not allow him to remain in his Company; whereat such an enmity arose between the two that no greater or more deadly can be imagined.

The Ensign, that wickedest of all bad men, now turned his thought to injuring the Moor; and seeking out the Captain, whose wound was by this time healed, and who went about with a wooden leg in place of the one that had been cut off, he said to him, "'tis time you should be avenged for your lost limb; and if you will come with me to Venice, I'll tell you who the malefactor is, whom I dare not mention to you here for many reasons; and I will bring you proofs."

The Captain of the troop, whose anger returned fiercely but without knowing why, thanked the Ensign, and went with him to Venice. On arriving there the Ensign told him it was the Moor who had cut off his leg, on account of the suspicion he had formed of Disdemona's conduct with him; and for that reason he had slain her, and then spread the report that the ceiling had fallen and killed her. Upon hearing which, the Captain accused the Moor to the Signoria, both of having cut off his leg and killed his wife, and called the Ensign to witness the truth of what he said. The Ensign declared both charges to be true, for that the Moor had disclosed to him the whole plot, and had tried to persuade him to perpetrate both crimes; and that, having afterwards killed his wife out of jealousy he[1] had conceived, he had narrated to him the manner in which he had perpetrated her death.

The Signoria of Venice, when they heard of the cruelty inflicted by a barbarian upon a lady of their city, commanded the Moor's arms should be pinioned[2] in Cyprus, and he be brought to Venice, where, with many tortures, they sought to draw from him the truth. But the Moor, bearing with unyielding courage all the torment, denied the whole charge so resolutely that no confession could be drawn from him. But, although by his constancy and firmness he escaped death, he was, after being confined for several days in prison, condemned to perpetual banishment, in which he was eventually slain by the kinsfolk of Disdemona, as he merited. The Ensign returned to his own country, and, following up his wonted° villainy, he accused one of his companions of having sought to persuade him to kill an enemy of his, who was a man of noble rank; whereupon this person was arrested and put to the torture; but when he denied the truth of what his accuser had declared, the Ensign himself was likewise tortured to make him prove the truth of his accusations; and he was tortured so that his body ruptured, upon which he

---

[1] i.e., the jealousy the Ensign had planted in the Moor
[2] bound, as a prisoner

was removed from prison and taken home, where he died a miserable death. Thus did Heaven avenge the innocence of Disdemona; and all these events were narrated by the Ensign's wife, who was privy to the whole, after his death, as I have told them here.

Translated by John Edward Taylor

Questions

1. A concern with racial difference, stereotypes, civility, and barbarity seems to linger just under the surface of this story. They may provoke the Moor's violent response to the Ensign's suggestions that Disdemona is unfaithful to him, but the reasons behind his violence are never fully developed in the story. Why do you think Cinthio makes so little of these details? Does Shakespeare follow suit?

2. At the very end of the text we learn that the entire story is based upon the report of the Ensign's wife, told to the narrator sometime after the death of the Ensign. What effect does this mode of storytelling have on our understanding of the story?

3. Does Shakespeare's decision to make Emilia, not the Ensign, the one who takes Disdemona's handkerchief seem to you a significant change to Cinthio's story?

4. Deep characterization of the kind we are used to now is not one of Cinthio's strengths as an author—and nor was it for most writers of the sixteenth century. As you imagine the interior lives of Disdemona, the Moor, the Ensign, or the Captain of a troop, what do you find?

5. The murder scene is quite different in Cinthio's story compared to Shakespeare's. What are the differences? How much do they matter?

6. With its tidy moral conclusion, Cinthio's tale does not really end as tragedies usually do. What are the major changes that Shakespeare made to transform this story into a tragedy?

Robert Greene,
Pandosto. The Triumph of Time.
The History of Dorastus and Fawnia
(1588)

The Winter's Tale

In writing *The Winter's Tale*, probably first performed in early 1611, Shakespeare once again went to the popular prose literature of his age for his storyline, this time to a prose romance entitled *Pandosto. The Triumph of Time* by the prolific Elizabethan writer Robert Greene. This is the same Robert Greene who in 1592 had attacked the young playwright for being a rising star in London's competitive theatrical world, calling him an "upstart crow" who "beautified" himself with feathers stolen from writers of more learning and more experience (see the General Introduction).

The play comes from the last years of Shakespeare's career, and it is among the last he wrote without the significant collaboration of any other playwright. Even though he had well over thirty plays to his name by this time, Shakespeare used a strategy that had served him throughout his career, namely rewriting a popular story that had already demonstrated that it could capture the attention of a wide audience. In this case, his audience was formed of readers with a taste for the staples of the romance genre: the faraway, the exotic, and the sentimental. Greene's story features a distant Mediterranean setting—in keeping with romance tradition, the setting is more imaginary than real—and action revolving around courtiers, shepherds, disguises, sudden reversals of fortune, mistaken identities, honest servants and imperious tyrants, an ancient oracle, and perhaps most necessary of all, a mostly happy ending. This was the kind of literary fare that Elizabethan England's readers—in an age of widespread illiteracy, readers were still a minority of the overall population—simply could not get enough of. More often than not, popular romances of this period were continental works translated or adapted for English readers. But Greene's tale is an outlier in this respect: it is a native English product aware of the conventions of continental romances but with no known source.

If the number of reprints of the first edition of 1588 is anything to go by (and reprints are usually a very good guide), *Pandosto* was immensely popular. The story reappeared in new editions in 1592, 1595, 1600, 1607, and 1609, all prior to Shakespeare's stage version; it also continued to be republished long after it, with over thirty English editions and two French translations—as well as two French stage versions—by the mid eighteenth century. In fact, the tale continued to be printed in cheap, popular editions in England and beyond until 1843, for a total of more than sixty editions in prose, verse, and drama.

We cannot be sure which published version of the story Shakespeare used, though a small but significant change introduced into the 1607 edition suggests that he must have used one of the early editions. This textual crux concerns a single but important word contained within Apollo's oracle. In the editions prior to 1607 the oracle states that "the King shall live without an heir if that which is lost be not found." In other words, Pandosto's fate will be to live in a perpetual state of uncertainty, heirless but (probably) living in hope that his castoff daughter might one day be found. However, beginning with the 1607 edition, the phrase changes to "the King shall *die* without an heir if that which is lost be not found" (my italics). Although the application of strict logic brings us to the same conclusion—that in both cases the king will, eventually, die without an heir if the girl who comes to be known as Fawnia be not found—the original wording that Shakespeare followed has a subtle evocative power that the revision does not. The prospect of a life spent in perpetual hope that the child he repudiated at birth might someday, somehow return and supply him with an heir seems to invite us back into the mental and moral universe of *King Lear*, the age-old story of parental loss and reunion he had retold just a few years before. Or we could compare this story to that of Prospero and his daughter Miranda in *The Tempest* (1611). Perhaps most obviously, the story of a daughter lost to her kingly father but alive and well and living elsewhere in the world, beyond his knowledge, also forms a significant theme in two other romances of this phase of Shakespeare's late career: *Pericles* (1607-8) and *Cymbeline* (1609-10).

We cannot be sure whether the change from "live without an heir" to "die without an heir" was a conscious decision by the early seventeenth-century publisher G. Potter, who appears to have obtained the rights to publish the story from its first publisher in about 1607, or an error or impromptu editorial decision made on the spot by a worker in the printing house, but we can rule out any change of heart by Robert Greene: he died in 1592, a constellation of self-destructive behaviours carrying him off soon after his thirty-fourth birthday.

Nor can we be exactly sure of what was contained in the 1588 edition because only one copy of it survives and that copy is missing almost twenty percent of its content. In all likelihood, the 1592 edition was composed directly from the prior edition, but there are enough differences between them that we cannot be sure what the exact contents of the missing pages were. The very fact that the first edition survives in just one copy is additional evidence of the story's popularity, however: much-loved books did not sit on shelves, surviving intact into later generations; they were passed around, handed down, shared, and eventually read to shreds. Our single surviving but mutilated copy of the first edition gives us yet another indication of the book's great popularity among Elizabethan readers.

As with Shakespeare's other plays, *The Winter's Tale* is not derived from a single source, but from an amalgam of stories that were combined as part of the playwright's creative process. Although he followed Greene's narrative line very closely in composing *The Winter's Tale*, when it came to the crucial plot point of Hermione's survival/revival, he was almost certainly influenced by his memories of Ovid's famous story of Pygmalion, who created a real woman out of a stone statue he himself had sculpted (see *Metamorphoses*, Book 10). Ovid was one of Shakespeare's most beloved authors, whom he read in both Latin and in a 1567 English translation by William Golding. He drew frequently from the *Metamorphoses* for his plays and for the main action of his narrative poem *Venus and Adonis*, and it seems almost self-evident that he had Ovid's story in mind when he made such a significant change to his source story.

He also drew upon an ancient Greek play by Euripides, *Alcestis* (438 BCE, but translated into Latin in 1566 by the Scottish humanist George Buchanan). That story provided the specific trope of a husband whose wife is restored to him after he presumes her dead, and it probably suggested the basis for the magnificent revelation scene in act 5, scene 3.

Greene's two titles (see illustration below) suggest something important about how his story is constructed: it contains two fairly distinct phases and offers the reader two quite different narrative environments. The first phase is set entirely in the court of Bohemia, a location more realistic and domestic than fantastic, and it corresponds to the action of *The Winter's Tale* through act 3, scene 2. The second is set principally in the Sicilian countryside, among shepherds, before the action returns to the court of Bohemia at the very end; it offers a much more fanciful setting, focused on a largely new set of characters and on the romance tropes of young love, disguise, and social mobility. The second phase links back to the first phase of the story only in the last pages, when the two generations are reunited and the mistaken identities and disagreements caused by Pandosto's rash actions in the first part of the story are finally resolved.

Shakespeare solved the problem of a divided story by introducing an allegorical figure named Time into his play. The character Time alerts the audience that we have skipped over sixteen years between the end of act 3 and the beginning of act 4. In a lengthy speech he supplies much of the middle part of Greene's original narrative in the form of reported rather than dramatised action. Despite being an obviously divided and in some ways imperfect story, Greene's tale holds together in a mythical, mysterious way that can still inspire the kind of admiration that pleased generations of readers and playgoers from 1588 until the middle of the nineteenth century, including Shakespeare. Perhaps we can read his attempt to fuse the two sections by introducing Time as his recognition that Greene's story needed a little remediation, despite its strangely powerful emotional effect.

Shakespeare transformed Greene's story into a very different tale. Although he clearly served as the model for Shakespeare's Leontes, King Pandosto is a notably different protagonist in at least one key moment that occurs at the end of the first phase of the story. Upon learning the truth from the Apollo's oracle and being publicly exposed as a jealous, tyrannical leader in front of his own court, Greene's protagonist is immediately repentant, willingly accepting the truth of the oracle and even trying to assuage his deep sense of guilt by taking his own life. He laments that "sith the gods mean to prolong my days to increase my dolour, I will offer my guilty blood a sacrifice to those sackless souls whose lives are lost by my rigorous folly."[1]

Pandosto is reduced to making daily visits to the sepulchre in which his dead wife and son are entombed; there he sits and weeps, bewailing his own folly, requiring no other company but his own sorrows and no other happiness but this ongoing ritual of repentance. The lines engraved in golden letters on the sepulchre proclaim the underlying moral of the first part of the story:

> Here lies entombed Bellaria fair,
> Falsely accused to be unchaste;
> Cleared by Apollo's sacred doom,
> Yet slain by jealousy at last.

Here we note sharp language of moral condemnation: Bellaria was "fair," "falsely accused," and "cleared" of any wrongdoing. And all who pass by

---

[1] sith: since; sackless: innocent

are enjoined to lay their curses on the jealous tyrant who behaved so irrationally and so destructively:

Whate'er thou be that passest by,
Curse him that caused this queen to die.

When Shakespeare worked with a source, a fundamental departure from the original was always just as possible as obedience to it. *The Winter's Tale* shows us this principle very clearly. What Shakespeare makes of Greene's penitent, tearful king is a rich question to consider. We might ask what the dramatist sought to gain by making Leontes reject the oracle, delaying his repentance until his son is reported dead, and then rewarding the king's eventual conversion with the gift of a wife apparently brought back to life by the magic of Paulina, a character who has no counterpart in *Pandosto*. The whole nexus of events around Leontes' slow change of behaviour from the moment when the messengers Cleomenes and Dion arrive from Delphos (act 3, scene 2) to the final scene (act 5, scene 3) invites us to consider how Shakespeare could read a story, absorb it, but follow it only up to a point when he came to re-write it.

Fascinating interpretive questions also emerge when we consider some of Shakespeare's other changes to Greene's story: Why did he switch the kings and their countries, making Leontes the king of Sicily and not Bohemia? Is there some underlying cultural logic that he sought to satisfy by identifying Leontes with Sicily rather than Bohemia, or is the change just a simple case of misremembering the original story? For that matter, why was he satisfied to use Greene's plot but not his characters' names? And why did he transfer a detail concerning the heritage of Egistus's wife, identified by Greene as the daughter of Emperor of Russia (though she never appears in the story or the play) to Hermione (see 3.2.)? And why, despite the most obvious geographical evidence, did he retain Greene's ludicrous mistake of giving landlocked Bohemia a shoreline? Why not just change the action to a country that had one?

In addition, Shakespeare abandoned both of Greene's titles and instead used *The Winter's Tale*. It is a curious choice, but one that has implications for imagining how he might have understood or appreciated Greene's story. In Shakespeare's time "a winter's tale" was a by-word for a pointless, unbelievable, and usually meandering tale designed to fill up the time—a yarn told to while away the long hours of winter. Is that what the playwright thought he was offering audiences with his play? Perhaps he was toying with their expectations by underselling his story, ultimately delivering a deep and serious meditation on the power of the human mind to succumb to its worst impulses—like jealousy—and its power to destroy everything and everyone in its path. Was he, too, imagining a repentance so deep and so total that it is rewarded with an apparently magical intervention that might gesture toward the central Christian story of resurrection and forgiveness? And what might it mean that this power of symbolic resurrection is invested in a female character, Paulina, who has no equivalent in Greene's story but is so central to this one? Indeed, the more one thinks about it, the thematic changes Shakespeare made to Greene's story are probably even more important to understanding *The Winter's Tale* than the elements he retained.

Perhaps most of all, why did Shakespeare allow characters to live when their models in Greene's story die? King Leontes lives to the end, but his predecessor King Pandosto dies by his own hand, darkening what was otherwise a grand final marriage celebration and reunion. And why does he bring Queen Hermione, based on Greene's Bellaria, back to life? Her revival might remind us of what happens to Hero in *Much Ado About Nothing*—another case of a woman set aside and brought back to reward and gratify a man who did her wrong by publicly shaming her. What does her revival signify? For many admirers of Shakespeare, these transformations are not only enticing pathways that might lead toward some understanding of *The Winter's Tale* central meaning(s), but they might also point us toward the creative, or moral, centre of Shakespeare's imagination.

A Note on the Text

Pandosto, The Triumph of Time. The History of Dorastus and Fawnia was published by Thomas Cadman (London, 1588). I compared early editions of this text, adding notes and glosses, modernising spelling and punctuation, and adjusting paragraph breaks in a few places. I retained many archaic verb forms (*bare* for *bore*, *bewray* for *betray*, *brake* for *broke*, *drave* for *drove*, *sate* for *sat*, *shew* for *show*, etc.) and some other forms (*sith* for *since*, *wise* for *way*) that present little or no difficulties for modern readers. Frequently repeated archaic words are footnoted on their first occurrence and thereafter noted with °, which refers readers to the glossary at the end of this volume.

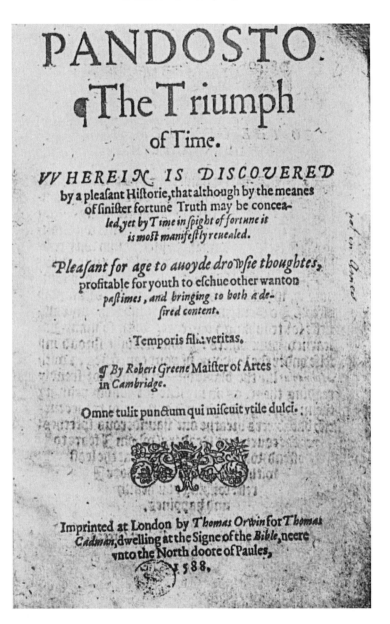

Fig. 6-1. The title page of Robert Greene's *Pandosto*

Pandosto.
The Triumph
of Time.

Wherein is discovered
by a pleasant history that, although by the means
of sinister fortune Truth may be concealed,
*yet by Time in spite of fortune it is
most manifestly revealed.*

Pleasant for age to avoid drowsy thoughts,
profitable for youth to eschew other wanton
*pastimes, and bringing to both a de-
sired content.*

Temporis filia veritas.[1]
By Robert Greene, Master of Arts
in *Cambridge.*
Omne tulit punctum qui miscuit utile dulci.[2]

Imprinted at London by *Thomas Orwin* for *Thomas
Cadman*, dwelling at the Sign of the Bible, near unto the North door of
Paul's,

1588.

The History of Dorastus and Fawnia

AMONG all the passions wherewith human minds are perplexed there is
none that so galleth with restless despite[3] as the infectious sore of jealousy;
for all other griefs are either to be appeased with sensible persuasions, to be
cured with wholesome counsel, to be relieved in want, or by tract of time to
be worn out, jealousy only excepted, which is so sauced[4] with suspicious

---

[1] "Truth is the daughter of Time," a popular proverb in the sixteenth century.
[2] "Whoever mixes the useful and the sweet wins all the points" (Horace, *Ars Poetica*,
    343).
[3] pesters with persistent sorrow
[4] seasoned

doubts and pinching mistrust that whoso seeks by friendly counsel to rase out[1] this hellish passion, it forthwith suspecteth that he giveth this advice to cover his own guiltiness. Yea, whoso is pained with this restless torment doubteth all, distrusteth himself, is always frozen with fear and fired with suspicion, having that wherein consisteth all his joy to be the breeder of his misery. Yea, it is such a heavy enemy to that holy estate of matrimony, sowing between the married couples such deadly seeds of secret hatred, as love being once rased out by spiteful distrust there oft ensueth bloody revenge, as this ensuing history manifestly proveth: wherein Pandosto, furiously incensed by causeless jealousy, procured the death of his most loving and loyal wife and his own endless sorrow and misery.

In the country of Bohemia there reigned a king called Pandosto, whose fortunate success in wars against his foes and bountiful courtesy towards his friends in peace made him to be greatly feared and loved of all men. This Pandosto had to wife a lady called Bellaria, by birth royal, learned by education, fair by nature, by virtues famous, so that it was hard to judge whether her beauty, fortune, or virtue won the greatest commendations. These two, linked together in perfect love, led their lives with such fortunate content that their subjects greatly rejoiced to see their quiet disposition. They had not been married long, but Fortune, willing to increase their happiness, lent them a son so adorned with the gifts of nature as the perfection of the child greatly augmented the love of the parents and the joy of their commons; in so much that the Bohemians, to show their inward joys by outward actions, made bonfires and triumphs throughout all the kingdom, appointing jousts and tourneys[2] for the honour of their young prince. Whither resorted not only his nobles but also divers[3] kings and princes which were his neighbours, willing to shew[4] their friendship they ought[5] to Pandosto and to win fame and glory by their prowess and valour. Pandosto, whose mind was fraught with princely liberality, entertained the kings, princes, and noblemen with such submiss[6] courtesy and magnifical[7] bounty, that they all saw how willing he was to gratify their good wills, making a general feast for his subjects, which continued by the space of twenty days, all which time the jousts and tourneys were kept to the great content both of the lords and ladies there present. This solemn triumph being

---

[1] eradicate
[2] arranging jousting matches and tournaments
[3] several, various (see glossary)
[4] show (one of several archaic forms I have left unmodernised: see glossary)
[5] owed
[6] humble
[7] sumptuous, splendid

once ended, the assembly taking their leave of Pandosto and Bellaria, the young son, who was called Garinter, was nursed up in the house to the great joy and content of the parents.

Fortune, envious of such happy success, willing to shew° some sign of her inconstancy, turned her wheel and darkened their bright sun of prosperity with the misty clouds of mishap and misery. For it so happened that Egistus, king of Sicilia,[1] who in his youth had been brought up with Pandosto, desirous to shew that neither tract of time nor distance of place could diminish their former friendship, provided a navy of ships and sailed into Bohemia to visit his old friend and companion, who hearing of his arrival, went himself in person and his wife Bellaria, accompanied with a great train of lords and ladies, to meet Egistus. And, espying him, alighted from his horse, embraced him very lovingly, protesting that nothing in the world could have happened more acceptable to him than his coming, wishing his wife to welcome his old friend and acquaintance: who to shew how she liked him whom her husband loved, entertained him with such familiar courtesy as Egistus perceived himself to be very well welcome. After they had thus saluted and embraced each other, they mounted again on horseback and rode toward the city, devising and recounting how being children they had passed their youth in friendly pastimes: where, by the means of the citizens, Egistus was received with triumphs and shows in such sort[2] that he marvelled how on so small a warning[3] they could make such preparation.

Passing the streets thus with such rare sights, they rode on to the palace, where Pandosto entertained Egistus and his Sicilians with such banqueting and sumptuous cheer, so royally as they all had cause to commend his princely liberality; yea, the very basest slave[4] that was known to come from Sicilia was used with such courtesy that Egistus might easily perceive how both he and his were honoured for his friend's sake. Bellaria, who in her time was the flower of courtesy, willing to shew how unfeignedly she loved her husband by his friend's entertainment, used him likewise so familiarly that her countenance bewrayed[5] how her mind was affected towards him, oftentimes coming herself into his bedchamber to see that nothing should be amiss to mislike[6] him. This honest familiarity increased daily more and more betwixt them; for Bellaria, noting in Egistus a princely and bountiful

---

[1] Sicily
[2] in such a way
[3] short a notice
[4] lowliest servant
[5] revealed (literally, betrayed)
[6] displease

mind, adorned with sundry[1] and excellent qualities, and Egistus, finding in her a virtuous and courteous disposition, there grew such a secret uniting of their affections that the one could not well be without the company of the other: in so much that when Pandosto was busied with such urgent affairs that he could not be present with his friend Egistus, Bellaria would walk with him into the garden, where they two in private and pleasant devices[2] would pass away the time to both their contents.

This custom still continuing betwixt them, a certain melancholy passion entering the mind of Pandosto drave[3] him into sundry and doubtful thoughts. First, he called to mind the beauty of his wife Bellaria, the comeliness and bravery of his friend Egistus, thinking that love was above all laws and therefore to be stayed with[4] no law; that it was hard to put fire and flax together without burning; that their open pleasures might breed his secret displeasures. He considered with himself that Egistus was a man and must needs love, that his wife was a woman and therefore subject unto love, and that where fancy forced, friendship was of no force.

These and such like doubtful thoughts, a long time smothering in his stomach, began at last to kindle in his mind a secret mistrust which, increased by suspicion, grew at last to a flaming jealousy that so tormented him as he could take no rest. He then began to measure all their actions and to misconstrue of their too private familiarity, judging that it was not for honest affection but for disordinate fancy,[5] so that he began to watch them more narrowly[6] to see if he could get any true or certain proof to confirm his doubtful suspicion. While thus he noted their looks and gestures and suspected their thoughts and meanings, they two silly[7] souls, who doubted[8] nothing of this his treacherous intent, frequented daily each other's company, which drave him into such a frantic passion that he began to bear a secret hate to Egistus and a louring[9] countenance to Bellaria; who marvelling unaccustomed frowns, began to cast beyond the moon and to enter into a thousand sundry thoughts which way she should[10] offend her husband. But finding in herself a clear conscience, ceased to muse until such

---

[1] various
[2] plan, strategy (see glossary)
[3] drove (see introduction)
[4] impeded by
[5] unnatural attraction
[6] closely
[7] innocent (see glossary)
[8] suspected
[9] sullen, downcast (see glossary)
[10] might have offended

time as she might find fit opportunity to demand the cause of his dumps.[1]

In the meantime Pandosto's mind was so far charged with jealousy that he did no longer doubt, but was assured, as he thought, that his friend Egistus had entered a wrong point in his tables, and so had played him false play:[2] whereupon, desirous to revenge so great an injury, he thought best to dissemble the grudge with a fair and friendly countenance and so under the shape of a friend to shew° him the trick of a foe. Devising[3] with himself a long time how he might best put away Egistus without suspicion of treacherous murder, he concluded at last to poison him; which opinion pleasing his humour, he became resolute in his determination and the better to bring the matter to pass he called unto him his cupbearer,[4] with whom in secret he brake[5] the matter, promising to him for the performance thereof to give him a thousand crowns of yearly revenues.

His cupbearer, either being of a good conscience or willing for fashion sake to deny such a bloody request, began with great reasons to persuade Pandosto from his determinate mischief, shewing him what an offence murder was to the gods, how such unnatural actions did more displease the heavens than men, that causeless cruelty did seldom or never escape without revenge. He laid before his face that Egistus was his friend, a king, and one that was come into his kingdom to confirm a league of perpetual amity betwixt them; that he had and did shew him a most friendly countenance; how Egistus was not only honoured of his own people by obedience but also loved of the Bohemians for his courtesy, and that if he now should without any just or manifest cause poison him, it would not only be a great dishonour to his majesty, and a means to sow perpetual enmity between the Sicilians and the Bohemians, but also his own subjects would repine[6] at such treacherous cruelty. These and such like persuasions of Franion—for so was his cupbearer called—could no whit prevail to dissuade him from his devilish enterprise, but remaining resolute in his determination (his fury so fired with rage as it could not be appeased with reason), he began with bitter taunts to take up his man, and to lay before him two baits, preferment and death, saying that if he should poison Egistus he would advance him to high dignities; if he refused to do it of an obstinate mind, no torture should be too great to requite his disobedience.

---

[1] melancholy
[2] The image comes from the game of backgammon: Pandosto is convinced that Egistus has cheated him.
[3] pondering
[4] trusted servant (one loyal enough to prevent a king being poisoned)
[5] revealed, spoke of (see glossary and introduction)
[6] show discontent

Franion, seeing that to persuade Pandosto any more was but to strive against the stream, consented as soon as opportunity would give him leave to dispatch Egistus: wherewith Pandosto remained somewhat satisfied, hoping now he should be fully revenged of such mistrusted injuries, intending also as soon as Egistus was dead to give his wife a sop of the same sauce[1] and so be rid of those which were the cause of his restless sorrow.

While thus he lived in this hope, Franion, being secret in his chamber, began to meditate with himself in these terms: "Ah, Franion, treason is loved of many but the traitor hated of all; unjust offences may for a time escape without danger, but never without revenge. Thou art servant to a king and must obey at command; yet Franion, against law and conscience it is not good to resist a tyrant with arms nor to please an unjust king with obedience. What shalt thou do? Folly refused gold, and frenzy preferment; wisdom seeketh after dignity, and counsel looketh for gain. Egistus is a stranger to thee and Pandosto thy sovereign: thou hast little cause to respect the one, and oughtest to have great care to obey the other. Think this, Franion, that a pound of gold is worth a ton of lead: great gifts are little gods and preferment to a mean man is a whetstone to courage. There is nothing sweeter than promotion nor lighter than report.[2] Care not then, though most count thee a traitor, so all call thee rich. Dignity, Franion, advanceth thy posterity and evil report can hurt but thyself. Know this, where eagles build falcons may prey; where lions haunt foxes may steal. Kings are known to command, servants are blameless to consent: fear not thou, then, to lift at[3] Egistus; Pandosto shall bear the burthen. Yea, but Franion, conscience is a worm that ever biteth but never ceaseth: that which is rubbed with the stone galactites[4] will never be hot. Flesh dipped in the Sea Aegeum will never be sweet; the herb tragion[5] being once bit with an aspis[6] never groweth, and conscience once stained with innocent blood is always tied to a guilty remorse. Prefer thy content before riches and a clear mind before dignity; so being poor thou shalt have rich peace, or else rich, thou shalt enjoy disquiet."

Franion, having muttered out these or such like words, seeing either he must die with a clear mind or live with a spotted conscience, he was so cumbered[7] with divers cogitations that he could take no rest until at last he

---

[1] the same treatment (literally, a taste of the same)
[2] rumour, gossip
[3] take arms against
[4] a legendary magical stone
[5] motherwort
[6] asp, serpent
[7] weighed down

determined to break the matter to[1] Egistus. But fearing that the king should either suspect or hear of such matters, he concealed the device° till opportunity would permit him to reveal it. Lingering thus in doubtful fear, in[2] an evening he went to Egistus' lodging and desirous to break with him of certain affairs that touched the king, after all were commanded out of the chamber Franion made manifest the whole conspiracy which Pandosto had devised against him, desiring Egistus not to account him a traitor for bewraying° his master's counsel, but to think that he did it for conscience, hoping that although his master, inflamed with rage or incensed by some sinister reports or slanderous speeches, had imagined such causeless mischief, yet when time should pacify his anger and try those talebearers[3] but flattering parasites, then he would count him as a faithful servant that with such care had kept his master's credit.

Egistus had not fully heard Franion tell forth his tale, but a quaking fear possessed all his limbs, thinking that there was some treason wrought and that Franion did but shadow his craft[4] with these false colours: wherefore[5] he began to wax in choler and said that he doubted not Pandosto, sith[6] he was his friend and there had never as yet been any breach of amity. He had not sought to invade his lands, to conspire with his enemies, to dissuade his subjects from their allegiance, but in word and thought he rested his at all times. He knew not, therefore, any cause that should move Pandosto to seek his death, but suspected it to be a compacted knavery[7] of the Bohemians to bring the king and him at odds.

Franion, staying him[8] in the midst of his talk, told him that to dally with princes was with the swans to sing against their death,[9] and that if the Bohemians had intended any such mischief it might have been better brought to pass than by revealing the conspiracy. Therefore his majesty did ill to misconstrue of his good meaning, sith° his intent was to hinder treason, not to become a traitor; and to confirm his promises, if it pleased his majesty

---

[1] open the topic with
[2] on
[3] those tattletales or "snitches"
[4] hide his plan
[5] at that (see glossary)
[6] since (see introduction and glossary)
[7] wicked conspiracy
[8] stopping himself
[9] Singing upon their own deaths was a legendary quality attributed to swans from at least the time of Aesop, 6th century BCE.

to fly[1] into Sicilia for the safeguard of his life he would go with him. And if then he found not such a practise to be pretended,[2] let his imagined treachery be repaid with most monstrous torments. Egistus, hearing the solemn protestation of Franion, began to consider that in love and kingdoms neither faith nor law is to be respected, doubting[3] that Pandosto thought by his death to destroy his men and with speedy war to invade Sicilia. These and such doubts thoroughly weighed, he gave great thanks to Franion, promising if he might with life return to Syracusa[4] that he would create him a duke in Sicilia, craving his counsel how he might escape out of the country. Franion, who, having some small skill in navigation, was well acquainted with the ports and havens, knew every danger in the sea, joining in counsel with the master of Egistus' navy, rigged all their ships, and setting them afloat, let them lie at anchor to be in the more readiness when time and wind should serve.

Fortune, although blind, yet by chance favouring this just cause, sent them within six days a good gale of wind, which Franion seeing fit for their purpose to put Pandosto out of suspicion, the night before they should sail he went to him and promised that the next day he would put the device in practice,[5] for he had got such a forcible poison as the very smell thereof would procure sudden death.

Pandosto was joyful to hear this good news and thought every hour a day till he might be glutted with bloody revenge. But his suit had but ill success. For Egistus, fearing that delay might breed danger, and willing that the grass should not be cut from under his feet, taking bag and baggage, by the help of Franion, conveyed himself and his men out at a postern[6] gate of the city so secretly and speedily that without any suspicion they got to the seashore, where with many a bitter curse, taking their leave of Bohemia, they went aboard. Weighing their anchors and hoisting sail, they passed as fast as wind and sea would permit towards Sicilia, Egistus being a joyful man that he had safely passed such treacherous perils.

But as they were quietly floating on the sea, so Pandosto and his citizens were in an uproar, for seeing that the Sicilians, without taking their leave, were fled away by night, the Bohemians feared some treason, and the king thought that without question his suspicion was true, seeing his cupbearer

---

[1] flee
[2] intended (by Pandosto)
[3] suspecting
[4] Syracuse, a city on Sicily's eastern shore
[5] go through with the plan
[6] secret, hidden

had bewrayed the sum of his secret pretence.[1] Whereupon he began to imagine that Franion and his wife Bellaria had conspired with Egistus, and that the fervent affection she bare[2] him was the only means of his secret departure; in so much that, incensed with rage, he commands that his wife should be carried to straight[3] prison until they heard further of his pleasure. The guard, unwilling to lay their hands on such a virtuous princess and yet fearing the king's fury, went very sorrowful to fulfil their charge. Coming to the queen's lodging, they found her playing with her young son Garinter, unto whom, with tears doing the message, Bellaria, astonished at such a hard censure and finding her clear conscience a sure advocate to plead in her case, went to the prison most willingly, where with sighs and tears she passed away the time till she might come to her trial.

But Pandosto, whose reason was suppressed with rage and whose unbridled folly was incensed with fury, seeing Franion had bewrayed his secrets and that Egistus might well be railed on but not revenged, determined to wreak all his wrath on poor Bellaria. He therefore caused a general proclamation to be made through all his realm that the queen and Egistus had, by the help of Franion, not only committed most incestuous adultery but also had conspired the king's death; whereupon the traitor Franion was fled away with Egistus and Bellaria was most justly imprisoned. This proclamation being once blazed[4] through the country, although the virtuous disposition of the queen did half discredit the contents. Yet the sudden and speedy passage of Egistus and the secret departure of Franion induced them, the circumstances thoroughly considered, to think that both the proclamation was true and the king greatly injured; yet they pitied her case, as sorrowful that so good a lady should be crossed with[5] such adverse fortune. But the king, whose restless rage would admit no pity, thought that although he might sufficiently requite his wife's falsehood with the bitter plague of pinching penury, yet his mind should never be glutted with revenge till he might have fit time and opportunity to repay the treachery of Egistus with a fatal injury. But a cursed cow hath oft-times short horns,[6] and a willing mind but a weak arm. For Pandosto, although he felt that revenge was a spur to war and that envy always proffereth steel, yet

---

[1] revealed the full extent of his plan

[2] bore (see glossary)

[3] secure

[4] circulated, broadcast

[5] hindered by

[6] An example of the proverbial wisdom invoked by Greene throughout his story: even a powerful animal like a cow can be "cursed" with short horns and therefore rendered powerless. The following sentence completes the meaning.

he saw that Egistus was not only of great puissance[1] and prowess to withstand him but had also many kings of his alliance to aid him if need should serve, for he married the Emperor's daughter of Russia. These and the like considerations something daunted Pandosto his courage,[2] so that he was content rather to put up a manifest injury with peace than hunt after revenge, dishonour and loss, determining since Egistus had escaped scot-free that Bellaria should pay for all at an unreasonable price.

Remaining thus resolute in his determination, Bellaria continuing still in prison and hearing the contents of the proclamation, knowing that her mind was never touched with such affection, nor that Egistus had ever offered her such discourtesy, would gladly have come to her answer that both she might have known her just accusers and cleared herself of that guiltless crime.

But Pandosto was so inflamed with rage and infected with jealousy as he would not vouchsafe[3] to hear her nor admit any just excuse, so that she was fain[4] to make a virtue of her need and with patience to bear those heavy injuries. As thus she lay crossed[5] with calamities, a great cause to increase her grief she found herself quick with child, which as soon as she felt stir in her body she burst forth into bitter tears, exclaiming against Fortune in these terms:

"Alas, Bellaria, how unfortunate art thou, because fortunate! Better thou hadst been born a beggar than a prince, so shouldest thou have bridled Fortune with want,[6] where now she sporteth herself with thy plenty. Ah, happy life, where poor thoughts and mean desires live in secure content, not fearing fortune because too low for Fortune! Thou seest now, Bellaria, that care is a companion to honour, not to poverty; that high cedars are crushed with tempests when low shrubs are not touched with the wind; precious diamonds are cut with the file when despised pebbles lie safe in the sand. Delphos[7] is sought to by princes, not beggars, and Fortune's altars smoke with kings' presents, not with poor men's gifts. Happy are such, Bellaria, that curse Fortune for contempt, not fear, and may wish they were, not sorrow they have been. Thou art a princess, Bellaria, and yet a prisoner, born to the one by descent, assigned to the other by despite, accused without cause, and therefore oughtest to die without care, for patience is a shield

---

[1] power
[2] dampened Pandosto's courage
[3] allow himself
[4] obliged
[5] beset by
[6] restrained Fortune with penury
[7] the site of Ancient Greece's most important oracle of Apollo, dating to at least the 9th century BCE

against Fortune, and a guiltless mind yieldeth to sorrow. Ah, but infamy galleth[1] unto death and liveth after death; report is plumed with Time's feathers and envy oftentime soundeth Fame's trumpet. Thy suspected adultery shall fly in the air and thy known virtues shall lie hid in the earth; one mole staineth the whole face and what is once spotted with infamy can hardly be worn out with time. Die then, Bellaria; Bellaria, die, for if the gods should say thou art guiltless, yet envy would hear the gods but never believe the gods. Ah, hapless wretch, cease these terms: desperate thoughts are fit for them that fear shame, not for such as hope for credit. Pandosto hath darkened thy fame but shall never discredit thy virtues. Suspicion may enter a false action but proof shall never put in his plea: care not then for envy, sith° report[2] hath a blister on her tongue, and let sorrow bite them which offend, not touch thee that art faultless. But alas, poor soul, how canst thou but sorrow? Thou art with child, and by him that, instead of kind pity, pincheth thee in cold prison." And with that, such gasping sighs so stopping her breath that she could not utter any more words, but wringing her hands and gushing forth streams of tears, she passed away the time with bitter complaints.

The jailor, pitying those her heavy passions, thinking that if the king knew she were with child he would somewhat appease his fury and release her from prison, went in all haste and certified[3] Pandosto what the effect of Bellaria's complaint was. Who no sooner heard the jailor say she was with child, but as one possessed with a frenzy he rose up in a rage, swearing that she and the bastard brat she was withal[4] should die if the gods themselves said no, thinking that surely by computation of time that Egistus and not he was the father to the child. This suspicious thought galled afresh this half healed sore, in so much as he could take no rest until he might mitigate his choler with a just revenge, which happened presently after. For Bellaria was brought to bed of a fair and beautiful daughter, which no sooner Pandosto heard but he determined that both Bellaria and the young infant should be burnt with fire.

His nobles, hearing of the king's cruel sentence, sought by persuasions to divert him from his bloody determination, laying before his face the innocency of the child and virtuous disposition of his wife, how she had continually loved and honoured him so tenderly that without due proof he

[1] vexes
[2] since rumour (The allegorical figure Rumour was often represented with a blistered tongue from spreading gossip.)
[3] informed
[4] carrying

could not nor ought not to appeach[1] her of that crime. And if she had faulted, yet it were more honourable to pardon with mercy than to punish with extremity and more kingly to be commended of pity than accused of rigour. And as for the child, if he should punish it for the mother's offence it were to strive against nature and justice, and that unnatural actions do more offend the gods than men; how causeless cruelty nor innocent blood never scapes[2] without revenge. These and such like reasons could not appease his rage, but he rested resolute in this, that Bellaria being an adulteress, the child was a bastard, and he would not suffer that such an infamous brat should call him father. Yet at last, seeing his noblemen were importunate upon[3] him, he was content to spare the child's life, and yet to put it to a worse death. For he found out this device,° that seeing, as he thought, it came by fortune, so he would commit it to the charge of Fortune. And therefore he caused a little cock-boat[4] to be provided, wherein he meant to put the babe and then send it to the mercies of the seas and the destinies. From this his peers in no wise[5] could persuade him, but that he sent presently two of his guard to fetch the child, who being come to the prison, and with weeping tears recounting their master's message, Bellaria no sooner heard the rigorous resolution of her merciless husband but she fell down in a swound[6] so that all thought she had been dead. Yet at last being come to herself, she cried and scratched out in this wise:°

"Alas, sweet unfortunate babe, scarce born before envied by Fortune! Would the day of thy birth had been the term of thy life, then shouldest thou have made an end to care and prevented thy father's rigour. Thy faults cannot yet deserve such hateful revenge; thy days are too short for so sharp a doom but thy untimely death must pay thy mother's debts and her guiltless crime must be thy ghastly curse. And shalt thou, sweet babe, be committed to fortune when thou art already spited by Fortune? Shall the seas be thy harbour and the hard boat thy cradle? Shall thy tender mouth, instead of sweet kisses, be nipped with bitter storms? Shalt thou have the whistling winds for thy lullaby and the salt sea foam instead of sweet milk? Alas, what destinies would assign such hard hap?[7] What father would be so cruel or what gods will not revenge such rigour? Let me kiss thy lips, sweet infant,

---

[1] accuse, charge
[2] escapes
[3] insistent with
[4] a small vessel
[5] in no way (*wise*: see glossary)
[6] swoon
[7] fate, fortune (see glossary)

and wet thy tender cheeks with my tears, and put this chain about thy little neck, that if Fortune save thee, it may help to succour thee. Thus, since thou must go to surge in the ghastful[1] seas, with a sorrowful kiss I bid thee farewell and I pray the gods thou mayest fare well."

Such and so great was her grief that her vital spirits being suppressed with sorrow, she fell again down into a trance, having her senses so sorted[2] with care that after she was revived yet she lost her memory and lay for a great time without moving, as one in a trance. The guard left her in this perplexity and carried the child to the king, who, quite devoid of pity, commanded that without delay it should be put in the boat, having neither sail nor rudder[3] to guide it, and so to be carried into the midst of the sea and there left to the wind and wave as the destinies please to appoint. The very shipmen, seeing the sweet countenance of the young babe, began to accuse the king of rigour and to pity the child's hard fortune. But fear constrained them to that which their nature did abhor, so that they placed it in one of the ends of the boat and with a few green boughs made a homely[4] cabin to shroud it as they could from wind and weather. Having thus trimmed the boat, they tied it to a ship and so haled[5] it into the main sea and then cut in sunder the cord, which they had no sooner done but there arose a mighty tempest which tossed the little boat so vehemently in the waves that the shipmen thought it could not continue long without sinking. Yea, the storm grew so great that with much labour and peril they got to the shore.

But leaving the child to her fortunes, again to Pandosto, who, not yet glutted with sufficient revenge, devised which way he should best increase his wife's calamity. But first assembling his nobles and counsellors, he called her for the more reproach into open court, where it was objected against her that she had committed adultery with Egistus and conspired with Franion to poison Pandosto her husband, but their pretence being partly spied, she counselled them to fly away by night for their better safety. Bellaria, who standing like a prisoner at the bar, feeling in herself a clear conscience to withstand her false accusers, seeing that no less than death could pacify her husband's wrath, waxed bold and desired that she might have law and justice, for mercy she neither craved nor hoped for, and that those perjured wretches which had falsely accused her to the king might be brought before her face to give in evidence.

But Pandosto, whose rage and jealousy was such as no reason nor equity

---

[1] frightful, dreadful
[2] filled, supplied
[3] rudder: emended from "nor other" in the 1588 edition
[4] simple
[5] dragged, tugged (as a tugboat might)

could appease, told her that for her accusers, they were of such credit as their words were sufficient witness and that the sudden and secret flight of Egistus and Franion confirmed that which they had confessed. And as for her, it was her part to deny such a monstrous crime and to be impudent in forswearing the fact, since she had passed all shame in committing the fault. But her stale countenance should stand for no coin, for as the bastard which she bare° was served, so she should with some cruel death be requited.[1]

Bellaria, no whit[2] dismayed with this rough reply, told her husband Pandosto that he spake upon choler and not conscience, for her virtuous life had been ever such as no spot of suspicion could ever stain. And if she had borne a friendly countenance to Egistus, it was in respect he was his friend and not for any lusting affection therefor. If she were condemned without any further proof it was rigour and not law.

The noblemen which sate[3] in judgement said that Bellaria spake reason and entreated the king that the accusers might be openly examined and sworn, and if then the evidence were such as the jury might find her guilty (for seeing she was a prince she ought to be tried by her peers[4]), then let her have such punishment as the extremity of the law will assign to such malefactors. The king presently made answer that in this case he might and would dispense with the law and that the jury being once panelled, they should take his word for sufficient evidence; otherwise, he would make the proudest of them repent it. The noblemen, seeing the king in choler, were all whist.[5] But Bellaria, whose life then hung in the balance, fearing more perpetual infamy than momentary death, told the king if his fury might stand for a law that it were vain to have the jury yield their verdict and therefore she fell down upon her knees and desired the king that for the love he bare° to his young son Garinter, whom she brought into the world, that he would grant her a request, which was this: that it would please his majesty to send six of his noblemen whom he best trusted to the Isle of Delphos, there to enquire of the oracle of Apollo whether she had committed adultery with Egistus or conspired to poison him with Franion. And if the god Apollo, who by his divine essence knew all secrets, gave answer that she was guilty she were content to suffer any torment were it never so terrible. The request was so reasonable that Pandosto could not for shame deny it unless he would be counted of all his subjects more wilful than wise. He therefore agreed that with as much speed as might be there should be certain ambassadors

---

[1] repaid
[2] not at all
[3] sat (see introduction)
[4] by her aristocratic equals—literally, peers of the realm
[5] silent

dispatched to the Isle of Delphos, and in the mean season[1] he commanded that his wife should be kept in close prison.

Bellaria, having obtained this grant, was now more careful[2] for her little babe that floated on the seas than sorrowful for her own mishap; for of that she doubted,[3] of herself she was assured, knowing if Apollo should give oracle according to the thoughts of the heart, yet[4] the sentence should go to her side. Such was the clearness of her mind in this case. But Pandosto, whose suspicious head still remained in one song, chose out six of his nobility whom he knew were scarce indifferent men in the queen's behalf, and providing all things fit for their journey, sent them to Delphos; they, willing to fulfil the king's command and desirous to see the situation and custom of the island, dispatched their affairs with as much speed as might be and embarked themselves to this voyage, which, the wind and weather serving fit for their purpose, was soon ended. For within three weeks they arrived at Delphos, where they were no sooner set on land but with great devotion they went to the temple of Apollo, and there offering sacrifice to the god and gifts to the priest, as the custom was, they humbly craved an answer of their demand. They had not long kneeled at the altar, but Apollo with a loud voice said: "Bohemians, what you find behind the altar take, and depart." They forthwith obeying the oracle, found a scroll of parchment wherein was written these words in letters of gold:

THE ORACLE
SUSPICION IS NO PROOF – JEALOUSY IS AN UNEQUAL JUDGE –
BELLARIA IS CHASTE – EGISTIS BLAMELESS – FRANION A TRUE SUBJECT –
PANDOSTO TREACHEROUS – HIS BABE AN INNOCENT, AND THE KING SHALL
LIVE[5] WITHOUT AN HEIR IF THAT WHICH IS LOST BE NOT FOUND

As soon as they had taken out this scroll the priest of the god commanded them that they should not presume to read it before they came in the presence of Pandosto, unless they would incur the displeasure of Apollo. The Bohemian lords, carefully obeying his command, taking their leave of the priest with great reverence, departed out of the temple and went to their ships, and as soon as wind would permit them, sailed toward Bohemia, whither in short time they safely arrived, and with great triumph issuing out

---

[1] meantime
[2] concerned
[3] worried
[4] so, naturally
[5] See the introduction for discussion of this textual crux: other editions read "die without an heir."

of their ships, went to the king's palace, whom they found in his chamber accompanied with other noblemen.

Pandosto no sooner saw them but with a merry countenance he welcomed them home, asking what news? They told his majesty that they had received an answer of the god written in a scroll, but with this charge, that they should not read the contents before they came in the presence of the king, and with that they delivered him the parchment. But his noblemen entreated him that, sith° therein was contained either the safety of his wife's life and honesty or her death and perpetual infamy, that he would have his nobles and commons assembled in the judgement hall, where the queen, brought in as prisoner, should hear the contents. If she were found guilty by the oracle of the god, then all should have cause to think his rigour proceeded of due desert;[1] if her grace were found faultless, then she should be cleared before all, sith she had been accused openly.

This pleased the king so that he appointed the day and assembled all his lords and commons and caused the queen to be brought in before the judgement seat, commanding that the indictment should be read wherein she was accused of adultery with Egistus and of conspiracy with Franion. Bellaria, hearing the contents, was no whit astonished but made this cheerful answer—"If the divine powers be privy to human actions—as no doubt they are—I hope my patience shall make Fortune blush and my unspotted life shall stain spiteful[2] discredit. For although lying report hath sought to appeach[3] mine honour and suspicion hath intended to soil my credit with infamy, yet where virtue keepeth the fort, report and suspicion may assail but never sack.[4] How I have led my life before Egistus' coming I appeal, Pandosto, to the gods and to thy conscience. What hath passed betwixt him and me the gods only know, and I hope will presently reveal: that I loved Egistus I cannot deny; that I honoured him I shame not to confess. To the one I was forced by his virtues, to the other for his dignities. But as touching lascivious lust, I say Egistus is honest and hope myself to be found without spot. For Franion, I can neither accuse him nor excuse him, for I was not privy to his departure. And that this is true which I have here rehearsed, I refer myself to the divine oracle."

Bellaria had no sooner said but the king commanded that one of his dukes should read the contents of the scroll, which after the commons had heard they gave a great shout, rejoicing and clapping their hands that the queen was clear of that false accusation. But the king, whose conscience

---

[1] deserving (see glossary)
[2] spiteful: emended from *spightfully*
[3] accuse
[4] conquer

was a witness against him of his witless fury and false suspected jealousy, was so ashamed of his rash folly that he entreated his nobles to persuade Bellaria to forgive and forget these injuries, promising not only to shew° himself a loyal and loving husband but also to reconcile himself to Egistus and Franion, revealing then before them all the cause of their secret flight and how treacherously he thought to have practised[1] his death if the good mind of his cupbearer had not prevented his purpose. As thus he was relating the whole matter there was word brought him that his young son Garinter was suddenly dead, which news so soon as Bellaria heard, surcharged before with extreme joy and now suppressed with heavy sorrow, her vital spirits were so stopped that she fell down presently dead and could be never revived.

This sudden sight so appalled the king's senses that he sank from his seat in a swound, so as he was fain to be carried[2] by his nobles to his palace, where he lay by the space of three days without speech. His commons were, as men in despair, diversely distressed. There was nothing but mourning and lamentation to be heard throughout all Bohemia: their young prince dead, their virtuous queen bereaved[3] of her life, and their king and sovereign in great hazard. This tragical discourse of Fortune so daunted them as they went like shadows, not men; yet somewhat to comfort their heavy hearts they heard that Pandosto was come to himself and had recovered his speech, who as in a fury brayed out these bitter speeches: "O miserable Pandosto! what surer witness than conscience? what thoughts more sour than suspicion? What plague more bad than jealousy? unnatural actions offend the gods more than men, and causeless cruelty never scapes without revenge. I have committed such a bloody fact,[4] as repent I may, but recall I cannot. Ah, jealousy! a hell to the mind and a horror to the conscience, suppressing reason and inciting rage, a worse passion than frenzy, a greater plague than madness. Are the gods just? Then let them revenge such brutish cruelty. My innocent babe I have drowned in the seas, my loving wife I have slain with slanderous suspicion, my trusty friend I have sought to betray, and yet the gods are slack[5] to plague such offences. Ah, unjust Apollo! Pandosto is the man that hath committed the fault. Why should Garinter, silly° child, abide the pain? Well, sith° the gods mean to prolong my days to increase my dolour, I will offer my guilty blood a sacrifice to those sackless[6] souls

---

[1] plotted
[2] sank from his seat in swoon and had to be carried
[3] robbed (see glossary)
[4] deed (literally, a "done thing")
[5] slow
[6] innocent

whose lives are lost by my rigorous folly."

And with that he reached at a rapier[1] to have murdered himself, but his peers being present stayed[2] him from such a bloody act, persuading him to think that the commonwealth consisted on his safety and that those sheep could not but perish that wanted a shepherd, wishing that if he would not live for himself yet he should have care of his subjects, and to put such fancies out of his mind, sith in sores past help salves do not heal but hurt, and in things past cure, care is a corrosive. With these and such like persuasions the king was overcome and began somewhat to quiet his mind; so that as soon as he could go abroad he caused his wife to be embalmed and wrapt in lead with her young son Garinter, erecting a rich and famous sepulchre wherein he entombed them both, making such solemn obsequies at her funeral as all Bohemia might perceive he did greatly repent him of his forepassed folly, causing[3] this epitaph to be engraven on her tomb in letters of gold—

The Epitaph
Here lies entombed Bellaria Fair
Falsely accused to be unchaste
Cleared by Apollo's sacred doom
Yet slain by jealousy at last.
What ere thou be that passest by
Curse him that caused this queen to die.

This epitaph being engraven, Pandosto would once a day repair to the tomb and there with watery plaints[4] bewail his misfortune, coveting no other companion but sorrow, nor no other harmony but repentance. But leaving him to his dolorous passions, at last let us come to shew° the tragical discourse of the young infant.

Who being tossed with wind and wave floated two whole days without succour, ready at every puff to be drowned in the sea, till at last the tempest ceased and the little boat was driven with the tide into the coast of Sicilia, where sticking upon the sands, it rested. Fortune, minding to be wanton,[5] willing to shew that as she hath wrinkles on her brows so she hath dimples in her cheeks, thought after so many sour looks to lend a feigned smile, and

---

[1] sword
[2] prevented
[3] commanding
[4] tearful lamentations
[5] having a mind to be capricious

after a puffing storm to bring a pretty calm, she began thus to dally.

It fortuned a poor mercenary shepherd that dwelled in Sicilia, who got his living by other men's flocks, missed one of his sheep, and thinking it had strayed into the covert that was hard by,[1] sought very diligently to find that which he could not see, fearing either that the wolves or eagles had undone him (for he was so poor as a sheep was half his substance), wandered down toward the sea cliffs to see if perchance the sheep was browsing on the sea ivy, whereon they greatly do feed. But not finding her there, as he was ready to return to his flock he heard a child cry but knowing there was no house near he thought he had mistaken the sound and that it was the bleating of his sheep. Wherefore, looking more narrowly,[2] as he cast his eye to the sea he spied a little boat from whence as he attentively listened he might hear the cry to come. Standing a good while in a maze,[3] at last he went to the shore and, wading to the boat, as he looked in he saw the little babe lying all alone, ready to die for hunger and cold, wrapped in a mantle of scarlet richly embroidered with gold and having a chain about the neck.

The shepherd, who before had never seen so fair a babe nor so rich jewels, thought assuredly that it was some little god and began with great devotion to knock on his breast. The babe, who writhed with the head to seek for the pap,[4] began again to cry afresh, whereby the poor man knew that it was a child which by some sinister means was driven thither by distress of weather, marvelling how such a silly° infant, which by the mantle[5] and the chain could not be but born of noble parentage, should be so hardly crossed[6] with deadly mishap. The poor shepherd, perplexed thus with divers thoughts, took pity of the child, and determined with himself to carry it to the king, that there it might be brought up according to the worthiness of birth, for his ability could not afford to foster it though his good mind was willing to further it.

Taking therefore the child in his arms, as he folded the mantle together the better to defend it from cold, there fell down at his foot a very fair and rich purse, wherein he found a great sum of gold; which sight so revived the shepherd's spirits as he was greatly ravished with joy and daunted with fear, joyful to see such a sum in his power and fearful if it should be known that it might breed his further danger. Necessity wished him at the least to retain the gold though he would not keep the child; the simplicity of his conscience

---

[1] into the covered area nearby
[2] closely
[3] in amazement
[4] mother's breast
[5] cloak-like garment
[6] afflicted, troubled by

feared[1] him from such deceitful bribery. Thus was the poor man perplexed with a doubtful dilemma until at last the covetousness of the coin overcame him, for what will not the greedy desire of gold cause a man to do? So that he was resolved in himself to foster the child and with the sum to relieve his want. Resting thus resolute in this point, he left seeking of his sheep and as covertly and secretly as he could, went by a by-way to his house, lest any of his neighbours should perceive his carriage.

As soon as he was got home, entering in at the door the child began to cry, which his wife hearing, and seeing her husband with a young babe in his arms, began to be somewhat jealous, yet marvelling that her husband should be so wanton abroad sith° he was so quiet at home. But as women are naturally given to believe the worst, so his wife, thinking it was some bastard, began to crow against her goodman[2] and taking up a cudgel (for the most master went breechless[3]) swore solemnly that she would make clubs trumps[4] if he brought any bastard brat within her doors. The goodman, seeing his wife in her majesty with her mace in her hand, thought it was time to bow for fear of blows and desired her to be quiet, for there was none such matter; but if she could hold her peace they were made for ever: and with that he told her the whole matter, how he had found the child in a little boat, without any succour, wrapped in that costly mantle, and having that rich chain about the neck.

But at last, when he shewed° her the purse full of gold, she began to simper something sweetly and taking her husband about the neck, kissed him after her homely fashion, saying that she hoped God had seen their want and now meant to relieve their poverty, and seeing they could get no children had sent them this little babe to be their heir.

"Take heed, in any case," quoth the shepherd, "that you be secret and blab it not out when you meet with your gossips,[5] for if you do we are like not only to lose the gold and jewels but our other goods and lives." "Tush," quoth his wife, "profit is a good hatch before the door.[6] Fear not, I have other things to talk of than this, but I pray you let us lay up the money surely and the jewels, lest by any mishap it be spied."

After that they had set all things in order the shepherd went to his sheep with a merry note and the good wife learned to sing lullaby at home with her young babe, wrapping it in a homely blanket instead of a rich mantle,

---

[1] deterred
[2] husband
[3] Women are masters of the home, despite not "wearing the breeches."
[4] raise a great domestic fuss
[5] friends
[6] a proverb meaning it is good to measure one's words or keep silent

nourishing it so cleanly and carefully as it began to be a jolly girl, in so much that they began both of them to be very fond of it, seeing as it waxed in age so it increased in beauty. The shepherd every night at his coming home would sing and dance it on his knee and prattle, that in short time it began to speak and call him Dad and her Mam. At last when it grew to ripe years that it was about seven years old, the shepherd left keeping of other men's sheep, and with the money he found in the purse he bought him the lease of a pretty farm and got a small flock of sheep which, when Fawnia (for so they named the child) came to the age of ten years he set her to keep, and she with such diligence performed her charge as the sheep prospered marvellously under her hand. Fawnia thought Porrus had been her father and Mopsa her mother (for so was the shepherd and his wife called), honoured and obeyed them with such reverence that all the neighbours praised the dutiful obedience of the child.

Porrus grew in short time to be a man of some wealth and credit, for fortune so favoured him in having no charge but Fawnia that he began to purchase land, intending after his death to give it to his daughter, so that divers rich farmers' sons came as wooers to his house. For Fawnia was something cleanly attired,[1] being of such singular beauty and excellent wit that whoso saw her would have thought she had been some heavenly nymph and not a mortal creature, in so much that when she came to the age of sixteen years she so increased with exquisite perfection both of body and mind as her natural disposition did bewray° that she was born of some high parentage; but the people thinking she was daughter to the shepherd Porrus rested only amazed at her beauty and wit. Yea, she won such favour and commendations in every man's eye as her beauty was not only praised in the country, but also spoken of in the court; yet such was her submiss[2] modesty that although her praise daily increased her mind was no whit puffed up with pride, but humbled herself as became a country maid and the daughter of a poor shepherd. Every day she went forth with her sheep to the field, keeping them with such care and diligence as all men thought she was very painful,[3] defending her face from the heat of the sun with no other veil but with a garland made of boughs and flowers, which attire became her so gallantly as she seemed to be the goddess Flora[4] herself for beauty.

Fortune, who all this while had shewed° a friendly face, began now to turn her back and to shew a louring° countenance, intending as she had given Fawnia a slender check, so she would give her a harder mate; to bring

---

[1] rather well dressed
[2] humble
[3] diligent in her care
[4] the ancient Roman goddess of springtime, flowers, gardens, and youthfulness

which to pass she laid her train on this wise.[1] Egistus had but one only son, called Dorastus, about the age of twenty years, a prince so decked and adorned with the gifts of nature, so fraught with beauty and virtuous qualities, as not only his father joyed to have so good a son, but all his commons rejoiced that God had lent them such a noble prince to succeed in the kingdom. Egistus, placing all his joy in the perfection of his son, seeing that he was now marriageable, sent ambassadors to the king of Denmark to entreat a marriage between him and his daughter, who willingly consenting made answer that the next spring, if it please Egistus with his son to come into Denmark, he doubted not but they should agree upon reasonable conditions.

Egistus, resting satisfied with this friendly answer, thought convenient in the meantime to break with[2] his son. Finding therefore on a day fit opportunity, he spake to him in these fatherly terms: "Dorastus, thy youth warneth me to prevent the worst and mine age to provide the best. Opportunities neglected are signs of folly; actions measured by time are seldom bitten with repentance. Thou art young, and I old; age hath taught me that which thy youth cannot yet conceive. I therefore will counsel thee as a father, hoping thou wilt obey as a child. Thou seest my white hairs are blossoms for the grave, and thy fresh colour fruit for time and fortune, so that it behoveth me to think[3] how to die and for thee to care how to live. My crown I must leave by death and thou enjoy my kingdom by succession, wherein I hope thy virtue and prowess shall be such, as though my subjects want[4] my person, yet they shall see in thee my perfection. That nothing either may fail to satisfy thy mind or increase thy dignities, the only care I have is to see thee well married before I die and thou become old."

Dorastus, who from his infancy delighted rather to die with Mars in the field than to dally with Venus in the chamber, fearing to displease his father and yet not willing to be wed, made him this reverent answer: "Sir, there is no greater bond than duty, nor no straiter[5] law than nature: disobedience in youth is often galled with despite[6] in age. The command of the father ought to be a constrain to the child: so parents' wills are laws, so they pass not all laws. May it please your grace, therefore, to appoint whom I shall love,

---

[1] The image derives from the game of chess: Fortune will follow a mild setback by delivering a harder blow, which she did in her own manner.
[2] open the topic with
[3] I must think
[4] lack
[5] stricter
[6] poisoned with regret

rather than by denial I should be appeached[1] of disobedience. I rest content
to love, though it be the only thing I hate."

Egistus, hearing his son to fly far from the mark, began to be somewhat
choleric, and, therefore, made him this hasty answer: "What, Dorastus, canst
thou not love? Cometh this cynical passion of prone[2] desires or peevish
frowardness? What, dost thou think thyself too good for all or none good
enough for thee? I tell thee, Dorastus, there is nothing sweeter than youth
nor swifter decreasing while it is increasing. Time passed with folly may be
repented, but not recalled.[3] If thou marry in age, thy wife's fresh colours
will breed in thee dead thoughts and suspicion and thy white hairs her
loathsomeness and sorrow; for Venus' affections are not fed with kingdoms,
or treasures, but with youthful conceits[4] and sweet amours. Vulcan was
allotted to shake the tree, but Mars[5] allowed to reap the fruit. Yield,
Dorastus, to thy father's persuasions, which may prevent thy perils. I have
chosen thee a wife, fair by nature, royal by birth, by virtues famous, learned
by education and rich by possessions, so that it is hard to judge whether her
bounty or fortune, her beauty or virtue, be of greater force. I mean, Dorastus,
Euphania, daughter and heir to the king of Denmark."

Egistus, pausing here awhile, looking when his son should make him
answer and seeing that he stood still as one in a trance, he shook him up thus
sharply: "Well, Dorastus, take heed; the tree Alpya[6] wasteth not with fire,
but withereth with the dew: that which love nourisheth not perisheth with
hate. If thou like Euphania, thou breedest my content and in loving her thou
shalt have my love; otherwise"—and with that he flung from his son in a
rage, leaving him a sorrowful man in that he had by denial displeased his
father and half angry with himself that he could not yield to that passion
whereto both reason and his father persuaded him. But see how Fortune is
plumed with Time's feathers and how she can minister strange causes to
breed strange effects.

It happened not long after this that there was a meeting of all the farmers'
daughters in Sicilia, whither Fawnia was also bidden as the mistress of the
feast, who, having attired herself in her best garments, went among the rest
of her companions to the merry meeting, there spending the day in such
homely pastimes as shepherds use.[7] As the evening grew on and their sports

---

[1] accused
[2] naturally inclined
[3] another instance of Greene's proverbial language
[4] emotions, conceptions
[5] The god Vulcan was traditionally represented as an old man, Mars as a youth.
[6] It appears that Greene invented the name of this tree.
[7] usually engage in

ceased, each taking their leave at other, Fawnia, desiring one of her companions to bear her company, went home by the flock to see if they were well folded and as they returned it fortuned that Dorastus, who all that day had been hawking and killed store of game, encountered by the way these two maids. And casting his eye suddenly on Fawnia, he was half afraid, fearing that with Actaeon he had seen Diana,[1] for he thought such exquisite perfection could not be found in any mortal creature. As thus he stood in a maze,[2] one of his pages told him that the maid with the garland on her head was Fawnia, the fair shepherd whose beauty was so much talked of in the court. Dorastus, desirous to see if nature had adorned her mind with any inward qualities, as she had decked her body with outward shape, began to question with her whose daughter she was, of what age, and how she had been trained up? who answered him with such modest reverence and sharpness of wit[3] that Dorastus thought her outward beauty was but a counterfeit to darken her inward qualities, wondering how so courtly behaviour could be found in so simple a cottage and cursing fortune that had shadowed wit and beauty with such hard fortune.

As thus he held her a long while with chat, Beauty seeing him at discovert[4] thought not to lose the vantage, but struck him so deeply with an envenomed shaft as he wholly lost his liberty and became a slave to love, which[5] before contemned love, glad now to gaze on a poor shepherd who before refused the offer of a rich princess. For the perfection of Fawnia had so fired his fancy as he felt his mind greatly changed and his affections altered, cursing love that had wrought such a change and blaming the baseness of his mind that would make such a choice, but thinking that these were but passionate toys that might be thrust out at pleasure to avoid the siren that enchanted him, he put spurs to his horse and bade this fair shepherd farewell.

Fawnia, who all this while had marked the princely gesture of Dorastus, seeing his face so well featured, and each limb so perfectly framed, began greatly to praise his perfection, commending him so long till she found herself faulty and perceived that if she waded but a little further she might

---

[1] The hunter Actaeon accidently saw the goddess Diana naked and bathing in a stream. She punished him by turning him into a stag, which was then killed by his own dogs (Ovid, *Metamorphosis*, Book 3). The tale was often used allegorically to suggest the dangers of prying into matters beyond one's station or indulging irrational passions.

[2] in amazement

[3] intelligence or good sense (rather than wittiness)

[4] uncovered, exposed

[5] Dorastus, who had previously condemned love

slip over her shoes.[1] She therefore, seeking to quench that fire which never was put out, went home and feigning herself not well at ease got her to bed, where casting a thousand thoughts in her head, she could take no rest. For if she waked, she began to call to mind his beauty and, thinking to beguile such thoughts with sleep, she then dreamed of his perfection. Pestered thus with these unacquainted passions, she passed the night as she could in short slumbers.

Dorastus, who all this while rode with a flea in his ear,[2] could not by any means forget the sweet favour of Fawnia, but rested so bewitched with her wit and beauty as he could take no rest. He felt fancy to give the assault and his wounded mind ready to yield as vanquished, yet he began with divers considerations to suppress this frantic affection, calling to mind that Fawnia was a shepherd, one not worthy to be looked at of a prince, much less to be loved of such a potentate, thinking what a discredit it were to himself and what a grief it would be to his father, blaming fortune and accusing his own folly that should be so fond[3] as but once to cast a glance at such a country slut.[4] As thus he was raging against himself, Love, fearing if she dallied long to lose her champion, stepped more nigh and gave him such a fresh wound as it pierced him at the heart that he was fain to yield, maugre[5] his face, and to forsake the company and get him to his chamber, where being solemnly set, he burst into these passionate terms: "Ah, Dorastus, art thou alone? No, not alone while thou art tired with[6] these unacquainted passions. Yield to fancy thou canst not by thy father's counsel, but in a frenzy thou art by just destinies. Thy father were content if thou couldst love, and thou therefore discontent because thou dost love. O, divine love! feared of men because honoured of the gods, not to be suppressed by wisdom, because not to be comprehended by reason; without law and therefore above all law. How now, Dorastus! why dost thou blaze that with praises which thou hast cause to blaspheme with curses?[7] Yet why should they curse love that are in love? Blush, Dorastus, at thy fortune, thy choice, thy love: thy thoughts cannot be uttered without shame nor thy affections without discredit. Ah, Fawnia, sweet Fawnia, thy beauty, Fawnia! Shamest not thou, Dorastus, to

---

[1] a proverb meaning becoming fully immersed: in this case, falling head over heels in love
[2] with a feeling nagging and exciting him (in this case love)
[3] foolish (see glossary)
[4] a girl of no social standing (but not a comment on her sexual mores)
[5] forced to yield, in spite of
[6] beset by (literally, dressed in). The author might have intended the word *tried* (tested), as it appears in the 1607 edition.
[7] to lavish with praises one (Fawnia) you have reason to scorn with curses

name one unfit for thy birth, thy dignities, thy kingdoms? Die, Dorastus; Dorastus, die. Better hadst thou perish with high desires than live in base thoughts. Yea, but beauty must be obeyed because it is beauty, yet framed of the gods to feed the eye, not to fetter the heart.

Ah, but he that striveth against love shooteth with them of Scyrum against the wind, and with the cockatrice pecketh against the steel.[1] I will therefore obey because I must obey. Fawnia, yea Fawnia, shall be my fortune in spite of Fortune. The gods above disdain not to love women beneath. Phoebus liked Sibylla, Jupiter Io,[2] and why not I then Fawnia, one something[3] inferior to these in birth but far superior to them in beauty, born to be a shepherd, but worthy to be a goddess. Ah, Dorastus, wilt thou so forget thyself as to suffer affection to suppress wisdom, and love to violate thine honour? How sour will thy choice be to thy father, sorrowful to thy subjects, to thy friends a grief, most gladsome[4] to thy foes! Subdue then thy affections and cease to love her whom thou couldst not love, unless blinded with too much love. Tush, I talk to the wind, and in seeking to prevent the causes I further the effects. I will yet praise Fawnia, honour, yea, and love Fawnia, and at this day follow content, not counsel. Do, Dorastus, thou canst but repent."

And with that his page came into the chamber, whereupon he ceased from his complaints, hoping that time would wear out that which fortune had wrought. As thus he was pained, so poor Fawnia was diversely perplexed, for the next morning getting up very early she went to her sheep, thinking with hard labours to pass away her new conceived amours, beginning very busily to drive them to the field and then to shift the folds. At last, wearied with toil, she sat her down, where (poor soul) she was more tried with fond° affections, for love began to assault her in so much that as she sate upon the side of a hill she began to accuse her own folly in these terms:

"Unfortunate Fawnia and therefore unfortunate because Fawnia! Thy shepherd's hook sheweth° thy poor state, thy proud desires an aspiring mind: the one declareth thy want, the other thy pride. No bastard hawk must

---

[1] While Greene's reference to Scyrum is obscure, the general sense here is clear: fighting against the wind is futile. The cockatrice, or basilisk, was a legendary bird that killed those who looked upon it (see Pliny, *Natural History*, Book 8).

[2] Both pairs are famous classical instances of gods stooping to abduct mortal women for their pleasures (Ovid, *Metamorphoses*, Books 1 and 14).

[3] somewhat

[4] pleasing

soar so high as the hobby, no fowl gaze against the sun but the eagle.[1] Actions wrought against nature reap despite[2] and thoughts above fortune disdain. Fawnia, thou art a shepherd, daughter to poor Porrus: if thou rest content with this thou art like to stand; if thou climb thou art sure to fall. The herb anita, growing higher than six inches, becometh a weed. Nylus, flowing more than twelve cubits, procureth a dearth.[3] Daring affections that pass measure are cut short by time or fortune: suppress then, Fawnia, those thoughts which thou mayest shame to express. But ah, Fawnia, love is a lord who will command by power and constrain by force. Dorastus, ah, Dorastus is the man I love! The worse is thy hap,[4] and the less cause hast thou to hope. Will eagles catch at flies? Will cedars stoop to brambles, or mighty princes look at such homely trulls?[5] No, no. Think this: Dorastus' disdain is greater than thy desire; he is a prince respecting his honour, thou a beggar's brat forgetting thy calling. Cease then not only to say, but to think to love Dorastus, and dissemble thy love, Fawnia, for better it were to die with grief than to live with shame. Yet, in despite of love, I will sigh to see if I can sigh out love."

Fawnia, somewhat appeasing her griefs with these pithy persuasions, began after her wonted[6] manner to walk about her sheep, and to keep them from straying into the corn,[7] suppressing her affection with the due consideration of her base estate, and with the impossibilities of her love, thinking it were frenzy, not fancy, to covet that which the very destinies did deny her to obtain.

But Dorastus was more impatient in his passions, for love so fiercely assailed him that neither company nor music could mitigate his martyrdom, but did rather far the more increase his malady. Shame would not let him crave counsel in this case nor fear of his father's displeasure reveal it to any secret friend, but he was fain to make a secretary of himself and to

---

[1] The hobby was a prized species of falcon, used for sport. The eagle, alone among birds, was thought to have the power to look directly into the sun (see Pliny, *Natural History*, Book 10 and Lucan, *Pharsalia*, Book 6).

[2] misery

[3] Just as the herb anita (anise) becomes a weed when it grows too tall, the River Nile creates scarcity when it reaches more than 12 cubits. These conventional images are used to express Fawnia's ambivalence about her desire to be with Prince Dorastus.

[4] fortune

[5] simple, low-born girls (as with slut, above, not a comment on her sexual mores)

[6] usual

[7] grain of any sort

participate his thoughts with his own troubled mind.[1] Lingering thus awhile in doubtful suspense, at last stealing secretly from the court without either men or page, he went to see if he could espy Fawnia walking abroad in the field. But as one having a great deal more skill to retrieve the partridge with his spaniels than to hunt after such a strange prey, he sought but was little the better. Which cross luck[2] drave him into a great choler that he began both to accuse love and fortune. But, as he was ready to retire, he saw Fawnia sitting all alone under the side of a hill, making a garland of such homely[3] flowers as the fields did afford. This sight so revived his spirits that he drew nigh, with more judgement to take a view of her singular perfection, which he found to be such as, in that country attire she stained[4] all the courtly dames of Sicilia. While thus he stood gazing with piercing looks on her surpassing beauty, Fawnia cast her eye aside and spied Dorastus, which sudden sight made the poor girl to blush and to dye her crystal cheeks with a vermilion red, which gave her such a grace as she seemed more beautiful. And with that she rose up, saluting the prince with such modest curtesies[5] as he wondered how a country maid could afford such courtly behaviour. Dorastus, repaying her curtesy with a smiling countenance, began to parley[6] with her on this manner:

"Fair maid," quoth he, "either your want is great or a shepherd's life very sweet, that your delight is in such country labours. I cannot conceive what pleasure you should take unless you mean to imitate the nymphs, being yourself so like a nymph. To put me out of this doubt, shew° me what is to be commended in a shepherd's life and what pleasures you have to countervail[7] these drudging labours."

Fawnia, with blushing face, made him this ready answer: "Sir, what richer state than content, or what sweeter life than quiet? We shepherds are not born to honour, nor beholding unto beauty the less care we have to fear fame or fortune. We count our attire brave[8] enough if warm enough, and our food dainty if to suffice nature. Our greatest enemy is the wolf, our only care in safe keeping our flock. Instead of courtly ditties we spend the days

---

[1] forced to be his own secretary so as to keep his own secrets and share them only with himself
[2] ill luck
[3] humble
[4] outshone
[5] The original spelling could mean either courtesies or curtsies.
[6] speak
[7] compensate for
[8] good

with country songs: our amorous conceits[1] are homely thoughts, delighting as much to talk of Pan and his country pranks as ladies to tell of Venus and her wanton toys.[2] Our toil is in shifting the folds looking to the lambs' easy labours, oft singing and telling tales, homely pleasures. Our greatest wealth not to covet, our honour not to climb, our quiet not to care. Envy looketh not so low as shepherds: shepherds gaze not so high as ambition. We are rich in that we are poor with content and proud only in this, that we have no cause to be proud."

This witty answer of Fawnia so inflamed Dorastus' fancy, as he commended himself for making so good a choice, thinking if her birth were answerable to her wit and beauty that she were a fit mate for the most famous prince in the world. He, therefore, began to sift her more narrowly[3] on this manner: "Fawnia, I see thou art content with country labours because thou knowest not courtly pleasures. I commend thy wit and pity thy want, but wilt thou leave thy father's cottage and serve a courtly mistress?"

"Sir," quoth she, "beggars ought not to strive against fortune, nor to gaze after honour, lest either their fall be greater or they become blind. I am born to toil for the court, not in the court, my nature unfit for their nurture: better live, then, in mean degree than in high disdain."

"Well said, Fawnia," quoth Dorastus: "I guess at thy thoughts; thou art in love with some country shepherd."

"No, sir," quoth she: "shepherds cannot love that are so simple, and maids may not love that are so young."

"Nay, therefore," quoth Dorastus, "maids must love because they are young; for Cupid is a child, and Venus, though old, is painted with fresh colours."

"I grant," quoth she, "age may be painted with new shadows, and youth may have imperfect affections, but what art concealeth in one ignorance revealeth in the other."

Dorastus, seeing Fawnia held him so hard, thought it was vain so long to beat about the bush. Therefore he thought to have given her a fresh charge, but he was so prevented by certain of his men who, missing their master, came puffing to seek him, seeing that he was gone forth all alone. Yet before they drew so nigh that they might hear their talk, he used these speeches:

"Why, Fawnia, perhaps I love thee, and then thou must needs yield, for

---

[1] emotions

[2] Pan was the classical god of shepherds, associated with the rustic life, music and poetry, as well as sexuality; Venus was the goddess of love, famed for her irrational tricks and moods (wanton toys) in love.

[3] question her more closely

thou knowest I can command and constrain." "Truth, sir," quoth she, "but not to love, for constrained love is force, not love. And know this, sir, mine honesty is such as I had rather die than be a concubine, even to a king, and my birth is so base as I am unfit to be a wife to a poor farmer." "Why then," quoth he, "thou canst not love Dorastus." "Yes," said Fawnia, "when Dorastus becomes a shepherd." And with that the presence of his men broke off their parle,[1] so that he went with them to the palace and left Fawnia sitting still on the hill side, who seeing that the night drew on, shifted her folds and busied herself about other work to drive away such fond° fancies as began to trouble her brain. But all this could not prevail, for the beauty of Dorastus had made such a deep impression in her heart as it could not be worn out without cracking, so that she was forced to blame her own folly in this wise:°

"Ah, Fawnia, why dost thou gaze against the sun, or catch at the wind? Stars are to be looked at with the eye, not reached at with the hand; thoughts are to be measured by fortunes, not by desires; falls come not by sitting low, but by climbing too high. What, then, shall all fear to fall because some hap to fall? No, luck cometh by lot, and Fortune windeth those threads which the destinies spin. Thou art favoured, Fawnia, of a prince, and yet thou art so fond to reject desired favours: thou hast denial at thy tongue's end, and desire at thy heart's bottom, a woman's fault to spurn at that with her foot which she greedily catcheth at with her hand. Thou lovest Dorastus, Fawnia, and yet seemest to lour.° Take heed: if he retire thou wilt repent, for unless he love thou canst but die. Die, then, Fawnia, for Dorastus doth but jest: the lion never preyeth on the mouse, nor falcons stoop not to dead stales.[2] Sit down then in sorrow, cease to love, and content thyself that Dorastus will vouchsafe to flatter Fawnia, though not to fancy Fawnia.[3] Heigh ho! Ah fool, it were seemlier for thee to whistle as a shepherd than to sigh as a lover." And with that she ceased from these perplexed passions, folding her sheep and hying[4] home to her poor cottage.

But such was the incessant sorrow of Dorastus to think on the wit and beauty of Fawnia and to see how fond° he was, being a prince, and how froward she was, being a beggar, that he began to lose his wonted° appetite, to look pale and wan; instead of mirth, to feed on melancholy, for courtly dances to use cold dumps[5] in so much that not only his own men but his father and all the court began to marvel at his sudden change, thinking that

---

[1] conversation
[2] decoy birds used to trap birds
[3] Dorastus will stoop to flatter, but not to love Fawnia.
[4] hurrying
[5] to change courtly dances for melancholy

some lingering sickness had brought him into this state. Wherefore he
caused physicians to come, but Dorastus neither would let them minister nor
so much as suffer them to see his urine,[1] but remained still so oppressed
with these passions as he feared in himself a farther inconvenience. His
honour wished him to cease from such folly but love forced him to follow
fancy. Yea, and in despite of honour, love won the conquest, so that his hot
desires caused him to find new devices.° For he presently made himself a
shepherd's coat, that he might go unknown and with the less suspicion to
prattle with Fawnia, and conveyed it secretly into a thick grove hard joining
to[2] the palace, whither, finding fit time and opportunity, he went all alone.
And putting off his princely apparel, got on those shepherd's robes and
taking a great hook in his hand, which he had also gotten, he went very
anciently[3] to find out the mistress of his affection. But as he went by the
way, seeing himself clad in such unseemly rags, he began to smile at his
own folly and to reprove his fondness in these terms.

"Well," said Dorastus, "thou keepest a right decorum—base desires and
homely attires. Thy thoughts are fit for none but a shepherd and thy apparel
such as only becomes a shepherd. A strange change from a prince to a
peasant! What, is it thy wretched fortune or thy wilful folly? Is it thy cursed
destinies or thy crooked desires that appointeth thee this penance? Ah,
Dorastus, thou canst but love and unless thou love, thou art like to perish
for love. Yet, fond° fool, choose flowers, not weeds; diamonds, not pebbles;
ladies which may honour thee, not shepherds which may disgrace thee.
Venus is painted in silks, not in rags, and Cupid treadeth on disdain when
he reacheth at dignity. And yet, Dorastus, shame not at thy shepherd's
weed.[4] The heavenly gods have sometime[5] earthly thoughts. Neptune
became a ram, Jupiter a bull, Apollo a shepherd: they gods, and yet in love,
and thou a man appointed to love."

Devising thus with himself, he drew nigh to the place where Fawnia was
keeping her sheep, who casting her eye aside and seeing such a mannerly
shepherd perfectly limbed and coming with so good a pace, she began half
to forget Dorastus and to favour this pretty shepherd, whom she thought she
might both love and obtain. But as she was in these thoughts she perceived
then it was the young Prince Dorastus, wherefore she rose up and reverently
saluted him. Dorastus, taking her by the hand, repaid her courtesy with a
sweet kiss and praying her to sit down by him, he began thus to lay the

---

[1] Urine was used to make a medical diagnoses.
[2] nearby
[3] in an old-fashioned way
[4] garment
[5] sometimes

battery:[1] "If thou marvel, Fawnia, at my strange attire, thou wouldest more muse at my unaccustomed thoughts: the one disgraceth but my outward shape, the other disturbeth my inward senses. I love, Fawnia, and therefore what love liketh I cannot mislike. Fawnia, thou hast promised to love, and I hope thou wilt perform no less. I have fulfilled thy request and now thou canst but grant my desire. Thou wert content to love Dorastus when he ceased to be a prince and to become a shepherd, and see I have made the change and therefore not to miss of my choice."

"Truth," quoth Fawnia, "but all that wear cowls are not monks: painted eagles are pictures, not eagles. Zeuxis' grapes[2] were like grapes, yet shadows. Rich clothing make not princes, nor homely attire beggars: shepherds are not called shepherds because they wear hooks and bags, but that they are born poor and live to keep sheep; so this attire hath not made Dorastus a shepherd, but to seem like a shepherd."

"Well, Fawnia," answered Dorastus, "were I a shepherd, I could not but like thee, and being a prince, I am forced to love thee. Take heed, Fawnia, be not proud of beauty's painting, for it is a flower that fadeth in the blossom. Those which disdain in youth are despised in age. Beauty's shadows are tricked up with Time's colours, which being set to dry in the sun, are stained with the sun, scarce pleasing the sight ere[3] they begin not to be worth the sight, not much unlike the herb ephemeron, which flourisheth in the morning and is withered before the sun setting.[4] If my desire were against law, thou mightest justly deny me by reason; but I love thee, Fawnia, not to misuse thee as a concubine, but to use thee as my wife I can promise no more and mean to perform no less."

Fawnia, hearing this solemn protestation of Dorastus, could no longer withstand the assault, but yielded up the fort in these friendly terms: "Ah, Dorastus, I shame to express that thou forcest me with thy sugared speech to confess: my base birth causeth the one and thy high dignities the other. Beggars' thoughts ought not to reach so far as kings, and yet my desires reach as high as princes. I dare not say, Dorastus, I love thee, because I am a shepherd; but the gods know I have honoured Dorastus (pardon if I say amiss), yea, and loved Dorastus with such dutiful affection as Fawnia can perform or Dorastus desire. I yield, not overcome with prayers but with

---

[1] a metaphor comparing love to a military campaign (a battery), continued below

[2] Zeuxis of Heraclea (5th century BCE) painted a scene of grapes so realistic that birds pecked at it. In this section Fawnia offers several conventional images to describe the differences between appearances and realities.

[3] before (see glossary)

[4] Classical and medieval authors described plants and insects that were born and died the same day.

love, resting Dorastus' handmaid, ready to obey his will if no prejudice at
all to his honour nor to my credit."

Dorastus, hearing this friendly conclusion of Fawnia, embraced her in
his arms, swearing that neither distance, time, nor adverse fortune, should
diminish his affection; but that, in despite of the destinies, he would remain
loyal unto death. Having thus plighted their troth[1] each to other, seeing they
could not have the full fruition of their love in Sicilia, for that Egistus'
consent would never be granted to so mean[2] a match, Dorastus determined,
as soon as time and opportunity would give them leave, to provide a great
mass of money and many rich and costly jewels for the easier carriage, and
then to transport themselves and their treasure into Italy,[3] where they should
lead a contented life until such time as either he could be reconciled to his
father or else by succession come to the kingdom. This device° was greatly
praised of Fawnia, for she feared if the king his father should but hear of the
contract that his fury would be such as no less than death would stand for
payment. She therefore told him that delay bred danger, that many mishaps
did fall out between the cup and the lip, and that to avoid danger it were best
with as much speed as might be to pass out of Sicilia, lest fortune might
prevent their pretence with some new despite.[4] Dorastus, whom love
pricked forward with desire, promised to dispatch his affairs with as great
haste as either time or opportunity would give him leave, and so resting
upon this point, after many embracings and sweet kisses they departed.

Dorastus, having taken his leave of his best beloved Fawnia, went to the
grove where he had his rich apparel, and there, uncasing[5] himself as secretly
as might be, hiding up his shepherd's attire till occasion should serve again
to use it, he went to the palace, shewing° by his merry countenance that
either the state of his body was amended or the case of his mind greatly
redressed.[6] Fawnia, poor soul, was no less joyful, that being a shepherd,
fortune had favoured her so as to reward her with the love of a prince,
hoping in time to be advanced from the daughter of a poor farmer to be the
wife of a rich king. So that she thought every hour a year till by their
departure they might prevent danger, not ceasing still to go every day to her
sheep, not so much for the care of her flock as for the desire she had to see
her love and lord Dorastus, who oftentimes when opportunity would serve
repaired thither to feed his fancy with the sweet content of Fawnia's

---

[1] formally pledged their love
[2] low
[3] At this time Italy and Sicily were separate realms.
[4] Fortune might frustrate their plan with some new setback.
[5] undressing
[6] improved

presence. And although he never went to visit her but in his shepherd's rags, yet his oft repair[1] made him not only suspected, but known to divers[2] of their neighbours who for the good will they bare° to old Porrus told him secretly of the matter, wishing him to keep his daughter at home lest she went so oft to the field that she brought him home a young son, for they feared that Fawnia, being so beautiful, the young prince would allure her to folly. Porrus was stricken into a dump at these news, so that thanking his neighbours for their good will, he hied him home to his wife and calling her aside, wringing his hands and shedding forth tears, he brake[3] the matter to her in these terms: "I am afraid, wife, that my daughter Fawnia hath made herself so fine that she will buy repentance too dear. I hear news, which if they be true, some will wish they had not proved true. It is told me by my neighbours that Dorastus, the king's son, begins to look at our daughter Fawnia. Which, if it be so, I will not give her a halfpenny for her honesty[4] at the year's end. I tell thee, wife, nowadays beauty is a great stale[5] to trap young men and fair words and sweet promises are two great enemies to a maiden's honesty; and thou knowest where poor men entreat and cannot obtain, there princes may command and will obtain. Though kings' sons dance in nets, they may not be seen; but poor men's faults are spied at a little hole.[6] Well, it is a hard case where kings' lusts are laws, and that they should bind poor men to that which they themselves wilfully break."

"Peace, husband," quoth his wife, "take heed what you say: speak no more than you should lest you hear what you would not: great streams are to be stopped by sleight,[7] not by force, and princes to be persuaded by submission, not by rigour. Do what you can but no more than you may, lest in saving Fawnia's maidenhead you lose your own head. Take heed, I say: it is ill jesting with edged tools and bad sporting with kings. The wolf had his skin pulled over his ears for but looking into the lion's den."

"Tush, wife," quoth he, "thou speakest like a fool: if the king should know that Dorastus had begotten our daughter with child, as I fear it will fall out little better, the king's fury would be such as, no doubt, we should

---

[1] frequent visits

[2] several

[3] revealed (literally, broke)

[4] virginity

[5] lure

[6] Greene plays upon a proverb "you dance in a net and think nobody sees you." The sense is that princes get away with misbehaviour that commoners cannot because their subjects cannot criticise their behaviour. The following sentence completes the meaning.

[7] craft, cunning

both lose our goods and lives. Necessity, therefore, hath no law. And I will prevent this mischief with a new device° that is come in my head, which shall neither offend the king nor displease Dorastus. I mean to take the chain and the jewels that I found with Fawnia and carry them to the king, letting him then to understand how she is none of my daughter, but that I found her beaten up with the water, alone in a little boat, wrapped in a rich mantle, wherein was enclosed this treasure. By this means I hope the king will take Fawnia into his service, and we, whatsoever chanceth,[1] shall be blameless." This device pleased the good wife very well, so that they determined, as soon as they might know the king at leisure, to make him privy to[2] this case.

In the meantime, Dorastus was not slack in his affairs, but applied his matters with such diligence that he provided all things fit for their journey. Treasure and jewels he had gotten great store, thinking there was no better friend than money in a strange country; rich attire he had provided for Fawnia, and because he could not bring the matter to pass without the help and advice of someone, he made an old servant of his, called Capnio, who had served him from his childhood, privy to his affairs. Who, seeing no persuasions could prevail to divert him from his settled determination, gave his consent, and dealt so secretly in the cause that within short space he had gotten a ship ready for their passage.

The mariners, seeing a fit gale of wind for their purpose, wished Capnio to make no delays, lest if they pretermitted[3] this good weather they might stay long ere they had such a fair wind. Capnio, fearing that his negligence should hinder the journey, in the night time conveyed the trunks full of treasure into the ship, and by secret means let Fawnia understand that the next morning they meant to depart. She, upon this news, slept very little that night but got up very early and went to her sheep, looking every minute when she should see Dorastus, who tarried not long for fear delay might breed danger, but came as fast as he could gallop; and without any great circumstance took Fawnia up behind him and rode to the haven where the ship lay, which was not three quarters of a mile distant from that place. He no sooner came there, but the mariners were ready with their cock-boat[4] to set them aboard, where, being couched together in a cabin, they passed away the time in recounting their old loves till their man Capnio should come.

Porrus, who had heard that this morning the king would go abroad to take the air, called in haste to his wife to bring him his holiday hose and his best jacket, that he might go, like an honest, substantial man, to tell his tale.

---

[1] whatever happens
[2] informed of
[3] missed
[4] small vessel

His wife, a good, cleanly wench, brought him all things fit, and sponged[1] him up very handsomely, giving him the chains and jewels in a little box, which Porrus, for the more safety, put in his bosom. Having thus all his trinkets in a readiness, taking his staff in his hand, he bade his wife kiss him for good luck and so he went towards the palace. But as he was going, Fortune, who meant to shew° him a little false play, prevented his purpose in this wise.°

He met by chance in his way Capnio, who, trudging as fast as he could with a little coffer under his arm to the ship and spying Porrus, whom he knew to be Fawnia's father, going towards the palace, being a wily fellow, began to doubt[2] the worst and therefore crossed him by the way and asked him whither he was going so early this morning? Porrus, who knew by his face that he was one of the court, meaning simply,[3] told him that the king's son Dorastus dealt hardly with him, for he had but one daughter who was a little beautiful, and that the neighbours told him the young prince had allured her to folly. He went, therefore, now to complain to the king how greatly he was abused.

Capnio, who straightway smelt the whole matter, began to soothe him in his talk and said that Dorastus dealt not like a prince to spoil any poor man's daughter in that sort:° he therefore would do the best for him he could because he knew he was an honest man. "But," quoth Capnio, "you lose your labour in going to the palace, for the king means this day to take the air of the sea and to go aboard of a ship that lies in the haven. I am going before, you see, to provide all things in a readiness, and if you will follow my counsel, turn back with me to the haven, where I will set you in such a fit place as you may speak to the king at your pleasure." Porrus, giving credit to Capnio's smooth tale, gave him a thousand thanks for his friendly advice and went with him to the haven, making all the way his complaints of Dorastus, yet concealing secretly the chain and the jewels.

As soon as they were come to the sea side, the mariners, seeing Capnio, came a land with their cock-boat, who, still dissembling the matter, demanded of Porrus if he would go see the ship, who, unwilling and fearing the worst because he was not well acquainted with Capnio, made his excuse that he could not brook the sea, therefore would not trouble him. Capnio, seeing that by fair means he could not get him aboard, commanded the mariners that by violence they should carry him into the ship; who, like sturdy knaves, hoisted the poor shepherd on their backs, and bearing him to the boat launched from the land.

---

[1] cleaned or "spruced"
[2] suspect
[3] speaking innocently (or naively)

Porrus, seeing himself so cunningly betrayed, durst[1] not cry out, for he saw it would not prevail, but began to entreat Capnio and the mariners to be good to him and to pity his estate: he was but a poor man that lived by his labour. They, laughing to see the shepherd so afraid, made as much haste as they could and set him aboard. Porrus was no sooner in the ship but he saw Dorastus walking with Fawnia, yet he scarce knew her, for she had attired herself in rich apparel which so increased her beauty that she resembled rather an angel than a mortal creature.

Dorastus and Fawnia were half astonished to see the old shepherd, marvelling greatly what wind had brought him thither, till Capnio told him all the whole discourse: how Porrus was going to make his complaint to the king, if by policy[2] he had not prevented him, and therefore now sith° he was aboard for the avoiding of further danger it were best to carry him into Italy.

Dorastus praised greatly his man's device° and allowed of his counsel, but Fawnia, who still feared Porrus as her father, began to blush for shame that by her means he should either incur danger or displeasure.

The old shepherd, hearing this hard sentence that he should on such a sudden be carried from his wife, his country, and kinsfolk, into a foreign land amongst strangers, began with bitter tears to make his complaint and on his knees to entreat Dorastus, that, pardoning his unadvised folly, he would give him leave to go home, swearing that he would keep all things as secret as they could wish. But these protestations could not prevail, although Fawnia entreated Dorastus very earnestly; but the mariners hoisting their mainsails weighed anchors and haled[3] into the deep, where we leave them to the favour of the wind and seas and return to Egistus, who having appointed this day to hunt in one of his forests, called for his son Dorastus to go sport himself because he saw that of late he began to lour.° But his men made answer that he was gone abroad, none knew whither except he were gone to the grove to walk all alone, as his custom was to do every day.

The king, willing to waken him out of his dumps, sent one of his men to go seek him, but in vain, for at last he returned, but find him he could not, so that the king went himself to go see the sport. Where, passing away the day, returning at night from hunting, he asked for his son, but he could not be heard of, which drave the king into a great choler, whereupon most of his noblemen and other courtiers posted abroad[4] to seek him, but they could not hear of him through all Sicilia, only they missed Capnio, his man, which again made the king suspect that he was not gone far.

---

[1] dared (see glossary)
[2] strategy (see glossary)
[3] launched
[4] hurried away

Two or three days being passed and no news heard of Dorastus, Egistus began to fear that he was devoured with some wild beasts, and upon that made out a great troop of men to go seek him, who coasted through all the country and searched in every dangerous and secret place until at last they met with a fisherman that was mending his nets when Dorastus and Fawnia took shipping. Who, being examined if he either knew or heard where the king's son was, without any secrecy at all revealed the whole matter, how he was sailed two days past and had in his company his man Capnio, Porrus, and his fair daughter Fawnia. This heavy news was presently carried to the king, who, half dead for sorrow, commanded Porrus' wife to be sent for. She, being come to the palace, after due examination, confessed that her neighbours had oft told her that the king's son was too familiar with Fawnia, her daughter; whereupon, her husband, fearing the worst, about two days past, hearing the king should go an hunting, rose early in the morning and went to make his complaint. But since she neither heard of him nor saw him.

Egistus, perceiving the woman's unfeigned simplicity, let her depart without incurring further displeasure, conceiving such secret grief for his son's reckless folly that he had so forgotten his honour and parentage by so base a choice to dishonour his father and discredit himself, that with very care and thought he fell into a quartan fever,[1] which was so unfit for his aged years and complexion that he became so weak as the physicians would grant him no life.

But his son Dorastus little regarded either father, country, or kingdom in respect of his lady Fawnia, for Fortune, smiling on this young novice, lent him so lucky a gale of wind for the space of a day and a night that the mariners lay and slept upon the hatches. But on the next morning about the break of day the air began to overcast, the winds to rise, the seas to swell, yea, presently there arose such a fearful tempest as the ship was in danger to be swallowed up with every sea; the mainmast with the violence of the wind was thrown overboard, the sails were torn, the tacklings went in sunder, the storm raging still so furiously that poor Fawnia was almost dead for fear, but that she was greatly comforted with the presence of Dorastus. The tempest continued three days, all which time the mariners every minute looked for death, and the air was so darkened with clouds that the master could not tell by his compass in what coast they were. But upon the fourth day, about ten of the clock, the wind began to cease, the sea to wax calm, and the sky to be clear, and the mariners descried the coast of Bohemia, shooting off their ordnance for joy that they had escaped such a fearful tempest.

---

[1] With intense worry and thought he fell into a violent fever.

Dorastus, hearing that they were arrived at some harbour, sweetly kissed
Fawnia and bade her be of good cheer. When they told him that the port
belonged unto the chief city of Bohemia, where Pandosto kept his court,
Dorastus began to be sad, knowing that his father hated no man so much as
Pandosto, and that the king himself had sought secretly to betray Egistus.
This considered, he was half afraid to go on land, but that Capnio counselled
him to change his name and his country until such time as they could get
some other bark to transport them into Italy. Dorastus, liking this device,°
made his case privy to the mariners, rewarding them bountifully for their
pains and charging them to say that he was a gentleman of Trapolonia[1]
called Meleagrus.

The shipmen, willing to shew° what friendship they could to Dorastus,
promised to be as secret as they could or he might wish. And upon this they
landed in a little village a mile distant from the city, where after they had
rested a day, thinking to make provision for their marriage, the fame of
Fawnia's beauty was spread throughout all the city, so that it came to the
ears of Pandosto, who then being about the age of fifty had, notwithstanding,
young and fresh affections, so that he desired greatly to see Fawnia. And to
bring this matter the better to pass, hearing they had but one man and how
they rested at a very homely house, he caused them to be apprehended as
spies, and sent a dozen of his guard to take them: who, being come to their
lodging, told them the king's message.

Dorastus, no whit dismayed, accompanied with Fawnia and Capnio,
went to the court (for they left Porrus to keep the stuff), who being admitted
to the king's presence, Dorastus and Fawnia with humble obeisance[2] saluted
his majesty.

Pandosto, amazed at the singular perfection of Fawnia, stood half
astonished viewing her beauty, so that he had almost forgot himself what he
had to do. At last, with stern countenance he demanded their names, and of
what country they were, and what caused them to land in Bohemia. "Sir,"
quoth Dorastus, "know that my name Meleagrus is, a knight born and
brought up in Trapolonia, and this gentlewoman, whom I mean to take to
my wife, is an Italian, born in Padua, from whence I have now brought her.
The cause I have so small a train with me is for that, her friends unwilling
to consent, I intended secretly to convey her into Trapolonia; whither, as I
was sailing, by distress of weather I was driven into these coasts. Thus have
you heard my name, my country, and the cause of my voyage." Pandosto,
starting from his seat as one in choler, made this rough reply: "Meleagrus, I

---

[1] Traplonia is apparently Greene's invented city.
[2] obedience

fear this smooth tale hath but small truth and that thou coverest a foul skin with fair paintings. No doubt, this lady by her grace and beauty is of her degree more meet¹ for a mighty prince than for a simple knight and thou, like a perjured traitor, hath bereft her of her parents, to their present grief and her ensuing sorrow. Till, therefore, I hear more of her parentage and of thy calling I will stay² you both here in Bohemia."

Dorastus, in whom rested nothing but kingly valour, was not able to suffer the reproaches of Pandosto, but that he made him this answer:

"It is not meet° for a king, without due proof, to appeach any man of ill behaviour, nor upon suspicion to infer belief: strangers ought to be entertained with courtesy, not to be entreated with cruelty, lest being forced by want to put up injuries, the gods revenge their cause with rigour."

Pandosto, hearing Dorastus utter these words, commanded that he should straight be committed to prison, until such time as they heard further of his pleasure, but as for Fawnia, he charged that she should be entertained in the court with such courtesy as belonged to a stranger and her calling. The rest of the shipmen he put into the dungeon.

Having thus hardly handled the supposed Trapolonians, Pandosto, contrary to his aged years, began to be somewhat tickled with the beauty of Fawnia, in so much that he could take no rest but cast in his old head a thousand new devices.° At last he fell into these thoughts: "How art thou pestered, Pandosto, with fresh affections, and unfit fancies, wishing to possess with an unwilling mind and a hot desire, troubled with a cold disdain! Shall thy mind yield in age to that thou hast resisted in youth? Peace, Pandosto: blab not out that which thou mayest be ashamed to reveal to thyself. Ah, Fawnia is beautiful and it is not for thine honour, fond° fool, to name her that is thy captive and another man's concubine. Alas, I reach at that with my hand which my heart would fain° refuse, playing like the bird ibis in Egypt, which hateth serpents yet feedeth on their eggs. Tush, hot desires turn oftentimes to cold disdain; love is brittle, where appetite, not reason, bears the sway; king's thoughts ought not to climb so high as the heavens, but to look no lower than honour; better it is to peck at the stars with the young eagles than to prey on dead carcasses with the vulture. 'Tis more honourable for Pandosto to die by concealing love than to enjoy such unfit love. Doth Pandosto then love? Yea. Whom? A maid unknown, yea, and perhaps immodest, straggled out of her own country, beautiful but not therefore chaste, comely in body but perhaps crooked in mind. Cease, then, Pandosto, to look at Fawnia, much less to love her: be not overtaken with a

---

¹ fitting, suitable
² hold, keep

woman's beauty, whose eyes are framed by art to enamour, whose heart is framed by nature to enchant, whose false tears know their true times, and whose sweet words pierce deeper than sharp swords."

Here Pandosto ceased from his talk but not from his love. For although he sought by reason and wisdom to suppress this frantic affection, yet he could take no rest, the beauty of Fawnia had made such a deep impression in his heart. But, on a day, walking abroad into a park which was hard adjoining to his house, he sent by one of his servants for Fawnia, unto whom he uttered these words: "Fawnia, I commend thy beauty and wit, and now pity thy distress and want. But if thou wilt forsake Sir Meleagrus, whose poverty, though a knight, is not able to maintain an estate answerable to thy beauty, and yield thy consent to Pandosto, I will both increase thee with dignities and riches."

"No, sir," answered Fawnia, "Meleagrus is a knight that hath won me by love and none but he shall wear[1] me. His sinister mischance shall not diminish my affection, but rather increase my good will. Think not, though your grace hath imprisoned him without cause, that fear shall make me yield my consent. I had rather be Meleagrus' wife and a beggar than live in plenty and be Pandosto's concubine."

Pandosto, hearing the assured answer of Fawnia, would, notwithstanding, prosecute his suit to the uttermost, seeking with fair words and great promises to scale the fort of her chastity, swearing that if she would grant to his desire Meleagrus should not only be set at liberty but honoured in his court amongst his nobles. But these alluring baits could not entice her mind from the love of her new betrothed mate Meleagrus. Which Pandosto seeing, he left her alone for that time to consider more of the demand. Fawnia, being alone by herself, began to enter into these solitary meditations:

"Ah, unfortunate Fawnia! Thou seest to desire above fortune is to strive against the gods and Fortune. Who gazeth at the sun weakeneth his sight; they which stare at the sky fall oft into deep pits. Haddest thou rested content to have been a shepherd, thou needest not to have feared mischance: better had it been for thee by sitting low to have had quiet than by climbing high to have fallen into misery. But alas, I fear not mine own danger, but Dorastus' displeasure. Ah, sweet Dorastus, thou art a prince but now a prisoner by too much love procuring thine own loss. Haddest thou not loved Fawnia thou hadst been fortunate. Shall I then be false to him that hath forsaken kingdoms for my cause? No: would my death might deliver him, so mine honour might be preserved!" With that, fetching a deep sigh, she ceased from her complaints and went again to the palace, enjoying a liberty

---

[1] possess and enjoy

without content and proffered pleasure with small joy.

But poor Dorastus lay all this while in close[1] prison, being pinched with a hard restraint and pained with the burden of cold and heavy irons, sorrowing sometimes that his fond° affection had procured him this mishap, that by the disobedience[2] of his parents he had wrought his own despite,[3] another while cursing the gods and Fortune that they should cross him with such sinister chance, uttering at last his passions in these words:

"Ah, unfortunate wretch! born to mishap, now thy folly hath his desert:° art thou not worthy for thy base mind to have bad fortune? Could the destinies favour thee, which hast forgot thine honour and dignities? Will not the gods plague him in despite, that paineth his father with disobedience? O, gods! If any favour or justice be left, plague me but favour poor Fawnia and shroud[4] her from the tyrannies of wretched Pandosto. But let my death free her from mishap, and then welcome death." Dorastus, pained with these heavy passions, sorrowed and sighed but in vain, for which he used the more patience.

But again to Pandosto, who, broiling at the heat of unlawful lust, could take no rest, but still felt his mind disquieted with his new love, so that his nobles and subjects marvelled greatly at this sudden alteration, not being able to conjecture the cause of this his continued care. Pandosto, thinking every hour a year till he had talked once again with Fawnia, sent for her secretly into his chamber, whither though Fawnia unwillingly coming, Pandosto entertained her very courteously, using these familiar speeches which Fawnia answered as shortly in this wise:°

PANDOSTO
"Fawnia, are you become less wilful and more wise to prefer the love of a king before the liking of a poor knight? I think, ere this, you think it is better to be favoured of a king than of a subject."

FAWNIA
"Pandosto, the body is subject to victories but the mind not to be subdued by conquest; honesty is to be preferred before honour, and a dram of faith weigheth down a ton of gold. I have promised to Meleagrus to love and will perform no less."

---

[1] secure
[2] i.e., by disobeying his parents
[3] ill condition
[4] protect

PANDOSTO

"Fawnia, I know thou art not so unwise in thy choice as to refuse the offer
of a king, nor so ungrateful as to despise a good turn. Thou art now in that
place where I may command and yet thou seest I entreat: my power is such
as I may compel by force and yet I sue by prayers. Yield, Fawnia, thy love
to him which burneth in thy love. Meleagrus shall be set free, thy
countrymen discharged, and thou both loved and honoured."

FAWNIA

"I see, Pandosto, where lust ruleth it is a miserable thing to be a virgin. But
know this, that I will always prefer fame before life and rather choose death
than dishonour."

Pandosto, seeing that there was in Fawnia a determinate courage to love
Meleagrus and a resolution without fear to hate him, flung away from her
in a rage, swearing if in short time she would not be won with reason, he
would forget all courtesy and compel her to grant by rigour. But these
threatening words no whit dismayed Fawnia, but that she still both despited[1]
and despised Pandosto.

While thus these two lovers strove, the one to win love, the other to live
in hate, Egistus heard certain news by merchants of Bohemia that his son
Dorastus was imprisoned by Pandosto, which made him fear greatly that his
son should be but hardly entreated. Yet, considering that Bellaria and he
was[2] cleared by the Oracle of Apollo from that crime wherewith Pandosto
had unjustly charged them, he thought best to send with all speed to
Pandosto, that he should set free his son Dorastus and put to death Fawnia
and her father Porrus. Finding this by the advice of counsel the speediest
remedy to release his son, he caused presently two of his ships to be rigged
and thoroughly furnished with provision of men and victuals, and sent
divers of his nobles ambassadors into Bohemia; who, willing to obey their
king and receive their young prince, made no delays for fear of danger, but
with as much speed as might be sailed towards Bohemia. The wind and seas
favoured them greatly, which made them hope of some good hap,[3] for
within three days they were landed. Which Pandosto no sooner heard of
their arrival, but he in person went to meet them, entreating them with such
sumptuous and familiar courtesy that they might well perceive how sorry he
was for the former injuries he had offered to their king, and how willing, if
it might be, to make amends.

As Pandosto made report to them, how one Meleagrus, a knight of

---

[1] held in contempt
[2] Elizabethan usage sometimes permitted a singular verb for a plural subject.
[3] fortune

Trapolonia, was lately arrived with a lady, called Fawnia, in his land, coming very suspiciously, accompanied only with one servant and an old shepherd. The ambassadors perceived by the half what the whole tale meant and began to conjecture that it was Dorastus, who for fear to be known had changed his name; but, dissembling the matter, they shortly arrived at the court, where after they had been very solemnly and sumptuously feasted, the noblemen of Sicilia being gathered together, they made report of their embassage, where they certified[1] Pandosto that Meleagrus was son and heir to the king Egistus, and that his name was Dorastus, how contrary to the king's mind he had privily[2] conveyed away that Fawnia, intending to marry her, being but daughter to that poor shepherd Porrus. Whereupon, the king's request was that Capnio, Fawnia, and Porrus might be murdered and put to death and that his son Dorastus might be sent home in safety.

Pandosto, having attentively and with great marvel heard their embassage, willing to reconcile himself to Egistus and to shew° him how greatly he esteemed his favour, although love and fancy forbade him to hurt Fawnia, yet in despite of love he determined to execute Egistus' will without mercy. And therefore he presently sent for Dorastus out of prison, who, marvelling at this unlooked-for courtesy, found at his coming to the king's presence that which he least doubted of,[3] his father's ambassadors, who no sooner saw him but with great reverence they honoured him. And Pandosto, embracing Dorastus, set him by him very lovingly in a chair of estate. Dorastus, ashamed that his folly was bewrayed,[4] sate a long time as one in a muse till Pandosto told him the sum of his father's embassage, which he had no sooner heard but he was touched at the quick for the cruel sentence that was pronounced against Fawnia. But neither could his sorrow nor his persuasions prevail, for Pandosto commanded that Fawnia, Porrus, and Capnio should be brought to his presence, who were no sooner come but Pandosto, having his former love turned to a disdainful hate, began to rage against Fawnia in these terms:

"Thou disdainful vassal, thou currish kite,[5] assigned by the destinies to base fortune and yet with an aspiring mind gazing after honour, how durst° thou presume, being a beggar, to match with a prince? By thy alluring looks to enchant the son of a king to leave his own country to fulfil thy disordinate lusts? O despiteful mind! A proud heart in a beggar is not unlike to a great fire in a small cottage, which warmeth not the house but burneth it. Assure

---

[1] informed
[2] secretly
[3] suspected
[4] revealed
[5] doglike vulture

thyself that thou shalt die. And thou, old doting fool whose folly hath been such as to suffer thy daughter to reach above thy fortune, look for no other meed[1] but the like punishment. But Capnio, thou which hast betrayed the king, and hast consented to the unlawful lust of thy lord and master, I know not how justly I may plague thee: death is too easy a punishment for thy falsehood and to live[2] (if not in extreme misery) were not to shew° thee equity. I therefore award that thou shalt have thine eyes put out, and continually while thou diest, grind in a mill like a brute beast."

The fear of death brought a sorrowful silence upon Fawnia and Capnio, but Porrus seeing no hope of life burst forth into these speeches:

"Pandosto, and ye noble ambassadors of Sicilia, seeing without cause I am condemned to die, I am yet glad I have opportunity to disburden my conscience before my death. I will tell you as much as I know and yet no more than is true. Whereas I am accused that I have been a supporter of Fawnia's pride and she disdained as a vile beggar, so it is that I am neither father unto her nor she daughter unto me. For so it happened that I, being a poor shepherd in Sicilia, living by keeping other men's flocks, one of my sheep straying down to the sea side, as I went to seek her I saw a little boat driven upon the shore, wherein I found a babe of six days old wrapped in a mantle of scarlet, having about the neck this chain. I, pitying the child and desirous of the treasure, carried it home to my wife, who with great care nursed it up and set it to keep sheep. Here is the chain and the jewels, and this Fawnia is the child whom I found in the boat. What she is or of what parentage I know not, but this I am assured that she is none of mine."

Pandosto would scarce suffer him to tell out his tale but that he enquired the time of the year, the manner of the boat, and other circumstances, which when he found agreeing to his count, he suddenly leapt from his seat and kissed Fawnia, wetting her tender cheeks with his tears, and crying, "My daughter Fawnia! Ah sweet Fawnia! I am thy father, Fawnia." This sudden passion of the king drave them all into a maze,[3] especially Fawnia and Dorastus. But, when the king had breathed himself a while in this new joy, he rehearsed before the ambassadors the whole matter, how he had entreated[4] his wife Bellaria for jealousy and that this was the child whom he had sent to float in the seas.

Fawnia was not more joyful that she had found such a father than Dorastus was glad he should get such a wife. The ambassadors rejoiced that their young prince had made such a choice, that those kingdoms which

---

[1] reward
[2] permit you to live
[3] drove them all into amazement
[4] treated

through enmity had long time been dissevered should now through perpetual amity be united and reconciled. The citizens and subjects of Bohemia, hearing that the king had found again his daughter which was supposed dead, joyful that there was an heir apparent to his kingdom, made bonfires and shows throughout the city. The courtiers and knights appointed jousts and tourneys to signify their willing minds in gratifying the king's hap.[1]

Eighteen days being passed in these princely sports, Pandosto, willing to recompense old Porrus, of a shepherd made him a knight. Which done, providing a sufficient navy to receive him and his retinue, accompanied with Dorastus, Fawnia, and the Sicilian ambassadors, he sailed towards Sicilia, where he was most princely entertained by Egistus, who hearing this most comical event, rejoiced greatly at his son's good hap° and without delay (to the perpetual joy of the two young lovers) celebrated the marriage. Which was no sooner ended, but Pandosto, calling to mind how first he betrayed his friend Egistus, how his jealousy was the cause of Bellaria's death, that contrary to the law of nature he had lusted after his own daughter, moved with these desperate thoughts he fell into a melancholy fit and, to close up the comedy with a tragical stratagem, he slew himself. Whose death being many days bewailed of Fawnia, Dorastus, and his dear friend Egistus, Dorastus, taking his leave of his father, went with his wife and the dead corpse into Bohemia, where, after they were sumptuously entombed, Dorastus ended his days in contented quiet.

FINIS

---

[1] celebrating the king's fortune

Questions

1. *Temporis filia veritas*—"truth is the daughter of time." What does this saying tell us about the story Robert Greene seems to want to tell?

2. *Pandosto* is a story in which painful consequences follow directly from bad behaviour. But by changing the fate of the protagonist and reviving his queen in *The Winter's Tale*, Shakespeare seems to offer us a story in which there are ultimately far fewer ill consequences. Would you agree?

3. Describe the narrative voice of this story: how does the narration shape your relationship to the story told?

4. Paulina has no equivalent in *Pandosto*. Why was she added to *The Winter's Tale*?

5. Leontes does not take his own life, as Pandosto does. Why do you think Shakespeare changed this key detail in his ending?

THE TRUE CHRONICLE HISTORY OF KING LEIR AND HIS THREE DAUGHTERS, GONORILL, RAGAN, AND CORDELLA (1605)

KING LEAR

The most direct source for the plot of Shakespeare's *King Lear*, published in 1608 but first acted in late 1605 or 1606, is an anonymous play bearing a title very similar to Shakespeare's own: *The True Chronicle History of King LEIR and His Three Daughters, Gonorill, Ragan, and Cordella*. Despite intensive efforts by scholars over many years, no consensus has ever formed concerning the earlier play's authorship; nor is there complete agreement among specialists concerning when and in what form Shakespeare might have encountered this now-anonymous work. The London impresario Philip Henslowe's diary records that it was performed at least twice in London in 1594, relatively early in Shakespeare's dramatic career and at a time when the young actor-playwright may have been especially receptive to a powerful or popular performance. Some scholars have suggested that he might have been an actor in the company that performed the play. Although we have no eye-witness reports of this production and nothing but very circumstantial evidence to connect it to William Shakespeare, it may well be that he saw *King Leir* in 1594, vividly remembered it, and came back to the story more than ten years and half a career later when the printed edition appeared in 1605.

And yet *The True Chronicle History* does not tell the full story of Shakespeare's sources for his own version of the old tale. His *King Lear* follows the broad plot outlines of the earlier play, from Leir's ill-fated "love test" of his three daughters to his eventual reconciliation with the one he rejected, in close enough detail that many scholars posit that he must have had the printed play at hand when he composed his own *King Lear*. But he also departed from and augmented the source in some very significant ways. With the addition of the Gloucester-Edmund-Edgar family story that opens *King Lear* and runs through it as a parallel to the royal story, Shakespeare's version adds a significant subplot, one which many scholars and thespians praise as the playwright's finest experiment of its kind, and indeed one of literature's great examples of an interwoven dual plot. And with the addition of the Fool and many imaginative plot details such as the blinding of Gloucester, Edgar's disguise as Tom O'Bedlam, and Lear's mock-trial of Goneril and Regan, an entirely different theatrical or reading experience emerges from *King Lear* compared to *The True Chronicle History*.

For many of these added details Shakespeare went to several other contemporary and near-contemporary sources to fill out the story. He drew from Sir Philip Sidney's 1590 prose romance *Arcadia* for the basic story line and most of the details for the Gloucester-Edmund-Edgar plot, to Edmund Spenser's national epic *The Faerie Queene* (published in 1590 and expanded in 1596) for a key detail concerning Cordelia's death (an event that never takes place in the source play), and to sections of several different English histories, political tracts, and literary works for many small details of action and language that shaped his own version. One of the most notable of these works was an anti-Catholic treatise of 1603 by Samuel Harsnett entitled *A Declaration of Egregious Popish Impostures*, from which Shakespeare drew some of the disguised Edgar's most striking speeches when he is in the guise of Tom O'Bedlam, as well as some of the outlandish imagery and phrasing offered by King Lear during the storm scene of act 3, scene 2. Harsnett also seems to have inspired some of Lear's most vivid misogynistic imagery linking women's genitalia with "hell," "darkness," and "the sulphurous pit" in act 4, scene 6.

In addition, a notorious legal case in 1603-4 may well have had an influence on Shakespeare's decision to dramatise the old story. An aged pensioner of Queen Elizabeth named Brian Annesley had three grown daughters, the first of whom attempted to have him declared mentally incompetent so that she and her husband could control his estate. His youngest daughter successfully appealed to Sir Robert Cecil, a key minister to Queen Elizabeth I and later to King James I, to block her sister's legal manoeuvre and thus to allow her father to continue to control his affairs for himself. That daughter was named Cordell.

To this amalgam of Elizabethan and early Jacobean sources and influences so typical of Shakespeare's eclectic habits of composition we must add the weight of tradition. Even in the early seventeenth century, the story of King Leir and his three daughters was the stuff of folklore, with dozens of written versions dating back to Geoffrey of Monmouth's account in the first half of the twelfth century, and folk elements such as the love test reaching back into the very origins of oral storytelling. For example, the story appeared in Holinshed's *Chronicle* of 1577, which was republished in 1587 in an expanded version. This later edition became one of Shakespeare's favourite sources, as well as one of Elizabethan England's triumphant documents of national identity. In other words, Shakespeare was taking on not only a story that had already been told, literally, hundreds of times over several centuries, but also one with a clear moral outcome. Up until Shakespeare, the standard or received version of the King Leir family saga was a story of renewal and restoration—a tale with a happy ending. That his version is so radically different both in tone and in outcome from all prior ones is one of the best reasons to study his direct source carefully.

But to return to our main subject: *The True Chronicle History* fits squarely into the early modern genre of romance. Printed and stage romances offered readers and spectators lively tales of danger and heroism, often featuring exotic locations, fantastic sea voyages, amazing coincidences, and sometimes elements of magic. The world of romance is one typically populated by exaggeratedly good or evil characters. Disguises might temporarily create confusion—princesses might don the garments of shepherdesses, and malevolent sorcerers may take on the guise of handsome princes, and so on—but in romance the true will eventually distinguish itself from the false. Grand, heroic, selfless gestures of great courtesy, kindness, and self-denial present a positive picture of human motivations; romance offers us a world where powerful kings take pity on lowly commoners or embrace their homespun wisdom, which sometimes means the difference between life and death. It is a world that ennobles humankind by portraying our actions and our motives as better than they really are, our ability to control our environment as greater than it is in real life. Above all, the world of romance is a place where honesty and virtue triumph, even if it may take some time or exact some price during the course of the story for them to emerge victorious. Indeed, one of the delights of the genre is that the journey to such triumphs is dangerous and exciting, but the outcome never really in doubt.

The True Chronicle History is just such a work. Aged King Leir (Shakespeare was the first to spell his name Lear) makes the mistake of believing his two eldest daughters' empty professions of love, slowly realises their insincerity, and eventually acknowledges his own faulty wisdom and rashness; he repents and sets off to France, both to humble himself before the truthful, virtuous daughter he wronged and to seek asylum with her and her superhumanly benevolent husband, the Gallian King (i.e., the King of France). The play presents us with a narrative of renewal and restoration. A providential force—symbolised perhaps most obviously in the thunder and lightning that frightens the murderer sent to kill the old king and his counsellor—and exaggeratedly loyal characters such as Perillus, Cordella, and the Gallian King combine in this play to assure theatregoers and readers that by the end all the deserts will be just.

And indeed, they are: as King Leir is restored to his rightful place, he exclaims his gratitude, "First to the heavens, next, thanks to you my son, / By whose good means I repossess the same." But in pure romance form, he immediately resigns his newly recovered crown to his younger benefactors, completing the handover of power and the retirement from political life that he sought at the very beginning of the play. A natural, beautiful life cycle is laid out for us in the final act as all loose ends are tied up: King Leir embraces his truthful daughter and thanks his loyal followers Perillus and Mumford, the kingdom is restored, evil is purged, and harmony returns to his once-divided kingdom.

At the same time, the play does something Shakespeare's does not: it gives us reasons for things that are not explained, or not fully explained, in *King Lear*. Let us take as an example the wicked behaviour of Cordella's sisters: their petty jealousy over her beauty, which they reveal early in the play, places them neatly in the ranks of folkloric wicked sisters, a category probably most familiar to us in Cinderella's evil step-sisters. The text's explicitness, especially when combined with Cordella's much more developed speeches during her father's love-test, creates a scene in which the lines of good and evil are more clearly drawn than in the equivalent scene of Shakespeare's play, which is much more ambiguously, even mysteriously developed. The earlier play's generic conventions of black and white, good and evil, make it easy for us to know where we are meant to stand morally, from the beginning to the very end.

The play also has many notable literary and dramatic features. Perhaps most obviously, it mixes the pieties and securities we would expect in a world governed by providence with the idioms, and even the vulgarities, of its own cultural moment. High, noble, selfless expressions of faith in God and the king exist side by side with low humour and word-play that might earn the play an "adults-only" rating if it were a film in today's world: the comic sidekick Mumford has only one thing on his mind—sex with an English girl. And Cordella, though pious in every way and devoted to her father, participates in sexual *double-entendres* that must have drawn spirited laughter from the play's first audiences. The anonymous author's language is also learned in a modest way, with several characters invoking well-known classical myths and a making a number of biblical allusions of the sort good Elizabethan Christians would approve. Compared to Shakespeare's *King Lear*, the play is more calculated and self-aware in its careful balancing of comic scenes and comic characters—the hapless drunken Watchmen, most obviously, but also the Murderer sent to kill King Leir and Perillus—with scenes and characters designed to portray human behaviour at its most noble.

Because all is restored at the play's end, with villainy punished and good rewarded, and because the anonymous author intermingled scenes of human nobility with examples of human grossness, we can well imagine that the play made for a pleasant and uplifting few hours of theatrical entertainment in the 1590s. It must have made its first audiences feel good to know that God looks out for us all and is not above expressing divine will through messages of thunder and lightning when needed, that evil will be discovered and punished, and that political and natural order will be restored in ancient Britain.

As you read *The True Chronicle History of King Leir*, first consider the play in its own right and ask yourself some of the basic questions that its first audience might have: how well or poorly does it convey its story? Does it conform to its own generic conventions? Is it a good story or a bad one? A satisfying one? What kind of message or moral does this play seek to communicate? Is it artistically whole? Do you like the story?

After you have made some determinations about what the play aimed to be as its own art form, ask yourself some questions about its relationship to Shakespeare's play. Which major details from this source did Shakespeare retain and which did he abandon? Why? Do his decisions suggest any overarching artistic or philosophical motive? More detailed questions might follow from these. For example, what does the Gloucester-Edmund-Edgar plot add in Shakespeare's version, especially now that you have read a full version of the story without that additional plot line? What about the storm in *King Lear*—does it have any antecedent in *The True Chronicle History of King Leir*? What does it mean in Shakespeare's story? Why does King Lear go mad in Shakespeare's story but never in the prior one? What does the addition of the Fool do to the story?

Perhaps most of all, what are we to make of the radically different endings? What do you think it would have been like to see this performed in London in 1594? Then imagine yourself in an audience in about 1606, remembering a delightful, uplifting version of the story of King Leir and his three daughters you saw some dozen years earlier, returning to the theatre to experience Shakespeare's version of what you *thought* was a familiar old tale?

A Note on the Text

The author of *The True Chronicle History of King Leir, and His Three Daughters* is no longer known. The only early modern edition, published in 1605 by John Wright, presents several editorial challenges because it does not contain consistent act and scene divisions or stage directions, verse and prose are sometimes printed indiscriminately, and its punctuation is particularly challenging for modern readers. In preparing my text, I added notes and glosses. I also modernised spelling and punctuation, but whenever it seemed advantageous to do so, retained early modern spellings that present no significant difficulties for modern readers (*vild* for *vile*, *perfit* for *perfect*). I left several ambiguously or erroneously printed speeches in the hybrid verse-prose of the original. Frequently repeated archaic words are footnoted on their first occurrence and thereafter noted with °, which refers readers to the glossary at the end of this volume.

I also supplied many stage directions (in square brackets to distinguish them from those of the 1605 edition, which I have left as printed) and regularised speech prefixes; I included within square brackets the act and scene divisions first established by Sidney Lee in his edition of the play (London and New York, 1909). In preparing my text, I consulted the editions of Sidney Lee, W. W. Greg (London: Chatto and Windus, 1909), Donald M. Michie (New York and London: Garland, 1991), and Tiffany Stern (London: Routledge, 2002).

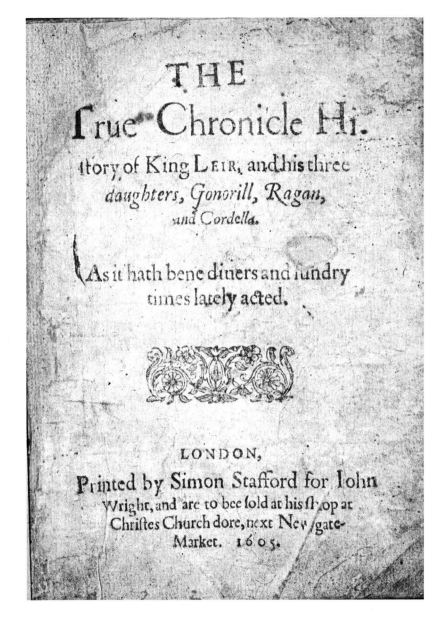

Fig. 7-1. The title page of *The True Chronicle History of King Leir*

The True Chronicle History of King Leir, and His Three Daughters, Gonorill, Ragan, and Cordella

Enter King Leir and Nobles.

KING LEIR Thus, to our grief, the obsequies[1] performed
Of our (too late) deceas'd and dearest queen,
Whose soul, I hope, possess'd of heavenly joys,
Doth ride in triumph 'mongst the cherubins,[2]
Let us request your grave advice, my lords,
For the disposing of[3] our princely daughters,
For whom our care is specially employed,
As nature bindeth to advance their states,
In royal marriage with some princely mates.
For wanting[4] now their mother's good advice,
Under whose government they have received
A perfit[5] pattern of a virtuous life,
Left as it were a ship without a stern,
Or silly[6] sheep without a pastor's care.
Although ourselves[7] do dearly tender[8] them,
Yet are we ignorant of their affairs,
For fathers best do know to govern sons,
But daughters' steps the mother's counsel turns.
A son we want° for to succeed our crown
And course of time hath cancelled the date
Of further issue from our withered loins.
One foot already hangeth in the grave
And age hath made deep furrows in my face.
The world of me, I of the world am weary,
And I would fain[9] resign these earthly cares
And think upon the welfare of my soul,
Which by no better means may be effected

---

[1] funeral rites
[2] cherubim: an order of angels
[3] providing for
[4] lacking (see glossary)
[5] a perfect example (see glossary)
[6] innocent (see glossary)
[7] King Leir uses the "royal we" here.
[8] value
[9] rather, prefer to (see glossary)

Than by resigning up the crown from me
In equal dowry to my daughters three.

SKALLIGER A worthy care, my liege, which well declares
The zeal you bare[1] unto our *quondam*[2] queen.
And since your grace hath licens'd me to speak,
I censure[3] thus: your majesty, knowing well
What several suitors your princely daughters have,
To make them each a jointure[4] more or less,
As is their worth, to them that love profess.

KING LEIR No more, nor less, but even all alike:
My zeal is fixed, all fashion'd in one mould.
Wherefore unpartial shall my censure be;[5]
Both old and young shall have alike for me.

NOBLE My gracious lord, I heartily do wish
That God had lent you an heir indubitate,[6]
Which might have set[7] upon your royal throne
When fates should loose the prison of your life,
By whose succession all this doubt might cease;
And as by you, by him we might have peace.
But after-wishes ever come too late
And nothing can revoke the course of fate.
Wherefore, my Liege, my censure° deems it best,
To match them with some of your neighbour kings
Bord'ring within the bounds of Albion,[8]
By whose united friendship this our state
May be protected 'gainst all foreign hate.

KING LEIR Herein, my lords, your wishes sort[9] with mine
And mine (I hope) do sort with heavenly powers:

---

[1] love you bore
[2] one-time, erstwhile
[3] advise (see glossary)
[4] portion of inheritance
[5] For that reason, impartial shall be my decision be.
[6] unquestioned heir (i.e., a son)
[7] sat
[8] ancient name for the British Isles
[9] concur, agree

For at this instant two near neighbouring kings
Of Cornwall and of Cambria, motion love
To my two daughters, Gonorill and Ragan.
My youngest daughter, fair Cordella, vows
No liking to a monarch, unless love allows.
She is solicited by divers[1] peers,
But none of them her partial fancy[2] hears.
Yet, if my policy[3] may her beguile,
I'll match her to some king within this ile
And so establish such a perfit peace
As Fortune's force shall ne'er prevail to cease.

PERILLUS Of us and ours, your gracious care, my lord,
Deserves an everlasting memory,
To be enroll'd in chronicles of fame
By never-dying perpetuity.
Yet to become so provident a prince,
Lose not the title of a loving father.
Do not force love where fancy cannot dwell,
Lest streams, being stopp'd, above the banks do swell.

KING LEIR I am resolv'd, and even now my mind
Doth meditate a sudden stratagem
To try[4] which of my daughters loves me best,
Which, till I know, I cannot be in rest.
This granted, when they jointly shall contend
Each to exceed the other in their love,
Then at the vantage[5] will I take Cordella,
Even as she doth protest she loves me best.
I'll say, "then, daughter, grant me one request
To shew[6] thou lovest me as thy sisters do:
Accept a husband, whom myself will woo."
This said, she cannot well deny my suit,
Although (poor soul) her senses will be mute.
Then will I triumph in my policy

---

[1] various, several (see glossary)
[2] inclination to love
[3] strategy (see glossary)
[4] test (see glossary)
[5] with this advantage
[6] show (see glossary)

And match her with a king of Brittany.

SKALLIGER *[aside]* I'll to them before and bewray[1] your secrecy.

PERILLUS *[aside]* Thus fathers think their children to beguile,
And oftentimes themselves do first repent
When heavenly powers do frustrate their intent. *Exeunt.*

[1.2]   Enter Gonorill and Ragan.

GONORILL I marvel, Ragan, how you can endure
To see that proud pert peat,[2] our youngest sister,
So slightly to account of us, her elders,
As if we were no better than herself!
We cannot have a quaint device[3] so soon,
Or new made fashion of our choice invention,
But if she like it, she will have the same,
Or study newer to exceed us both.
Besides, she is so nice[4] and so demure,
So sober, courteous, modest, and precise,
That all the court hath work enough to do
To talk how she exceedeth me and you.

RAGAN What should I do? Would it were in my power
To find a cure for this contagious ill.
Some desperate medicine must be soon applied
To dim the glory of her mounting fame,
Else ere't be long she'll have both prick and praise
And we must be set by for working days.[5]
Do you not see what several[6] choice of suitors
She daily hath, and of the best degree?
Say, amongst all, she hap[7] to fancy one
And have a husband when as we have none,

---

[1] I will go to them first and betray (*bewray*: see glossary)
[2] forward girl
[3] bauble, trinket
[4] picky, finicky
[5] or else before long she will be the object (of men's love) and we will be we will be
    treated as ordinary
[6] various
[7] happen

Why then, by right, to her we must give place,
Though it be ne'er so much to our disgrace.

GONORILL By my virginity, rather than she shall have
A husband before me
I'll marry one or other in his shirt.[1]
And yet I have made half a grant[2] already
Of my good will unto the king of Cornwall.

RAGAN Swear not so deeply, sister. Here cometh my lord Skalliger.
Something his hasty coming doth import.

Enter Skalliger.

SKALLIGER Sweet Princesses, I am glad I met you here so luckily,
Having good news which doth concern you both
And craveth speedy expedition.

RAGAN For God's sake tell us what it is, my lord.
I am with child[3] until you utter it.

SKALLIGER Madam, to save your longing, this it is:
Your father in great secrecy today
Told me he means to marry you out of hand[4]
Unto the noble Prince of Cambria,
[to Gonerill] You, madam, to the King of Cornwall's grace.
Your younger sister he would fain° bestow
Upon the rich King of Hibernia,[5]
But that he doubts[6] she hardly will consent,
For hitherto she ne'er could fancy him.
If she do yield, why then, between you three
He will divide his kingdom for your dowries.
But yet there is a further mystery,
Which, so you will conceal, I will disclose.

---

[1] any poor man
[2] a pledge provisionally or partially given
[3] about to burst (as if pregnant)
[4] immediately
[5] Ireland
[6] fears (see glossary)

GONORILL What e're thou speak'st to us, kind Skalliger,
Think that thou speak'st it only to thyself.

SKALLIGER He earnestly desireth for to know
Which of you three do bear most love to him,
And on your loves he so extremely dotes
As never any did, I think, before.
He presently doth mean to send for you
To be resolv'd of this tormenting doubt.
And look, whose answer pleaseth him the best,
They shall have most unto their marriages.

RAGAN Oh, that I had some pleasing mermaid's voice
For to enchant his senseless senses with!

SKALLIGER For he supposeth that Cordella will
(Striving to go beyond you in her love)
Promise to do whatever he desires.
Then will he straight enjoin her for his sake
The Hibernian king in marriage for to take.
This is the sum of all I have to say,
Which, being done, I humbly take my leave,
Not doubting but your wisdom will foresee
What course will best unto your good agree.

GONORILL Thanks, gentle Skalliger, thy kindness undeserved,
Shall not be unrequited, if we live.[1] *Exit Skalliger.*

RAGAN Now have we fit occasion offer'd us
To be reveng'd upon her unperceiv'd.

GONORILL Nay, our revenge we will inflict on her
Shall be accounted piety in us:
I will so flatter with my doting father,
As he was ne'er so flatt'red in his life.
Nay, I will say that if it be his pleasure
To match me to a beggar, I will yield:
For, why, I know whatever I do say,
He means to match me with the Cornwall king.

---

[1] shall not be unrewarded as long as we live

RAGAN I'll say the like, for I am well assured
Whate'er I say to please the old man's mind,
Who dotes as if he were a child again,
I shall enjoy the noble Cambrian prince.
Only to feed his humour will suffice
To say I am content with anyone
Whom he'll appoint me; this will please him more
Than e'er Apollo's music pleased Jove.[1]

GONORILL I smile to think in what a woeful plight
Cordella will be when we answer thus,
For she will rather die than give consent
To join in marriage with the Irish king.
So will our father think she loveth him not
Because she will not grant[2] to his desire,
Which we will aggravate in such bitter terms
That he will soon convert his love to hate,
For he, you know, is always in extremes.

RAGAN Not all the world could lay a better plot.
I long till it be put in practice. *Exeunt.*

[1.3]   Enter King Leir and Perillus.

KING LEIR Perillus, go seek my daughters,
Will[3] them immediately come and speak with me.

PERILLUS I will, my gracious lord. *Exit.*

KING LEIR Oh, what a combat feels my panting heart
Twixt children's love and care of commonweal![4]
How dear my daughters are unto my soul
None knows but He that knows my thoughts and secret deeds.
Ah, little do they know the dear regard
Wherein I hold their future state to come.
When they securely sleep on beds of down

---

[1] The ancient Greek god Apollo was associated with music, among other pursuits.
[2] accede
[3] command
[4] commonwealth

These aged eyes do watch[1] for their behalf.
While they like wantons sport in youthful toys[2]
This throbbing heart is pierced with dire annoys.
As doth the sun exceed the smallest star,
So much the father's love exceeds the child's.
Yet my complaints are causeless, for the world
Affords not children more conformable.[3]
And yet, methinks, my mind presageth[4] still
I know not what, and yet I fear some ill.

Enter Perillus, with the three daughters.

Well, here my daughters come. I have found out
A present means to rid me of this doubt.

GONORILL Our royal lord and father, in all duty
We come to know the tenor of your will,
Why you so hastily have sent for us?

KING LEIR Dear Gonorill, kind Ragan, sweet Cordella,
Ye flourishing branches of a kingly stock,
Sprung from a tree that once did flourish green,
Whose blossoms now are nipped with winter's frost,
And pale grim death doth wait upon my steps
And summons me unto his next assizes,[5]
Therefore, dear daughters, as ye tender[6] the safety
Of him that was the cause of your first being,
Resolve a doubt which much molests my mind:
Which of you three to me would prove most kind,
Which loves me most, and which at my request
Will soonest yield unto their father's hest?[7]

GONORILL I hope my gracious father makes no doubt
Of any of his daughters' love to him.

---

[1] remain awake
[2] while they like reckless ones occupy themselves in silly pastimes
[3] compliant, tractable
[4] predicts
[5] court session (i.e., day of reckoning)
[6] value
[7] request, behest

Yet, for my part, to shew° my zeal to you,
Which cannot be in windy words rehears'd,
I prize my love to you at such a rate,
I think my life inferior to my love.
Should you enjoin me for to tie a millstone
About my neck and leap into the sea
At your command I willingly would do it.
Yea, for to do you good, I would ascend
The highest turret in all Brittany
And from the top leap headlong to the ground.
Nay, more: should you appoint me for to marry
The meanest vassal in the spacious world,
Without reply I would accomplish it.
In brief, command whatever you desire,
And if I fail, no favour I require.

KING LEIR Oh, how thy words revive my dying soul!

CORDELLA *[aside]* Oh, how I do abhor this flattery!

KING LEIR But what sayeth Ragan to her father's will?

RAGAN Oh, that my simple utterance could suffice
To tell the true intention of my heart,
Which burns in zeal of duty to your grace
And never can be quench'd but by desire
To shew° the same in outward forwardness.
Oh, that there were some other maid that durst[1]
But make a challenge of her love with me:
I'd make her soon confess she never loved
Her father half so well as I do you.
Ay,[2] then my deeds should prove in plainer case
How much my zeal aboundeth to your grace.
But for them all, let this one mean[3] suffice
To ratify my love before your eyes:
I have right noble suitors to my love,
No worse than kings, and haply[4] I love one.

---

[1] dared (see glossary)
[2] indeed (see glossary)
[3] means (see glossary)
[4] perhaps

Yet, would you have me make my choice anew,
I'd bridle fancy,[1] and be ruled by you.

KING LEIR Did never Philomel[2] sing so sweet a note.

CORDELLA *[aside]* Did never flatterer tell so false a tale.

KING LEIR Speak now, Cordella, make my joys at full
And drop down nectar from thy honey lips.

CORDELLA I cannot paint my duty forth in words;
I hope my deeds shall make report for me.
But look what love the child doth owe the father,
The same to you I bear, my gracious lord.

GONORILL Here is an answer answerless indeed:
Were you my daughter, I should scarcely brook[3] it.

RAGAN Dost thou not blush, proud peacock as thou art,
To make our father such a slight reply?

KING LEIR Why, how now, minion, are you grown so proud?
Doth our dear love make you thus peremptory?
What, is your love become so small to us
As that you scorn to tell us what it is?
Do you love us as every child doth love
Their father? True indeed, as some
Who by disobedience short[4] their father's days,
And so would you. Some are so father-sick
That they make means to rid them from the world,
And so would you. Some are indifferent
Whether their aged parents live or die,
And so are you. But didst thou know, proud girl,
What care I had to foster thee to this,
Ah, then thou wouldst say as thy sisters do:
"Our life is less than love we owe to you."

---

[1] restrain (my) love
[2] After Tereus raped and cut out the tongue of his sister-in-law Philomel to silence her,
   she was transformed into a nightingale (Ovid, *Metamorphoses*, Book 6.590-977).
[3] tolerate (see glossary)
[4] shorten

CORDELLA Dear father, do not so mistake my words,
Nor my plain meaning be misconstrued;
My tongue was never us'd to flattery.

GONORILL You were not best say I flatter. If you do,
My deeds shall shew° I flatter not with you.
I love my father better than thou canst.

CORDELLA The praise were great, spoke from another's mouth,
But it should seem your neighbours dwell far off.[1]

RAGAN Nay, here is one that will confirm as much
As she hath said, both for myself and her.
I say thou dost not wish my father's good.

CORDELLA Dear father—

KING LEIR Peace, bastard imp, no issue of King Leir!
I will not hear thee speak one tittle[2] more.
Call not me father if thou love thy life,
Nor these thy sisters once presume to name.
Look for no help henceforth from me nor mine;
Shift as thou wilt and trust unto thyself.
My kingdom will I equally divide
'Twixt thy two sisters to their royal dower[3]
And will bestow them worthy their deserts.[4]
This done, because thou shalt not have the hope
To have a child's part in the time to come,
I presently will dispossess myself
And set up these upon my princely throne.

GONORILL I ever thought that pride would have a fall.

RAGAN Plain-dealing sister, your beauty is so sheen[5]
You need no dowry to make you be a queen.

---

[1] But they who might vouch for you are not to be found.
[2] iota, jot
[3] dowry (see glossary)
[4] deserving, merit (see glossary)
[5] shining, resplendent

Exeunt King Leir, Gonorill, Ragan.

CORDELLA Now whither, poor forsaken, shall I go
When mine own sisters triumph in my woe?
But unto Him which doth protect the just,
In Him will poor Cordella put her trust.
These hands shall labour for to get my spending[1]
And so I'll live until my days have ending.

PERILLUS *[aside]* Oh, how I grieve to see my lord thus fond,[2]
To dote so much upon vain flattering words.
Ah, if he but with good advice had weighed
The hidden tenure of her humble speech
Reason to rage should not have given place,
Nor poor Cordella suffer such disgrace. *Exit.*

[2.1]   Enter the Gallian King with Mumford, and three Nobles more.

GALLIAN KING Dissuade me not, my lords, I am resolv'd
This next fair wind to sail for Brittany
In some disguise, to see if flying fame[3]
Be not too prodigal in the wondrous praise
Of these three nymphs, the daughters of King Leir.
If present view do answer absent praise
And eyes allow of what our ears have heard,
And Venus stand auspicious to my vows,
And Fortune favour what I take in hand,
I will return seized of as rich a prize
As Jason, when he wan the golden fleece.[4]

MUMFORD Heavens grant you may; the match were full of honour
And well beseeming the young Gallian king.
I would your grace would favour me so much
As make me partner of your pilgrimage.
I long to see the gallant British dames
And feed mine eyes upon their rare perfections,

---

[1] money to live on
[2] foolish
[3] rumours
[4] With his followers the Argonauts, Jason went in search of and won (*wan*) the
golden fleece of Phrixus (Ovid, *Metamorphoses*, Book 7).

For till I know the contrary I'll say
Our dames in France are far more fair than they.

GALLIAN KING Lord Mumford, you have saved me a labour,
In off'ring that which I did mean to ask.
And I most willingly accept your company,
Yet first I will enjoin you to observe
Some few conditions which I shall propose.

MUMFORD So that you do not tie mine eyes for looking
After the amorous glances of fair dames,
So that you do not tie my tongue from speaking,
My lips from kissing when occasion serves,
My hands from congés,[1] and my knees to bow
To gallant girls, which were a task more hard
Than flesh and blood is able to endure.
Command what else you please, I rest content.

GALLIAN KING To bind thee from a thing thou canst not leave[2]
Were but a mean° to make thee seek it more,
And therefore speak, look, kiss, salute for me;
In these myself am like to second thee.
Now hear thy task. I charge thee from the time
That first we set sail for the British shore
To use no words of dignity to me,
But in the friendliest manner that thou canst
Make use of me as thy companion:
For we will go disguised in palmer's weeds,[3]
That no man shall mistrust us what we are.

MUMFORD If that be all, I'll fit your turn, I warrant you. I am some kin to the Blunts[4] and, I think, the bluntest of all my kindred; therefore, if I be too blunt with you, thank yourself for praying me to be so.

---

[1] polite gestures or shows of deference
[2] avoid
[3] pilgrim's garments
[4] Mumford may suggest here that he is of the Blount (Blunt) family, whose baronial title was Mountjoy, possibly a variation on the name Mumford (see Lee edition, p. xxxv: see introduction).

GALLIAN KING Thy pleasant company will make the way seem short.
It resteth¹ now that in my absence hence
I do commit the government to you,
My trusty lords and faithful councillors.
Time cutteth off the rest I have to say:
The wind blows fair, and I must needs away.

NOBLES Heavens send your voyage to as good effect
As we your land do purpose² to protect. *Exeunt.*

*[2.2]   Enter the King of Cornwall and his man booted and spurred, a
riding wand and a letter in his hand.*

CORNWALL But how far distant are we from the court?

SERVANT Some twenty miles, my lord, or thereabouts.

CORNWALL It seemeth to me twenty thousand miles,
Yet hope I to be there within this hour.

SERVANT *[to himself]* Then are you like to ride alone for me.
I think my lord is weary of his life.

CORNWALL Sweet Gonorill, I long to see thy face,
Which hast so kindly gratified my love.

*Enter the King of Cambria booted and spurred, and his man with a wand
and a letter.*

CAMBRIA *[He looks on the letter.]*
Get a fresh horse, for by my soul I swear
I am past patience longer to forbear
The wished sight of my beloved mistress,
Dear Ragan, stay³ and comfort of my life.

SERVANT *[to himself]* Now what in God's name doth my lord intend?
He thinks he ne'er shall come at's journey's end.
I would he had old Daedalus' waxen wings,

¹ remains to be done
² intend
³ prop, support

That he might fly, so I might stay behind,
For e'er we get to Troynovant, I see,
He quite will tire himself, his horse, and me.[1] *Cornwall and Cambria look*
one upon another, and start to see each other there.

CORNWALL Brother of Cambria, we greet you well,
As one whom here we little did expect.

CAMBRIA Brother of Cornwall, met in happy time!
I thought as much to have met with the Souldan[2] of Persia
As to have met you in this place, my lord.
No doubt, it is about some great affairs,
That makes you here so slenderly accompanied.[3]

CORNWALL To say the truth, my lord, it is no less,
And for your part some hasty wind of chance
Hath blown you hither thus upon the sudden.

CAMBRIA My lord, to break off further circumstances,[4]
For at this time I cannot brook° delays,
Tell you your reason, I will tell you mine.

CORNWALL In faith, content, and therefore to be brief,
For I am sure my haste's as great as yours.
I am sent for to come unto King Leir,
Who by these present letters promiseth
His eldest daughter, lovely Gonorill,
To me in marriage, and for present dowry
The moiety of half his regiment.[5]
The lady's love I long ago possess'd,
But until now I never had the father's.

CAMBRIA You tell me wonders, yet I will relate

---

[1] The servant wishes for the famous waxen wings of the artificer Daedalus (Ovid, *Metamorphoses*, Book 8.183-235) in order to carry his lord Cambria more quickly and easily to London, or Troynouvant, the "New Troy"of English legend.

[2] sultan

[3] meagrely attended (by his entourage)

[4] to get to the point

[5] half his rule or realm

Strange news, and henceforth we must brothers call.[1]
Witness these lines: his honourable age,
Being weary of the troubles of his crown,
His princely daughter Ragan will bestow
On me in marriage, with half his seigneuries,[2]
Whom I would gladly have accepted of
With the third part, her complements[3] are such.

CORNWALL If I have one half, and you have the other,
Then between us we must needs have the whole.

CAMBRIA The hole! how mean you that? 'Zlood,[4] I hope,
We shall have two holes between us.

CORNWALL Why, the whole kingdom.

CAMBRIA Ay, that's very true.

CORNWALL What then is left for his third daughter's dowry,
Lovely Cordella, whom the world admires?

CAMBRIA 'Tis very strange. I know not what to think,
Unless they mean to make a nun of her.

CORNWALL 'Twere pity such rare beauty should be hid
Within the compass of a cloister's wall,
But howsoe'er, if Leir's words prove true,
It will be good, my lord, for me and you.

CAMBRIA Then let's haste all danger to prevent,
For fear delays[5] do alter his intent. *Exeunt.*

[2.3]   Enter Gonorill and Ragan.

GONORILL Sister, when did you see Cordella last,
That pretty piece, that thinks none good enough

---

[1] call each other brother
[2] dominions
[3] personal qualities
[4] by God's blood (a profanity)
[5] for fear that our own delays

To speak to her because (sir-reverence)[1]
She hath a little beauty extraordinary?

RAGAN Since time my father warned[2] her from his presence
I never saw her that I can remember.
God give her joy of her surpassing beauty;
I think her dowry will be small enough.

GONORILL I have incens'd my father so against her
As he will never be reclaim'd again.

RAGAN I was not much behind to do the like.

GONORILL Faith, sister, what moves you to bear her such good will?

RAGAN In truth, I think, the same that moveth you:
Because she doth surpass us both in beauty.

GONORILL Beshrew[3] your fingers, how right you can guess.
I tell you true, it cuts me to the heart.

RAGAN But we will keep her low enough, I warrant,
And clip her wings for mounting up too high.

GONORILL Whoever hath her shall have a rich marriage of her.

RAGAN She were right fit to make a parson's wife,[4]
For they, men say, do love fair women well
And many times do marry them with nothing.

GONORILL With nothing! Marry God forbid. Why, are there any such?

RAGAN I mean, no money.[5]

---

[1] with all respect (here sarcastic)
[2] forbid
[3] curse
[4] a proverbially poor woman
[5] The daughters' banter here continues the play's sexual humour introduced in the *whole/hole* pun of Cambria and Cornwall above: *nothing* could mean vagina and *will* (with a similar sound to *well*) could mean penis in Elizabethan slang. Gonorill is also saying that Cordella would spend her husband's entire benefice (the yearly stipend paid to ministers for their material support) in one gown.

GONORILL I cry you mercy, I mistook you much,
And she is far too stately for the church;
She'll lay her husband's benefice on her back,
Even in one gown, if she may have her will.

RAGAN In faith, poor soul, I pity her a little.
Would she were less fair, or more fortunate.
Well, I think long[1] until I see my Morgan,
The gallant Prince of Cambria, here arrive.

GONORILL And so do I until the Cornwall king
Present himself, to consummate my joys.
Peace, here cometh my father.

Enter King Leir, Perillus and others.

KING LEIR Cease, good my lords, and sue not to reverse
Our censure,° which is now irrevocable.
We have dispatched letters of contract
Unto the kings of Cambria and of Cornwall;
Our hand and seal will justify no less.
Then do not so dishonour me, my lords,
As to make shipwrack of our kingly word.
I am as kind as is the pelican,
That kills itself to save her young ones' lives;
And yet as jealous as the princely eagle,
That kills her young ones if they do but dazzle[2]
Upon the radiant splendour of the sun.
Within this two days I expect their coming.

Enter Kings of Cornwall and Cambria.

But in good time, they are arriv'd already.
This haste of yours, my lords, doth testify
The fervent love you bear unto my daughters;
And think yourselves as welcome to King Leir,
As ever Priam's[3] children were to him.

---

[1] I am impatient
[2] become confused by gazing
[3] King Priam of Troy was legendary for having fifty sons and many daughters.

CORNWALL My gracious lord, and father, too, I hope:
Pardon for that I made no greater haste,
But were my horse as swift as was my will
I long ere[1] this had seen your majesty.

CAMBRIA No other 'scuse of absence can I frame
Than what my brother hath inform'd your grace:
For our undeserved welcome we do vow
Perpetually to rest at your command.

CORNWALL But you, sweet love, illustrious Gonorill,
The regent and the sovereign of my soul,
Is Cornwall welcome to your excellency?

GONORILL As welcome as Leander was to Hero
Or brave Aeneas to the Carthage queen[2]
So and more welcome is your grace to me.

CAMBRIA Oh, may my fortune prove no worse than his
Since heavens do know my fancy is as much.
Dear Ragan, say if welcome unto thee:
All welcomes else will little comfort me.

RAGAN As gold is welcome to the covetous eye
As sleep is welcome to the traveller,
As is fresh water to sea-beaten men,
Or moistened showers unto the parched ground,
Or anything more welcomer than this,
So and more welcome lovely Morgan is.

KING LEIR What resteth,° then, but that we consummate
The celebration of these nuptial rites?
My kingdom I do equally divide.
Princes, draw lots and take your chance as falls. *Then they draw lots.*
These I resign as freely unto you
As erst[3] by true succession they were mine.
And here I do freely dispossess myself

---

[1] before (see glossary)

[2] Hero and Leander and Aeneas and Dido, queen of Carthage, were legendary
examples of fervent lovers who risked all for love.

[3] first, previously (see glossary)

And make you two my true adopted heirs.
Myself will sojourn with my son[1] of Cornwall
And take me to my prayers and my beads.
I know my daughter Ragan will be sorry
Because I do not spend my days with her.
Would I were able to be with both at once;
They are the kindest girls in Christendom.

PERILLUS I have been silent all this while, my lord,
To see if any worthier than myself
Would once have spoke in poor Cordella's cause,
But love or fear ties silence to their tongues.
Oh, hear me speak for her, my gracious lord,
Whose deeds have not deserv'd this ruthless doom
As thus to disinherit her of all.

KING LEIR Urge this no more and if[2] thou love thy life:
I say, she is no daughter that doth scorn
To tell her father how she loveth him.
Whoever speaketh hereof to me again,
I will esteem him for my mortal foe.
Come, let us in to celebrate with joy
The happy nuptials of these lovely pairs.
Exeunt omnes, manet Perillus.[3]

PERILLUS
Ah, who so blind as they that will not see
The near approach of their own misery?
Poor lady, I extremely pity her,
And whilst I live each drop of my heart blood
Will I strain forth, to do her any good. *Exit.*

[2.4]   Enter the Gallian King and Mumford, disguised like pilgrims.

MUMFORD My lord, how do you brook° this British air?

GALLIAN KING "My lord?" I told you of this foolish humour
And bound you to the contrary, you know.

---

[1] son-in-law
[2] if (see glossary)
[3] all exit; Perillus remains

MUMFORD Pardon me for once, my lord; I did forget.

GALLIAN KING "My lord again?" Then let's have nothing else
And so be ta'en for spies, and then 'tis well.

MUMFORD 'Swounds,[1] I could bite my tongue in two for anger!
For God's sake, name yourself some proper name.

GALLIAN KING Call me Tresillus; I'll call thee Denapoll.

MUMFORD Might I be made the monarch of the world
I could not hit upon these names, I swear.

GALLIAN KING Then call me Will; I'll call thee Jack.

MUMFORD Well, be it so, for I have well deserv'd to be call'd Jack.[2]

GALLIAN KING Stand close, for here a British lady cometh.

Enter Cordella

A fairer creature ne'er mine eyes beheld.

CORDELLA This is a day of joy unto my sisters,
Wherein they both are married unto kings;
And I, by birth as worthy as themselves,
Am turn'd into the world to seek my fortune.
How may I blame the fickle Queen of Chance
That maketh me a pattern[3] of her power?
Ah, poor weak maid, whose imbecility[4]
Is far unable to endure these brunts.[5]
Oh, father Leir, how dost thou wrong thy child,
Who always was obedient to thy will!
But why accuse I Fortune and my father?
No, no, it is the pleasure of my God

---

[1] by God's wounds (a profanity)
[2] Mumford plays with the sound of *well* / *Will* and gently rebukes himself for being a "Jack," a by-word for a foolish fellow.
[3] example
[4] powerlessness
[5] setbacks

And I do willingly embrace the rod.

GALLIAN KING It is no goddess, for she doth complaint[1]
On Fortune and th'unkindness of her father.

CORDELLA These costly robes ill fitting my estate
I will exchange for other meaner habit.

MUMFORD Now if I had a kingdom in my hands
I would exchange it for a milkmaid's smock and petticoat,
That she and I might shift our clothes together.

CORDELLA I will betake me to my thread and needle
And earn my living with my fingers' ends.

MUMFORD Oh, brave! God willing, thou shalt have my custom,
By sweet Saint Denis here I sadly swear,
For all the shirts and night gear that I wear.[2]

CORDELLA I will profess and vow a maiden's life.

MUMFORD Then I protest thou shalt not have my custom.

GALLIAN KING I can forbear no longer for to speak,
For if I do I think my heart will break.

MUMFORD 'Sblood,[3] Will, I hope you are not in love with my sempster.[4]

GALLIAN KING I am in such a labyrinth of love
As that I know not which way to get out.

MUMFORD You'll ne'er get out unless you first get in.

GALLIAN KING I prithee, Jack, cross not my passions.

---

[1] complain, lament
[2] Mumford humorously swears by God, Saint Denis, the patron saint of France, and his own clothing that he will give his "business" (custom) to Cordella. The punch line of the sexual joke follows. In this context "Oh, brave!" means "Oh, wonderful."
[3] by God's blood (a profanity)
[4] seamstress

MUMFORD Prithee, Will, to her and try° her patience.

GALLIAN KING *[to Cordella]* Thou fairest creature, whatsoe'er thou art,
That ever any mortal eyes beheld,
Vouchsafe to me, who have o'erheard thy woes,
To shew° the cause of these thy sad laments.

CORDELLA Ah, pilgrims, what avails to shew the cause
When there's no means to find a remedy?

GALLIAN KING To utter grief doth ease a heart o'ercharg'd.

CORDELLA To touch a sore doth aggravate the pain.

GALLIAN KING The silly° mouse by virtue of her teeth
Releas'd the princely lion from the net.[1]

CORDELLA Kind palmer, which so much desir'st to hear
The tragic tale of my unhappy youth,
Know this in brief: I am the hapless daughter
Of Leir, sometimes[2] king of Brittany.

GALLIAN KING Why, who debars his honourable age
From being still the king of Brittany?

CORDELLA None but himself hath dispossess'd himself
And given all his kingdom to the kings
Of Cornwall and of Cambria, with my sisters.

GALLIAN KING Hath he given nothing to your lovely self?

CORDELLA He lov'd me not and therefore gave me nothing,
Only because I could not flatter him;
And in this day of triumph to my sisters
Doth Fortune triumph in my overthrow.

GALLIAN KING Sweet Lady, say there should come a king,

---

[1] The Gallian King alludes to a tale of Aesop in which a mouse frees a lion by chewing through a lion hunter's net.
[2] formerly

As good as either of your sisters' husbands
To crave your love, would you accept of him?

CORDELLA Oh, do not mock with those in misery,
Nor do not think, though Fortune have the power
To spoil mine honour and debase my state,
That she hath any interest in my mind.
For if the greatest monarch on the earth
Should sue to me in this extremity,
Except my heart could love and heart could like
Better than any that I ever saw,
His great estate no more should move my mind
Than mountains move by blast of every wind.

GALLIAN KING Think not, sweet nymph, 'tis holy palmer's guise
To grieved souls fresh torments to devise;
Therefore, in witness of my true intent,
Let heaven and earth bear record of my words:
There is a young and lusty[1] Gallian king,
So like to me as I am to myself,
That earnestly doth crave to have thy love
And join with thee in Hymen's[2] sacred bonds.

CORDELLA The like to thee did ne'er these eyes behold.
Oh, live to add new torments to my grief:
Why didst thou thus entrap me unawares?
Ah, palmer, my estate doth not befit
A kingly marriage, as the case now stands.
Whilom when as[3] I liv'd in honour's height
A prince perhaps might postulate[4] my love.
Now misery, dishonour, and disgrace
Hath light on me, and quite revers'd the case.
Thy king will hold thee wise if thou surcease[5]
The suit, whereas° no dowry will ensue.
Then be advised, palmer, what to do:
Cease for thy king, seek for thyself, to woo.

---

[1] vigorous, full of health
[2] the Roman god of marriage
[3] at the time when
[4] attempt, claim
[5] give up

GALLIAN KING Your birth's too high for any but a king.

CORDELLA My mind is low enough to love a palmer
Rather than any king upon the earth.

GALLIAN KING Oh, but you never can endure their life,
Which is so straight[1] and full of penury.

CORDELLA Oh yes I can, and happy if I might:
I'll hold thy palmer's staff within my hand
And think it is the sceptre of a queen.
Sometime[2] I'll set thy bonnet on my head
And think I wear a rich imperial crown.
Sometime I'll help thee in thy holy prayers
And think I am with thee in paradise.
Thus I'll mock Fortune as she mocketh me
And never will my lovely choice repent.
For having thee, I shall have all content.

GALLIAN KING *[aside]* 'Twere sin to hold her longer in suspense,
Since that my soul hath vow'd she shall be mine.
[to Cordella] Ah, dear Cordella, cordial to my heart,
I am no palmer as I seem to be,
But hither come in this unknown disguise
To view th'admired beauty of those eyes.
I am the king of Gallia, gentle maid
(Although thus slenderly accompanied[3]),
And yet thy vassal by imperious love
And sworn to serve thee everlastingly.

CORDELLA Whate'er you be, of high or low descent,
All's one to me, I do request but this:
That as I am, you will accept of me
And I will have you whatsoe'er you be.
Yet well I know you come of royal race;
I see such sparks[4] of honour in your face.

---

[1] strict
[2] sometimes
[3] meagrely attended (by an entourage)
[4] natural signs

MUMFORD Have palmer's weeds[1] such power to win fair ladies?
Faith, then I hope the next that falls is mine.
Upon condition I no worse might speed,[2]
I would forever wear a palmer's weed.
I like an honest and plain dealing wench
That swears (without exceptions) "I will have you."

These foppets[3] that know not whether to love a man or no except they first
go ask their mothers' leave,[4] by this hand I hate them ten times worse than
poison.

GALLIAN KING What resteth,° then, our happiness to procure?

MUMFORD Faith, go to church to make the matter sure.

GALLIAN KING It shall be so, because the world shall say
King Leir's three daughters were wedded in one day.
The celebration of this happy chance
We will defer until we come to France.

MUMFORD I like the wooing that's not long a-doing.
Well, for her sake I know what I know:
I'll never marry whilst I live
Except[5] I have one of these British ladies.
My humour[6] is alienated from the maids of France. *Exeunt.*

[3.1]   Enter Perillus solus.

PERILLUS The king hath dispossess'd himself of all
Those to advance, which scarce will give him thanks.
His youngest daughter he hath turn'd away
And no man knows what is become of her.
He sojourns now in Cornwall with the eldest,
Who flatter'd him until she did obtain

---

[1] pilgrim's garments
[2] succeed, prosper
[3] little fools
[4] permission
[5] unless
[6] mood, inclination

That[1] at his hands which now she doth possess.
And now she sees he hath no more to give,
It grieves her heart to see her father live.
Oh, whom should man trust in this wicked age
When children thus against their parents rage?
But he, the mirror[2] of mild patience,
Puts up all wrongs, and never gives reply.
Yet shames she not in most opprobrious sort,[3]
To call him fool and dotard to his face
And sets her parasites[4] of purpose oft
In scoffing wise[5] to offer him disgrace.
O, iron[6] age! O, times! O, monstrous, vild,
When parents are contemned[7] of the child!
His pension she hath half restrain'd from him
And will e'er long the other half, I fear,
For she thinks nothing is bestowed in vain
But that which doth her father's life maintain.
Trust not alliance, but trust strangers rather,
Since daughters prove disloyal to the father.
Well, I will counsel him the best I can.
Would I were able to redress his wrong,
Yet what I can, unto my utmost power,
He shall be sure of to the latest hour. *Exit.*

[3.2]   Enter Gonorill, and Skalliger.

GONORILL I prithee, Skalliger, tell me what thou think'st:
Could any woman of our dignity
Endure such quips and peremptory taunts
As I do daily from my doting father?

---

[1] that which
[2] paragon, model (see glossary)
[3] in a most shameful way
[4] minions, courtiers
[5] in a scoffing way (*wise*: see glossary)
[6] For the classical writers Hesiod and Ovid, the Iron Age was an era that had fallen off or devolved from previous eras of greatness like the Golden, Silver, Bronze, and Heroic Ages. Perillus means that the present day is an age of misery, vile (*vild*: see glossary) because parents fall to the machinations of their own children.
[7] despised

Doth't not suffice that I him keep of alms,
Who is not able for to keep himself?
But as if he were our better, he should think
To check and snap me up at every word.[1]
I cannot make me a new-fashioned gown
And set it forth with more than common cost,
But his old doting doltish withered wit
Is sure to give a senseless check[2] for it.
I cannot make a banquet extraordinary
To grace myself and spread my name abroad,
But he, old fool, is captious[3] by and by
And sayeth the cost would well suffice for twice.
Judge then, I pray, what reason is't that I
Should stand alone charg'd with his vain expense
And that my sister Ragan should go free,
To whom he gave as much as unto me?
I prithee, Skalliger, tell me, if thou know,
By any means to rid me of this woe.

SKALLIGER Your many favours still bestowed on me
Bind me in duty to advise your grace
How you may soonest remedy this ill.
The large allowance which he hath from you
Is that which makes him so forget himself.
Therefore, abridge it half and you shall see
That having less he will more thankful be.
For why? Abundance maketh us forget
The fountains whence the benefits do spring.

GONORILL Well, Skalliger, for thy kind advice herein
I will not be ungrateful, if I live.
I have restrained half his portion already
And I will presently restrain the other,
That, having no means to relieve himself,
He may go seek elsewhere for better help. *Exit.*

SKALLIGER Go, viperous woman, shame to all thy sex.
The heavens, no doubt, will punish thee for this.

---

[1] criticise and quarrel with me at every chance
[2] impediment
[3] fault-finding, critical

And me a villain, that to curry favour,
Have given the daughter counsel 'gainst the father.
But us the world doth this experience give:
That he that cannot flatter cannot live. *Exit.*

[3.3]   *Enter King of Cornwall, King Leir, Perillus and Nobles.*

CORNWALL Father, what aileth you to be so sad?
Methinks you frolic not as you were wont.[1]

KING LEIR The nearer we do grow unto our graves
The less we do delight in worldly joys.

CORNWALL But if a man can frame himself to mirth
It is a mean° for to prolong his life.

KING LEIR Then welcome sorrow, Leir's only friend,
Who doth desire his troubled days had end.

CORNWALL Comfort yourself, father,[2] here comes your daughter,
Who much will grieve, I know, to see you sad.

Enter Gonorill.

KING LEIR But more doth grieve, I fear, to see me live.

CORNWALL My Gonorill, you come in wished time,
To put your father from these pensive dumps.[3]
In faith, I fear that all things go not well.

GONORILL What, do you fear that I have anger'd him?
Hath he complained of me unto my lord?
I'll provide him a piece of bread and cheese,
For in a time he'll practise[4] nothing else

---

[1] used to be
[2] Here and below Cornwall uses *father* in two possible—and possibly complementary—senses: to address his father-in-law or to show respect for an elderly man (a "father" in a non-familial sense). This same double sense is important in the scene below in which Cordella is reunited with King Leir.
[3] melancholy moods
[4] habitually do

Than carry tales from one unto another.
'Tis all his practise for to kindle strife
'Twixt you, my lord, and me your loving wife,
But I will take an order, if I can,
To cease th'effect, where first the cause began.

CORNWALL Sweet, be not angry in a partial cause.
He ne'er complained of thee in all his life.
Father, you must not weigh[1] a woman's words.

KING LEIR Alas, not I: poor soul, she breeds young bones
And that is it makes her so touchy, sure.

GONORILL What, breeds young bones already! You will make
An honest woman of me then, belike.[2]
O vild° old wretch! Whoever heard the like,
That seeketh thus his own child to defame?

CORNWALL I cannot stay to hear this discord sound. *Exit.*

GONORILL For any one that loves your company,
You may go pack and seek some other place
To sow the seed of discord and disgrace. *Exit.*

KING LEIR Thus, say or do the best that e'er I can,
'Tis wrested straight into another sense.
This punishment my heavy sins deserve,
And more than this ten thousand thousand times,
Else aged Leir them could never find
Cruel to him to whom he hath been kind.
Why do I over-live myself to see
The course of nature quite revers'd in me?
Ah, gentle Death, if ever any wight[3]
Did wish thy presence with a perfit° zeal,
Then come, I pray thee, even with all my heart,
And end my sorrows with thy fatal dart. *He weeps.*

PERILLUS Ah, do not so disconsolate yourself,

---

[1] consider seriously
[2] perhaps
[3] person, living being

Nor dew your aged cheeks with wasting tears.

KING LEIR What man art thou that tak'st any pity
Upon the worthless state of old Leir?

PERILLUS One who doth bear as great a share of grief
As if it were my dearest father's case.

KING LEIR Ah, good my friend, how ill art thou advised
For to consort with miserable men.
Go learn to flatter, where thou mayest in time
Get favour 'mongst the mighty and so climb.
For now I am so poor and full of want,
As that I ne'er can recompense thy love.

PERILLUS What's got by flattery doth not long endure
And men in favour live not most secure.
My conscience tells me if I should forsake you
I were the hateful'st excrement[1] on the earth,
Which well do know, in course of former time,
How good my lord hath been to me and mine.

KING LEIR Did I ere raise thee higher than the rest
Of all thy ancestors which were before?

PERILLUS I ne'er did seek it, but by your good grace
I still enjoyed my own with quietness.

KING LEIR Did I ere give thee living to increase
The due revenues which thy father left?

PERILLUS I had enough, my lord, and having that,
What should you need to give me any more?

KING LEIR Oh, did I ever dispossess myself
And give thee half my kingdom in good will?

PERILLUS Alas, my lord, there were no reason why
You should have such a thought to give it me.

---

[1] outcast: a general term of contempt

KING LEIR Nay, if thou talk of reason, then be mute,
For with good reason I can thee confute.
If they which first by nature's sacred law
Do owe to me the tribute of their lives;
If they to whom I always have been kind
And bountiful beyond comparison;
If they for whom I have undone myself
And brought my age unto this extreme want
Do now reject, contemn,[1] despise, abhor me,
What reason moveth thee to sorrow for me?

PERILLUS Where reason fails, let tears confirm my love
And speak how much your passions do me move.
Ah, good my lord, condemn not all for one.
You have two daughters left to whom, I know
You shall be welcome if you please to go.

KING LEIR Oh, how thy words add sorrow to my soul,
To think of my unkindness to Cordella!
Whom, causeless, I did dispossess of all
Upon th'unkind suggestions of her sisters.
And for her sake I think this heavy doom
Is fall'n on me, and not without desert.°
Yet unto Ragan was I always kind,
And gave to her the half of all I had.
It may be, if I should to her repair,
She would be kinder and entreat me fair.

PERILLUS No doubt she would, and practise[2] ere't be long
By force of arms for to redress your wrong.

KING LEIR Well, since thou dost advise me for to go
I am resolv'd to try the worst of woe. *Exeunt.*

[3.4]   Enter Ragan solus.

RAGAN
How may I bless the hour of my nativity,

---

[1] treat with contempt
[2] find a way

Which bodeth unto me such happy stars!
How may I thank kind Fortune, that vouchsafes
To all my actions such desir'd event!
I rule the King of Cambria as I please.
The states are all obedient to my will,
And look what ere I say, it shall be so;
Not anyone that dareth answer no.
My eldest sister lives in royal state
And wanteth° nothing fitting her degree,
Yet hath she such a cooling card withal,
As that her honey savoureth much of gall.[1]
My father with her is quarter-master[2] still
And many times restrains her of her will.
But if he were with me and serv'd me so
I'd send him packing somewhere else to go.
I'd entertain him with such slender[3] cost
That he should quickly wish to change his host. *Exit.*

[3.5]   *Enter Cornwall, Gonorill, and attendants.*

CORNWALL Ah, Gonorill, what dire unhappy chance
Hath sequestered thy father from our presence
That no report can yet be heard of him?
Some great unkindness hath been offer'd him
Exceeding far the bounds of patience,
Else all the world shall never me persuade
He would forsake us without notice made.

GONORILL Alas, my lord, whom doth it touch so near,
Or who hath interest in this grief, but I,
Whom sorrow had brought to her longest home,[4]
But that I know his qualities so well?
I know he is but stol'n upon my sister
At unawares to see her how she fares
And spend a little time with her to note
How all things go and how she likes her choice.
And when occasion serves, he'll steal from her

---

[1] Yet she has such personal qualities that her honey tastes of bitterness.
[2] superior, boss
[3] mean, meagre
[4] i.e., her grave

And unawares return to us again.
Therefore, my lord, be frolic[1] and resolve
To see my father here again e'er long.

CORNWALL I hope so too; but yet to be more sure, ,
I'll send a post[2] immediately to know
Whether he be arrived there or no. *Exit.*

GONORILL But I will intercept the messenger
And temper[3] him before he doth depart
With sweet persuasions and with sound rewards
That his report shall ratify my speech
And make my lord cease further to enquire.
If he be not gone to my sister's court,
As sure my mind presageth that he is,
He happily° may, by travelling unknown ways,
Fall sick and as a common passenger
Be dead and buried. Would God it were so well,
For then there were no more to do but this.
He went away and none knows where he is.
But say he be in Cambria with the king
And there exclaim against me, as he will:
I know he is as welcome to my sister
As water is into a broken ship.
Well, after him I'll send such thunderclaps
Of slander, scandal, and invented tales
That all the blame shall be remov'd from me
And unperceiv'd rebound upon himself.
Thus with one nail another I'll expel
And make the world judge that I used him well.

Enter the Messenger that should go to Cambria, with a letter[4] in his hand.

GONORILL My honest friend, whither away so fast?

MESSENGER To Cambria, Madam, with letters from the king.

---

[1] joyful
[2] messenger
[3] emotionally manipulate
[4] The messenger actually carries several letters, as the action of the scene shows.

GONORILL To whom?

MESSENGER Unto your father, if he be there.

GONORILL Let me see them. *She opens them.*

MESSENGER Madam, I hope your grace will stand
Between me and my neck-verse,[1] if I be
Called in question for opening the king's letters.

GONORILL 'Twas I that opened them, it was not thou.

MESSENGER Ay, but you need not care, and so must I,
A handsome[2] man, be quickly truss'd up.
And when a man's hang'd all the world cannot save him.

GONORILL He that hangs thee were better hang his father,
Or that but hurts thee in the least degree.
I tell thee, we make great account of thee.

MESSENGER I am o'er-joy'd, I surfeit of sweet words.
Kind queen, had I a hundred lives I would
Spend ninety-nine of them for you for that word.

GONORILL Ay, but thou wouldst keep one life still,
And that's as many as thou art like to have.

MESSENGER That one life is not too dear for my good queen. This sword,
this buckler, this head, this heart, these hands, arms, legs, trips, bowels,
and all the members else whatsoever are at your dispose; use me, trust me,
command me: if I fail in anything, tie me to a dung cart and make a
scavenger's horse of me, and whip me, so long as I have any skin on my
back.

GONORILL In token of further employment, take that. *Flings him a purse.*

---

[1] If an accused criminal could read or recite a "neck-verse," typically Psalm 51, he
or she could be spared hanging as a so-called benefit of clergy. The messenger
is using the term in a more general and figurative sense to mean "between me
and my death."

[2] proper (rather than attractive)

MESSENGER A strong bond, a firm obligation, good in law, good in law. If I keep not the condition, let my neck be the forfeiture of my negligence.

GONORILL I like thee well; thou hast a good tongue.

MESSENGER And as bad a tongue if it be set on it as any oyster wife at Billingsgate hath. Why, I have made many of my neighbours forsake their houses with railing upon them, and go dwell elsewhere; and so by my means houses have been good cheap in our parish. My tongue, being well whetted with choler, is more sharp than a razor of Palermo.[1]

GONORILL Oh, thou art a fit man for my purpose.

MESSENGER Commend me not, sweet queen, before you try° me. As my deserts° are, so do think of me.

GONORILL Well said, then this is thy trial: instead of carrying the king's letters to my father, carry thou these letters to my sister, which contain matter quite contrary to the other. There shall she be given to understand that my father hath detracted her, given out slanderous speeches against her, and that he hath most intolerably abused me, set my lord and me at variance, and made mutinies amongst the commons.

These things (although it be not so)
Yet thou must affirm them to be true
With oaths and protestations as will serve
To drive my sister out of love with him
And cause my will accomplished to be.
This do, thou win'st my favour forever and makest
A highway of preferment to thee and all thy friends.

MESSENGER It sufficeth. Conceit[2] it is already done:
I will so tongue-whip him that I will
Leave him as bare of credit, as a poulter
Leaves a coney when she pulls off his skin.[3]

GONORILL Yet there is a further matter.

---

[1] Oyster-sellers of the Billingsgate section of London were proverbially loud and foul-mouthed. The razor of Palermo was proverbially sharp.

[2] imagine that

[3] The messenger boasts that he will attack him verbally, figuratively skinning him the way a merchant literally skins a rabbit for sale in a marketplace.

MESSENGER I thirst to hear it.

GONORILL If my sister thinketh convenient, as my letters importeth, to make him away,[1] hast thou the heart to effect it?

MESSENGER Few words are best in so small a matter:
These are but trifles. By this book I will. *He kisses the paper.*

GONORILL About it presently. I long 'til it be done.

MESSENGER I fly, I fly. *Exeunt.*

[4.1]   Enter Cordella solus.[2]

CORDELLA I have been over-negligent today
In going to the temple of my God
To render thanks for all His benefits
Which He miraculously hath bestowed on me
In raising me out of my mean estate
When as I was devoid of worldly friends
And placing me in such a sweet content
As far exceeds the reach of my deserts.°
My kingly husband, mirror° of his time,
For zeal, for justice, kindness, and for care
To God, his subjects, me, and commonweal,[3]
By his appointment was ordain'd for me.
I cannot wish the thing that I do want;°
I cannot want the thing but I may have,
Save only this which I shall ne'er obtain:
My father's love—Oh, this I ne'er shall gain.
I would abstain from any nutriment
And pine my body to the very bones.
Barefoot I would on pilgrimage set forth
Unto the furthest quarters of the earth,
And all my life time would I sackcloth wear,
And mourning-wise° pour dust upon my head
So he but to forgive me once would please,
That his gray hairs might go to heaven in peace.

---

[1] to murder him
[2] alone
[3] commonwealth

And yet I know not how I him offended
Or wherein justly I have deserved blame.
O, sisters! you are much to blame in this:
It was not he but you that did me wrong.
Yet God forgive both him and you and me,
Even as I do in perfit° charity.
I will to church, and pray unto my Saviour
That ere I die I may obtain His favour. *Exit.*

[4.2]   Enter King Leir and Perillus faintly.

PERILLUS Rest on me, my lord, and stay[1] yourself.
The way seems tedious to your aged limbs.

KING LEIR Nay, rest on me, kind friend, and stay thyself.
Thou art as old as I, but more kind.

PERILLUS Ah, good my lord, it ill befits that I
Should lean upon the person of a king.

KING LEIR But it fits worse[2] that I should bring thee forth,
That had no cause to come along with me
Through these uncouth paths and tireful ways[3]
And never ease thy fainting limbs a whit.
Thou hast left all, ay, all to come with me
And I, for all, have naught to guerdon[4] thee.

PERILLUS Cease, good my lord, to aggravate[5] my woes,
With these kind words, which cuts my heart in two,
To think your will should want° the power to do.

KING LEIR Cease, good Perillus, for to call me lord,
And think me but the shadow of myself.

PERILLUS That honourable title will I give
Unto my lord so long as I do live.

---

[1] steady
[2] is less appropriate
[3] unknown paths and exhausting roads
[4] reward
[5] worsen

Oh, be of comfort, for I see the place
Whereas[1] your daughter keeps her residence.
And lo, in happy time the Cambrian Prince
Is here arriv'd to gratify[2] our coming.

Enter the Prince of Cambria, Ragan and Nobles: they look upon them, and whisper together.

KING LEIR Were I best speak, or sit me down and die?
I am asham'd to tell this heavy tale.

PERILLUS Then let me tell it, if you please, my lord:
'Tis shame for them that were the cause thereof.

CAMBRIA What two old men are those that seem so sad?
Methinks I should remember well their looks.

RAGAN No, I mistake not, sure it is my father!
I must dissemble kindness now of force.[3]
She runneth to him, and kneels down, saying:
Father, I bid you welcome, full of grief,
To see your grace used thus unworthily,
And ill befitting for your reverend age
To come on foot a journey so endurable.[4]
Oh, what disaster chance hath been the cause
To make your cheeks so hollow, spare and lean?
He cannot speak for weeping. For God's love, come.
Let us refresh him with some needful things
And at more leisure we may better know
Whence springs the ground of this unlook'd-for woe.

CAMBRIA Come, father,[5] e'er we any further talk
You shall refresh you after this weary walk. *Exeunt, manet Ragan.*[6]

---

[1] where
[2] grace, dignify
[3] out of necessity
[4] lengthy and strenuous
[5] father-in-law
[6] They exit, Ragan remains.

RAGAN Comes he to me with finger in the eye¹
To tell a tale against my sister here,
Whom, I do know, he greatly hath abused?
And now like a contentious crafty wretch
He first begins for to complain himself,
Whenas° himself is in the greatest fault.
I'll not be partial in my sister's cause,
Nor yet believe his doting vain reports,
Who for a trifle, safely I dare say,
Upon a spleen² is stolen thence away.
And here (forsooth) he hopeth to have harbour
And to be moan'd and made on³ like a child.
But ere't be long⁴ his coming he shall curse
And truly say he came from bad to worse.
Yet will I make fair weather to procure
Convenient means and then I'll strike it sure.   *Exit.*

[4.3]   *Enter Messenger solus.*

MESSENGER Now happily I am arrived here
Before the stately palace of the Cambrian king.
If Leir be here safe-seated and in rest,
To rouse him from it I will do my best.

Enter Ragan.

Now bags of gold, your virtue is (no doubt)
To make me in my message bold and stout.
  [to Ragan] The King of Heaven preserve your majesty
And send your highness everlasting reign.

RAGAN Thanks, good my friend. But what imports thy message?

MESSENGER Kind greetings from the Cornwall queen.
The residue⁵ these letters will declare. *She opens the letters.*

---

¹ falsely weeping
² fit of ill temper
³ fussed over
⁴ before long
⁵ remainder (of the message)

RAGAN How fares our royal sister?

MESSENGER I did leave her at my parting in good health.
She reads the letter, frowns and stamps.
[aside] See how her colour comes and goes again,
Now red as scarlet, now as pale as ash.
See how she knits her brow and bites her lips
And stamps and makes a dumb shew° of disdain
Mixed with revenge and violent extremes.
Here will be more work and more crowns for me.

RAGAN *[to herself]* Alas, poor soul, and hath he used her thus
And is he now come hither with intent
To set divorce betwixt my lord and me?
Doth he give out that he doth hear report
That I do rule my husband as I list,[1]
And therefore means to alter so the case
That I shall know my lord to be my head?
Well, it were best for him to take good heed
Or I will make him hop without a head[2]
For his presumption, dotard that he is.
In Cornwall he hath made such mutinies,
First setting of the king against the queen,
Then stirring up the commons 'gainst the king,
That had he there continued any longer
He had been call'd in question for his fact.[3]
So upon that occasion thence he fled
And comes thus slyly stealing unto us.
And now already since his coming hither
My lord and he are grown in such a league
That I can have no conference with his grace.
I fear he doth already intimate
Some forged cavillations[4] 'gainst my state.
'Tis therefore best to cut him off in time,
Lest slanderous rumours, once abroad dispers'd,
It is too late for them to be revers'd.
[to him] Friend, as the tenor of these letters shews,°

---

[1] like (see glossary)
[2] kill him (with pun on *head/head*, above)
[3] deed
[4] criticisms, quibbles

My sister puts great confidence in thee.

MESSENGER She never yet committed trust to me,
But that (I hope) she found me always faithful.
So will I be to any friend of hers
That hath occasion to employ my help.

RAGAN Hast thou the heart to act a stratagem
And give a stab or two if need require?

MESSENGER I have a heart compact of adamant,[1]
Which never knew what melting pity meant.
I weigh no more the murd'ring of a man
Than I respect the cracking of a flea
When I do catch her biting on my skin.
If you will have your husband or your father,
Or both of them, sent to another world,
Do but command me do't: it shall be done.

RAGAN It is enough, we make no doubt of thee:
Meet us tomorrow here at nine o'clock.
Meanwhile, farewell, and drink that for my sake.
[She offers him money.] Exit.

MESSENGER Ay, this is it will make me do the deed.
Oh, had I every day such customers,
This were[2] the gainfulest trade in Christendom!
A purse of gold giv'n for a paltry stab!
Why, here's a wench that longs to have a stab.
Well, I could give it her and ne'er hurt her neither.[3]

[4.4]   Enter the Gallian King, and Cordella.

GALLIAN KING When will these clouds of sorrow once disperse
And smiling joy triumph upon thy brow?

---

[1] a heart composed of hard rock
[2] would be
[3] This obvious sexual joke is repeated, in slightly less vulgar language, by the Gallian
    King two speeches below. The play's pieties and sentimentalism do not appear
    to be incompatible with vulgar sexual humour up and down the social hierarchies
    of the play. See also Mumford's sexual jokes, below.

When will this scene of sadness have an end
And pleasant acts ensue to move delight?
When will my lovely queen cease to lament
And take some comfort to her grieved thoughts?
If of thyself thou deign'st to have no care,
Yet pity me, whom thy grief makes despair.

CORDELLA Oh, grieve not you, my lord; you have no cause.
Let not my passions move your mind a whit,
For I am bound by nature to lament
For his ill will that life to me first lent.
If so the stock be dried with disdain,
Wither'd and sere the branch must needs remain.[1]

GALLIAN KING But thou art now graft in another stock;
I am the stock and thou the lovely branch
And from my root continual sap shall flow
To make thee flourish with perpetual spring.
Forget thy father and thy kindred now
Since they forsake thee like inhumane beasts.
Think they are dead, since all their kindness dies,
And bury them where black oblivion lies.
Think not thou art the daughter of old Leir,
Who did unkindly disinherit thee,
But think thou art the noble Gallian queen
And wife to him that dearly loveth thee.
Embrace the joys that present with thee dwell;
Let sorrow pack and hide herself in hell.

CORDELLA Not that I miss my country or my kin,
My old acquaintance or my ancient friends
Doth any whit distemperate my mind,
Knowing you, which are more dear to me,
Than country, kin, and all things else can be.
Yet pardon me, my gracious lord, in this,
For what can stop the course of nature's power?
As easy is it for four-footed beasts

---

[1] Cordella offers a metaphor in which she, the branch to King Leir's "stock," is made
    withered and dry (sere) because her father is "dried with disdain." Her husband
    tries to comfort her by suggesting that she is now grafted to him, a second stock
    from whom flows "continual sap."

To stay themselves[1] upon the liquid air
And mount aloft into the element
And overstrip the feathered fowls in flight;
As easy is it for the slimy fish
To live and thrive without the help of water;
As easy is it for the blackamoor[2]
To wash the tawny colour from his skin,
Which all oppose against the course of nature,
As I am able to forget my father.

GALLIAN KING Mirror of virtue, phoenix[3] of our age!
Too kind a daughter for an unkind father,
Be of good comfort; for I will dispatch
Ambassadors immediately for Britain
Unto the King of Cornwall's court, whereas°
Your father keepeth now his residence,
And in the kindest manner him entreat
That, setting former grievances apart,
He will be pleased to come and visit us.
If no entreaty will suffice the turn,
I'll offer him the half of all my crown.
If that moves not, we'll furnish out a fleet,
And sail to Cornwall for to visit him,
And there you shall be firmly reconcil'd
In perfit° love, as erst° you were before.

CORDELLA Where tongue cannot sufficient thanks afford,
The King of Heaven remunerate my lord.

GALLIAN KING Only be blithe and frolic, sweet, with me:
This and much more I'll do to comfort thee.

[4.5]   Enter Messenger solus.

MESSENGER It is a world to see, now I am flush,[4]
How many friends I purchase everywhere!

---

[1] to float or suspend themselves
[2] a Moorish or African person
[3] Like the mythical phoenix, a bird that never dies, Cordella is a "mirror," or paragon,
   of virtue.
[4] flush with money

How many seeks[1] to creep into my favour
And kiss their hands and bend their knees to me!
No more, here comes the queen; now shall I know her mind
And hope for to derive more crowns from her.

Enter Ragan.

RAGAN My friend, I see thou mind'st thy promise well
And art before me here, methinks, today.

MESSENGER I am a poor man, and it like[2] your grace,
But yet I always love to keep my word.

RAGAN Well, keep thy word with me and thou shalt see
That of a poor man I will make thee rich.

MESSENGER I long to hear it. It might have been dispatch'd[3]
If you had told me of it yesternight.

RAGAN It is a thing of right strange consequence
And well I cannot utter it in words.

MESSENGER It is more strange that I am not by this
Beside myself with longing for to hear it.
Were it to meet the devil in his den
And try a bout with him for a scratch'd face,
I'd undertake it, if you would but bid me.

RAGAN Ah, good my friend, that[4] I should have thee do
Is such a thing as I do shame to speak.
Yet it must needs be done.

MESSENGER I'll speak it for thee, queen: shall I kill thy father?
I know 'tis that, and if it be so, say.

RAGAN Ay.

---

[1] seek. Early modern usage sometimes permitted singular verbs for plural subjects.
[2] may it please (a polite formula)
[3] done, completed
[4] that which

MESSENGER Why, that's enough.

RAGAN And yet that is not all.

MESSENGER What else?

RAGAN Thou must kill that old man that came with him.

MESSENGER Here are two hands; for each of them is one.

RAGAN And for each hand here is a recompense. *[She offers him money.]*

MESSENGER Oh, that I had ten hands by miracle,
I could tear ten in pieces with my teeth,
So in my mouth you'ld put a purse of gold.
But in what manner must it be effected?

RAGAN Tomorrow morning ere the break of day
I by a wile[1] will send them to the thicket
That is about some two miles from the court
And promise them to meet them there myself
Because I must have private conference
About some news I have receiv'd from Cornwall.
This is enough; I know they will not fail.
And then be ready for to play thy part,
Which done, thou mayst right easily escape
And no man once mistrust thee for the fact.°
But yet, before thou prosecute the act,
Shew° him the letter which my sister sent.
There let him read his own indictment first
And then proceed to execution.
But see thou faint not, for they will speak fair.

MESSENGER Could he speak words as pleasing as the pipe
Of Mercury, which charm'd the hundred eyes
Of watchful Argos and enforc'd him sleep,[2]
[to the purse] Yet here are words so pleasing to my thoughts

---

[1] deception, ruse

[2] Hermes (Mercury) charmed the 100-eyed watchman Argos (or Argus) by playing
upon his pipes and telling him stories until he fell asleep, so that he could liberate
Io, the daughter of Jove (Jupiter).

As quite shall take away the sound of his. *Exit.*

RAGAN About it then, and when thou hast dispatch'd
I'll find a means to send thee after him. *Exit.*

[4.6]   Enter Cornwall and Gonorill.

CORNWALL I wonder that the messenger doth stay,
Whom we dispatch'd for Cambria so long since.
If that his answer do not please us well
And he do shew° good reason for delay
I'll teach him how to dally with his king
And to detain us in such long suspense.

GONORILL My lord, I think the reason may be this:
My father means to come along with him
And therefore 'tis his pleasure he shall stay
For to attend upon him on the way.

CORNWALL It may be so and therefore till I know
The truth thereof I will suspend my judgement.

Enter Servant.

SERVANT And't like[1] your grace, there is an ambassador
Arrived from Gallia[2] and craves admittance to your majesty.

CORNWALL From Gallia? what should his message
Hither import? is not your father happily[3]
Gone thither? well, whatsoe'er it be,
Bid him come in, he shall have audience.

Enter Ambassador.

What news from Gallia? Speak, ambassador.

AMBASSADOR The noble king and queen of Gallia first salutes,
By me, their honourable father, my lord Leir.

---

[1] may it please (a polite formula)
[2] France
[3] haply, possibly (see glossary)

Next, they commend them kindly to your graces,
As those whose welfare they entirely wish.
Letters I have to deliver to my lord Leir,
And presents too, if I might speak with him.

GONORILL If you might speak with him? Why, do you think
We are afraid that you should speak with him?

AMBASSADOR Pardon me, madam, for I think not so,
But say so only 'cause he is not here.

CORNWALL Indeed, my friend, upon some urgent cause
He is at this time absent from the court.
But if a day or two you here repose
'Tis very likely you shall have him here
Or else have certain notice where he is.

GONORILL Are not we worthy to receive your message?

AMBASSADOR I had in charge to do it to himself.

GONORILL *To herself.* It may be then 'twill not be done in haste.
[to the ambassador] How doth my sister brook° the air of France?

AMBASSADOR Exceeding well and never sick one hour
Since first she set her foot upon the shore.

GONORILL I am the more sorry.

AMBASSADOR I hope, not so, madam.

GONORILL Didst thou not say, that she was ever sick
Since the first hour that she arrived there?

AMBASSADOR No, madam, I said quite contrary.

GONORILL Then I mistook thee.

CORNWALL Then she is merry, if she have her health.

AMBASSADOR Oh no, her grief exceeds, until the time

That she be reconcil'd unto her father.

GONORILL God continue it.

AMBASSADOR What, madam?

GONORILL Why, her health.

AMBASSADOR Amen to that, but God release her grief
And send her father in a better mind
Than to continue always so unkind.

CORNWALL I'll be a mediator in her cause
And seek all means to expiate[1] his wrath.

AMBASSADOR Madam, I hope your grace will do the like.

GONORILL Should I be a mean to exasperate[2] his wrath
Against my sister, whom I love so dear? No, no.

AMBASSADOR To expiate or mitigate his wrath,
For he hath misconceived without a cause.

GONORILL Oh, ay, what else?

AMBASSADOR 'Tis pity it should be so. Would it were otherwise.

GONORILL It were great pity it should be otherwise.

AMBASSADOR Than how, madam?

GONORILL Than that they should be reconciled again.

AMBASSADOR It shews° you bear an honourable mind.

GONERILL *Speaks to herself.* It shews thy understanding to be blind
And that thou hadst need of an interpreter.
Well, I will know thy message ere't be long

---

[1] diminish
[2] a means to increase

And find a mean to cross it[1] if I can.

CORNWALL Come in, my friend, and frolic in our court
Till certain notice of my father[2] come. *Exeunt.*

[4.7]   Enter King Leir and Perillus.

PERILLUS My lord, you are up today before your hour;
'Tis news to you to be abroad so rathe.[3]

KING LEIR 'Tis news indeed. I am so extreme heavy
That I can scarcely keep my eye-lids open.

PERILLUS And so am I, but I impute the cause
To rising sooner than we use to do.[4]

KING LEIR Hither my daughter means to come disguis'd.
I'll sit me down and read until she come. *Pulls out a book and sits down.*

PERILLUS She'll not be long, I warrant you, my lord.
But say a couple of these they call good fellows[5]
Should step out of a hedge and set upon us,
We were in good case for to answer them.[6]

KING LEIR 'Twere not for us to stand upon our hands.[7]

PERILLUS I fear we scant should stand upon our legs.
But how should we do to defend ourselves?

KING LEIR Even pray to God to bless us from their hands,
For fervent prayer much ill hap[8] withstands.

PERILLUS I'll sit and pray with you for company;

---

[1] a means to thwart it
[2] father-in-law
[3] early
[4] usually do
[5] i.e., robbers
[6] we'd be in no shape to respond
[7] defend ourselves
[8] fortune

Yet was I ne'er so heavy in my life. *They fall both asleep.*

Enter the Messenger or murtherer with two daggers in his hands.

MESSENGER Were it not a mad jest, lest two or three of my profession
should meet me and lay me down in a ditch and play rob-thief with me and
perforce take my gold away from me whilst I act this stratagem, and by
this means the graybeards should escape? Faith, when I were at liberty
again I would make no more to do but go to the next tree and there hang
myself. *Sees them and starts.*

But stay, methinks my youths are here already[1]
And with pure zeal have prayed themselves asleep.
I think they know to what intent they came,
And are provided for another world. *He takes their books away.*
Now could I stab them bravely[2] while they sleep
And in a manner put them to no pain.
And doing so, I shewed° them mighty friendship,
For fear of death is worse than death itself,
But that my sweet queen will'd me for to shew
This letter to them ere I did the deed.
Mass,[3] they begin to stir: I'll stand aside;
So shall I come upon them unawares.

They wake and rise.

KING LEIR I marvel that my daughter stays so long.

PERILLUS I fear we did mistake the place, my lord.

KING LEIR God grant we do not miscarry in the place.
I had a short nap, but so full of dread
As much amazeth me to think thereof.

PERILLUS Fear not, my lord, dreams are but fantasies
And slight imaginations of the brain.

---

[1] But wait, I think my youths are already here (ironic since they are obviously old
   men).
[2] fearlessly
[3] by the mass (a profanity)

MESSENGER *[aside]* Persuade him so, but I'll make him and you
Confess that dreams do often prove too true.

PERILLUS I pray, my lord, what was the effect of it?
I may go near to guess what it pretends.[1]

MESSENGER *[aside]* Leave that to me; I will expound the dream.

KING LEIR Methought my daughters, Gonorill and Ragan,
Stood both before me with such grim aspects,
Each brandishing a falchion[2] in their hand,
Ready to lop a limb off where it fell,
And in their other hands a naked poniard[3]
Wherewith they stabb'd me in a hundred places,
And to their thinking left me there for dead.
But then my youngest daughter, fair Cordella,
Came with a box of balsam in her hand
And poured it into my bleeding wounds,
By whose good means I was recovered well,
In perfit° health as erst° I was before.
And with the fear of this I did awake,
And yet for fear my feeble joints quake.

MESSENGER *[aside]* I'll make you quake for something presently.
[to them] Stand, stand. *They reel.*

KING LEIR We do, my friend, although with much ado.

MESSENGER Deliver, deliver.[4]

PERILLUS Deliver us, good Lord, from such as he.

MESSENGER You should have prayed before while it was time,
And then perhaps you might have 'scap'd my hands,
But you, like faithful watchmen, fell asleep,
The whilst I came and took your halberds[5] from you.

---

[1] I can probably guess what it means
[2] curved-bladed sword
[3] dagger
[4] hand over your money
[5] weapons

They shew° their books.
And now you want° your weapons of defence,
How have you any hope to be delivered?
This comes because you have no better stay,°
But fall asleep, when you should watch and pray.[1]

KING LEIR My friend, thou seem'st to be a proper man.

MESSENGER 'Sblood,[2] how the old slave claws me by the elbow!
He thinks, belike,[3] to 'scape by scraping thus.

PERILLUS And it may be, are in some need of money.

MESSENGER That to be false: behold my evidence. *Shews° his purses.*

KING LEIR If that I have[4] will do thee any good,
I give it thee, even with a right good will. *The messenger takes his purse.*

PERILLUS Here, take mine too, and wish with all my heart
To do thee pleasure it were twice as much.
He takes his and weighs them both in his hands.

MESSENGER I'll none of them; they are too light for me.
Puts them in his pocket.

KING LEIR Why then farewell. And if° thou have occasion
In anything to use me to the queen
'Tis like enough that I can pleasure[5] thee. *They proffer to go.*

MESSENGER Do you hear, do you hear, sir?
If I had occasion to use you to the queen,
Would you do one thing for me I should ask?

KING LEIR Ay, anything that lies within my power.
Here is my hand upon it, so farewell. *They proffer to go.*

---

[1] Matthew 26:41: "Watch and pray, that ye enter not into temptation: the spirit indeed is willing, but the flesh is weak" (Geneva Bible).
[2] by God's blood (a profanity)
[3] perhaps
[4] anything I have
[5] help you out

MESSENGER Hear you sir, hear you? Pray, a word with you.
Methinks a comely honest ancient man
Should not dissemble with one for a vantage.
I know, when I shall come to try this gear,[1]
You will recant from all that you have said.

PERILLUS Mistrust not him, but try° him when thou wilt:
He is her father, therefore may do much.

MESSENGER I know he is, and therefore mean to try him.
You are his friend too; I must try you both.

KING LEIR AND PERILLUS Prithee do, prithee do. *They proffer to go out.*

MESSENGER Stay, graybeards, then, and prove men of your words.
The queen hath tied me by a solemn oath
Here in this place to see you both dispatch'd.
Now for the safeguard of my conscience
Do me the pleasure for to kill yourselves,
So shall you save me labour for to do it,
And prove yourselves true old men of your words.
And here I vow in sight of all the world
I ne'er will trouble you whilst I live again.

KING LEIR Affright us not with terror, good my friend,
Nor strike such fear into our aged hearts.
Play not the cat which dallieth with the mouse
And on a sudden maketh her a prey.
But if thou art mark'd for the man of death
To me and to my Damion,[2] tell me plain,
That we may be prepared for the stroke
And make ourselves fit for the world to come.

MESSENGER I am the last of any mortal race,
That ere your eyes are likely to behold,
And hither sent of purpose to this place
To give a final period[3] to your days,

---

[1] taste death
[2] Damon, or Damion, a proverbially loyal friend
[3] full-stop, end

Which[1] are so wicked and have lived so long
That your own children seek to short your life.

KING LEIR Cam'st thou from France of purpose to do this?

MESSENGER From France? Zoones,[2] do I look like a Frenchman? Sure I
have not mine own face on: somebody hath chang'd faces with me and I
know not of it. But I am sure my apparel is all English. Sirrah,[3] what
mean'st thou to ask that question? I could spoil the fashion o' this face for
anger. A French face!

KING LEIR Because my daughter, whom I have offended,
And at whose hands I have deserv'd as ill
As ever any father did of child
Is queen of France, no thanks at all to me,
But unto God, who my injustice see.[4]
If it be so that she doth seek revenge,
As with good reason she may justly do,
I will most willingly resign my life,
A sacrifice to mitigate her ire.
I never will entreat thee to forgive
Because I am unworthy for to live.
Therefore, speak soon and I will soon make speed,
Whether Cordella will'd thee do this deed?

MESSENGER As I am a perfit° gentleman, thou speak'st French to me.
I never heard Cordella's name before,
Nor never was in France in all my life.
I never knew thou hadst a daughter there,
To whom thou didst prove so unkind a churl,
But thy own tongue declares that thou hast been
A vile old wretch and full of heinous sin.

KING LEIR Ah no, my friend, thou art deceived much,
For her except, whom I confess I wrong'd
Through doting frenzy and o'er-jealous love,
There lives not any under heaven's bright eye

---

[1] who
[2] by God's wounds (a profanity)
[3] a term of condescension
[4] sees

That can convict me of impiety.
And therefore sure thou dost mistake the mark,
For I am in true peace with all the world.

MESSENGER You are the fitter for the King of Heaven.
And therefore, for to rid thee of suspense,
Know thou the queens of Cambria and Cornwall,
Thy own two daughters, Gonorill and Ragan,
Appointed me to massacre thee here.
Why wouldst thou then persuade me that thou art
In charity[1] with all the world? But now
When thy own issue hold thee in such hate
That they have hired me t'abridge thy fate—
Oh, fie upon such vile dissembling breath,
That would deceive even at the point of death.

PERILLUS Am I awake or is it but a dream?

MESSENGER Fear nothing, man, thou art but in a dream
And thou shalt never wake until doomsday.
By then, I hope, thou wilt have slept enough.

KING LEIR Yet, gentle friend, grant one thing ere I die.

MESSENGER I'll grant you anything except your lives.

KING LEIR Oh, but assure me by some certain token
That my two daughters hired thee to this deed.
If I were once resolv'd of that then I
Would wish no longer life but crave to die.

MESSENGER That to be true, in sight of heaven I swear.

KING LEIR Swear not by heaven, for fear of punishment.
The heavens are guiltless of such heinous acts.

MESSENGER I swear by earth, the mother of us all.

KING LEIR Swear not by earth, for she abhors to bear

---

[1] at peace

Such bastards as are murtherers of her sons.

MESSENGER Why then, by hell and all the devils I swear.

KING LEIR Swear not by hell, for that stands gaping wide
To swallow thee, and if° thou do this deed. *Thunder and lightning.*

MESSENGER *[aside]* I would that word were in his belly again,
It hath frighted me even to the very heart.
This old man is some strong magician:
His words have turn'd my mind from this exploit.
[to them] Then neither heaven, earth, nor hell be witness,
But let this paper witness for them all. *Shews° Gonorill's letter.*
[aside] Shall I relent, or shall I prosecute?
Shall I resolve or were I best recant?
I will not crack my credit with two queens
To whom I have already passed my word.
Oh, but my conscience for this act doth tell,
I get heaven's hate, earth's scorn, and pains of hell.

They bless themselves.

PERILLUS O just Jehovah, whose almighty power
Doth govern all things in this spacious world,
How canst thou suffer such outrageous acts
To be committed without just revenge?
O viperous generation and accurs'd,
To seek his blood, whose blood did make them first!

KING LEIR Ah, my true friend in all extremity,
Let us submit us to the will of God:
Things past all sense, let us not seek to know;
It is God's will, and therefore must be so.
My friend, I am prepared for the stroke:
Strike when thou wilt and I forgive thee here,
Even from the very bottom of my heart.

MESSENGER But I am not prepared for to strike.

KING LEIR Farewell, Perillus, even the truest friend
That ever lived in adversity:

The latest[1] kindness I'll request of thee
Is that thou go unto my daughter Cordella
And carry her her father's latest blessing.
Withal[2] desire her that she will forgive me,
For I have wrong'd her without any cause.
Now, Lord, receive me, for I come to Thee
And die, I hope, in perfit° charity.
Dispatch, I pray thee. I have lived too long.

MESSENGER Ay, but you are unwise to send an errand
By him that never meaneth to deliver it.
Why, he must go along with you to heaven:
It were not good you should go all alone.

KING LEIR No doubt he shall, when by the course of nature
He must surrender up his due to death.
But that time shall not come 'til God permit.

MESSENGER Nay, presently, to bear you company,
I have a passport for him in my pocket,
Already seal'd, and he must needs ride post.[3] *He shews° a bag of money.*

KING LEIR The letter which I read imports not so;
It only toucheth me, no word of him.

MESSENGER Ay, but the queen commands it must be so,
And I am paid for him as well as you.

PERILLUS I who have borne you company in life
Most willingly will bear a share in death.
It skilleth not for me, my friend, a whit,[4]
Nor for a hundred such as thou and I.

---

[1] final
[2] with that
[3] must hurry (to his own death)
[4] it does not matter at all to me, my friend

MESSENGER Marry,[1] but it doth, sir, by your leave: your good days are
past. Though it be no matter for you 'tis a matter for me; proper men are
not so rife.[2]

PERILLUS Oh, but beware how thou dost lay thy hand
Upon the high anointed of the Lord:
Oh, be advised ere thou dost begin:
Dispatch me straight but meddle not with him.[3]

KING LEIR Friend, thy commission is to deal with me
And I am he that hath deserved all.
The plot was laid to take away my life,
And here it is. I do entreat thee take it.
Yet for my sake and as thou art a man,
Spare this my friend that hither with me came:
I brought him forth, whereas° he had not been
But for good will to bear me company.
He left his friends, his country, and his goods
And came with me in most extremity.
Oh, if he should miscarry here and die,
Who is the cause of it, but only I?

MESSENGER Why that am I, let that ne'er trouble thee.

KING LEIR Oh no, 'tis I. O, had I now to give thee
The monarchy of all the spacious world
To save his life, I would bestow it on thee.
But I have nothing but these tears and prayer
And the submission of a bended knee. *He kneels.*
Oh, if all this to mercy move thy mind,
Spare him. In heaven thou shalt like mercy find.

MESSENGER *[aside]* I am as hard to be moved as another, and yet
methinks the strength of their persuasions stirs me a little.

PERILLUS My friend, if fear of the almighty power
Have power to move thee we have said enough,

---

[1] by the Virgin Mary (a profanity)
[2] Good men are not very plentiful.
[3] Perillus invokes the belief that the monarch was anointed by God. He warns the
messenger not to meddle with a king favoured with a "divine right."

But if thy mind be moveable with gold
We have not presently to give it thee.
Yet to thyself thou mayst do greater good,
To keep thy hands still undefiled from blood,
For do but well consider with thyself:
When thou hast finish'd this outrageous act
What horror still will haunt thee for the deed?
Think this again, that they which would incense[1]
Thee for to be the butcher of their father,
When it is done, for fear it should be known
Would make a means to rid thee from the world.
Oh, then art thou forever tied in chains
Of everlasting torments to endure,
Even in the hottest hole of grisly hell,
Such pains as never mortal tongue can tell.
It thunders. He quakes, and lets fall the dagger next to Perillus.

KING LEIR Oh, heavens be thanked, he will spare my friend.
Now when thou wilt come make an end of me.
He lets fall the other dagger.

PERILLUS Oh, happy sight. He mean° to save my lord.
The King of Heaven continue this good mind.[2]

KING LEIR Why stayst thou[3] to do execution?

MESSENGER I am as wilful as you for your life.
I will not do it, now you do entreat me.

PERILLUS Ah, now I see thou hast some spark of grace.

MESSENGER Beshrew[4] you for it, you have put it in me—
The parlousest[5] old men that ere I heard!
Well, to be flat, I'll not meddle with you:
Here I found you and here I'll leave you.

---

[1] incite

[2] good disposition

[3] do you hesitate

[4] curse

[5] *Parlous* is a variant of *perilous*—cunning, clever, or dangerous. The messenger is
   probably also punning on Perillus's name.

If any ask you why the case so stands
Say that your tongues were better than your hands. *Exit Messenger.*

PERILLUS Farewell. If ever we together meet,
It shall go hard, but I will thee regreet.[1]
Courage, my lord, the worst is overpast;
Let us give thanks to God and hie[2] us hence.

KING LEIR Thou art deceived, for I am past the best
And know not whither for to go from hence.
Death had been better welcome unto me
Than longer life to add more misery.

PERILLUS It were not good to return from whence we came,
Unto your daughter Ragan back again.
Now let us go to France, unto Cordella,
Your youngest daughter; doubtless she will succour you.

KING LEIR Oh, how can I persuade myself of that,
Since the other two are quite devoid of love,
To whom I was so kind, as that my gifts
Might make them love me, if 'twere nothing else?

PERILLUS No worldly gifts, but grace from God on high
Doth nourish virtue and true charity.
Remember well what words Cordella spake
What time[3] you ask'd her how she lov'd your grace.
She said her love unto you was as much
As ought a child to bear unto her father.

KING LEIR But she did find my love was not to her
As should a father bear unto a child.

PERILLUS That makes not her love to be any less
If she do love you as a child should do.
You have tried° two; try one more for my sake.
I'll ne'er entreat you further trial make.
Remember well the dream you had of late

---

[1] exchange greetings with you

[2] hasten (see glossary)

[3] that time

And think what comfort it foretells to us.

KING LEIR Come, truest friend that ever man possess'd,
I know thou counsel'st all things for the best.
If this third daughter play a kinder part,
It comes of God and not of my desert.° *Exeunt.*

[4.8]   Enter the Gallian Ambassador solus.

GALLIAN AMBASSADOR There is of late news come unto the court,
That old lord Leir remains in Cambria.[1]
I'll hie° me thither presently to impart
My letters and my message unto him.
I never was less welcome to a place
In all my life time than I have been hither,
Especially unto the stately queen,
Who would not cast one gracious look on me,
But still with louring[2] and suspicious eyes
Would take exceptions at each word I spake
And fain° she would have undermined me
To know what my ambassage[3] did import.
But she is like to hop without her hope[4]
And in this matter for to want° her will,
Though (by report) she'll have't in all things else.
Well, I will post[5] away for Cambria.
Within these few days I hope to be there. *Exit.*

[5.1]   Enter the King and Queen of Gallia, and Mumford.

GALLIAN KING By this our father understands our mind
And our kind greetings sent to him of late;
Therefore, my mind presageth ere't be long
We shall receive from Britain happy news.

CORDELLA I fear my sister will dissuade his mind,
For she to me hath always been unkind.

---

[1] Wales
[2] sullen, sour
[3] diplomatic message
[4] proceed without her hope fulfilled
[5] hasten

GALLIAN KING Fear not, my love, since that we know the worst,
The last means helps if that we miss the first:
If he'll not come to Gallia unto us
Then we will sail to Britain unto him.

MUMFORD Well, if I once see Britain again
I have sworn I'll ne'er come home without my wench.
And I'll not be forsworn.
I'll rather never come home while I live.

CORDELLA Are you sure, Mumford, she is a maid still?

MUMFORD Nay, I'll not swear she is a maid, but she goes for one:
I'll take her at all adventures, if I can get her.[1]

CORDELLA Ay, that's well put in.

MUMFORD Well put in? Nay, it was ill put in; for had it
Been as well put in, as ere I put in, in my days,
I would have made her follow me to France.[2]

CORDELLA Nay, you'd have been so kind as take her with you,
Or else, were I as she,
I would have been so loving as I'd stay behind you.
Yet I must confess you are a very proper man
And able to make a wench do more than she would do.

MUMFORD Well, I have a pair of slops for the nonce[3]
Will hold all your mocks.

GALLIAN KING Nay, we see you have a handsome hose.[4]

CORDELLA Ay, and of the newest fashion.

MUMFORD More bobs, more—put them in still. They'll serve instead of
bombast, yet put not in too many lest the seams crack and they fly out

---

[1] I'll take my chances on getting her.
[2] True to character, Mumford finds a sexual double-entendre in Cordella's comment.
[3] loose-fitting trousers for the occasion
[4] pair of fine stockings

amongst you again.[1] You must not think to outface me so easily in my mistress's quarrel, who if I see once again, ten team of horses shall not draw me away till I have full and whole possession.

GALLIAN KING Ay, but one team and a cart will serve the turn.

CORDELLA Not only for him, but also for his wench.[2]

MUMFORD Well, you are two to one, I'll give you over.
And since I see you so pleasantly disposed,
Which indeed is but seldom seen, I'll claim
A promise of you, which you shall not deny me.
For promise is debt, and by this hand you promis'd it me.
Therefore, you owe it me, and you shall pay it me
Or I'll sue you upon an action of unkindness.

GALLIAN KING Prithee, lord Mumford, what promise did I make thee?

MUMFORD Faith, nothing but this:
That the next fair weather, which is very now,
You would go in progress[3] down to the sea side,
Which is very near.

GALLIAN KING Faith, in this motion I will join with thee
And be a mediator to my queen.
Prithee, my love, let this march go forward.
My mind foretells 'twill be a lucky voyage.

CORDELLA Entreaty needs not[4] where you may command.
So you be pleased,[5] I am right well content.
Yet, as the sea I much desire to see,
So am I most unwilling to be seen.

---

[1] *Bobs* can mean both ornaments and jibes or jokes; bombast is stuffing used to fill and give dimension to Elizabethan garments. Mumford plays with words as he continues the conversation about clothing.

[2] The Gallian King and Cordella refer to the early modern practice of carting prostitutes through the streets.

[3] in royal procession

[4] entreaty is not needed

[5] so long as you are content

GALLIAN KING We'll go disguised, all unknown to any.

CORDELLA Howsoever you make one, I'll make another.

MUMFORD And I the third. Oh, I am overjoyed!
See what love is, which getteth with a word
What all the world besides could ne'er obtain!
But what disguises shall we have, my lord?

GALLIAN KING Faith, thus: my queen and I will be disguised
Like a plain country couple and you shall be Roger,
Our man, and wait upon us. Or if you will,
You shall go first and we will wait on you.

MUMFORD 'Twere more than time; this device is excellent.
Come let us about it.[1] *Exeunt.*

[5.2]   *Enter Cambria and Ragan, with Nobles.*

CAMBRIA What strange mischance or unexpected hap°
Hath thus depriv'd us of our father's presence?
Can no man tell us what's become of him,
With whom we did converse not two days since?
My lords, let everywhere light-horse[2] be sent
To scour about through all our regiment.
Dispatch a post[3] immediately to Cornwall
To see if any news be of him there.
Myself will make a strict inquiry here
And all about our cities near at hand
Till certain news of his abode[4] be brought.

RAGAN All sorrow is but counterfeit to mine,
Whose lips are almost sealed up with grief.
Mine is the substance, whilst they do but seem
To weep the loss, which tears cannot redeem.
Oh, ne'er was heard so strange a misadventure,
A thing so far beyond the reach of sense,

---

[1] This plan is excellent; let's get going with it.
[2] lightly armed cavalry
[3] messenger
[4] of where is is now (see glossary)

Since no man's reason in the cause can enter.
What hath remov'd my father thus from hence?
Oh, I do fear some charm or invocation
Of wicked spirits or infernal fiends
Stirred by Cordella moves this innovation[1]
And brings my father timeless[2] to his end.
But might I know that the detested witch
Were certain cause of this uncertain ill,
Myself to France would go in some disguise
And with these nails scratch out her hateful eyes,
For since I am deprived of my father
I loathe my life and wish my death the rather.

CAMBRIA The heavens are just and hate impiety
And will (no doubt) reveal such heinous crimes.
Censure not any till you know the right:
Let Him be Judge that bringeth truth to light.

RAGAN Oh, but my grief, like to a swelling tide,
Exceeds the bounds of common patience.
Nor can I moderate my tongue so much
To conceal them whom I hold in suspect.[3]

CAMBRIA This matter shall be sifted:[4] if it be she
A thousand Frances shall not harbour her.

Enter the Gallian Ambassador.

GALLIAN AMBASSADOR All happiness unto the Cambrian king.

CAMBRIA Welcome, my friend. From whence is thy ambassage?°

GALLIAN AMBASSADOR I came from Gallia, unto Cornwall sent
With letters to your honourable father,
Whom there not finding, as I did expect,
I was directed hither to repair.

---

[1] causes this development
[2] eternally
[3] suspicion
[4] investigated

RAGAN Frenchman, what is thy message to my father?

GALLIAN AMBASSADOR My letters, madam, will import the same,
Which my commission is for to deliver.

RAGAN In his absence you may trust us with your letters.

GALLIAN AMBASSADOR I must perform my charge in such a manner,
As I have strict commandment from the king.

RAGAN There is good packing¹ 'twixt your king and you.
You need not hither come to ask for him;
You know where he is better than ourselves.

GALLIAN AMBASSADOR Madam, I hope, not far off.

RAGAN Hath the young murd'ress, your outrageous queen,
No means to colour² her detested deeds
In finishing my guiltless father's days
(Because he gave her nothing to her dower°)
But by the colour of a feigned ambassage,°
To send him letters hither to our court?
Go carry them to them that sent them hither
And bid them keep their scrolls unto themselves.
They cannot blind us with such slight excuse
To smother up so monstrous vild° abuse.
And, were it not, it is 'gainst law of arms
To offer violence to a messenger,
We would inflict such torments on thyself,
As should enforce thee to reveal the truth.³

GALLIAN AMBASSADOR Madam, your threats no whit appal my mind.
I know my conscience guiltless of this act.
My king and queen, I dare be sworn, are free
From any thought of such impiety.
And therefore, madam, you have done them wrong,

---

¹ plotting, collusion
² disguise
³ Ambassadors were entitled to diplomatic immunity when performing their duties. Ragan's sense is clear enough, despite somewhat garbled syntax. Note what follows.

And ill beseeming with a sister's love,
Who in mere duty tender[1] him as much
As ever you respected him for dower.°
The king your husband will not say as much.

CAMBRIA I will suspend my judgement for a time
Till more apparance[2] give us further light.
Yet to be plain, your coming doth enforce
A great suspicion to our doubtful[3] mind,
And that you do resemble, to be brief,
Him that first robs and then cries "stop the thief!"

GALLIAN AMBASSADOR Pray God some near you have not done the like.

RAGAN Hence, saucy mate, reply no more to us,
She strikes him. For law of arms shall not protect thy tongue.

GALLIAN AMBASSADOR Ne'er was I off'red such discourtesy.
God and my king, I trust, ere it be long,
Will find a mean° to remedy this wrong. *Exit Gallian Ambassador.*

RAGAN How shall I live, to suffer this disgrace
At every base and vulgar peasant's hands?
It ill befitteth my imperial state
To be thus used and no man take my part. *She weeps.*

CAMBRIA What should I do? Infringe the law of arms
Were to my everlasting obloquy,[4]
But I will take revenge upon his master
Which sent him hither to delude us thus.

RAGAN Nay, if you put up this,[5] be sure, ere long,
Now that my father thus is made away,
She'll come and claim a third part of your crown
As due unto her by inheritance.

---

[1] value, esteem
[2] time to prepare
[3] doubting (and note the royal *our*)
[4] shame
[5] tolerate, permit

CAMBRIA But I will prove her title to be naught
But shame and the reward of parricide,
And make her an example to the world
For after-ages to admire her penance.
This will I do, as I am Cambria's king,
Or lose my life to prosecute revenge.
Come, first let's learn what news is of our father
And then proceed as best occasion fits. *Exeunt.*

[5.3]   Enter Leir, Perillus, and two Mariners, in sea-gowns and sea-caps.

PERILLUS My honest friends, we are asham'd to shew°
The great extremity of our present state,
In that at this time we are brought so low
That we want° money for to pay our passage.
The truth is so, we met with some good fellows[1]
A little before we came aboard your ship,
Which stripp'd us quite of all the coin we had
And left us not a penny in our purses.
Yet, wanting money, we will use the mean°
To see you satisfied to the uttermost.

FIRST MARINER *He looks on Leir.*
Here's a good gown; 'twould become me passing well.[2]
I should be fine in it.

SECOND MARINER *He looks on Perillus.*
Here's a good cloak; I marvel how I should look in it.

KING LEIR Faith, had we others to supply their room,[3]
Though ne'er so mean,[4] you willingly should have them.

FIRST MARINER Do you hear, sir? you look like an honest man; I'll not
stand to do you a pleasure: here's a good strong motley gabardine,[5] cost

---

[1] robbers
[2] would suit me well enough
[3] place
[4] no matter how lowly
[5] coat of simple, sturdy fabric

me fourteen good shillings at Billingsgate.[1] Give me your gown for it, and
your cap for mine, and I'll forgive your passage.[2]

KING LEIR With all my heart, and twenty thanks. *Leir and he changeth.*

SECOND MARINER Do you hear, sir? you shall have a better match than he
because you are my friend. Here is a good sheep's russet[3] seagown will
bide more stress, I warrant you, than two of his, yet for you seem to be an
honest gentleman I am content to change it for your cloak and ask you
nothing for your passage more. *He pulls off Perillus's cloak.*

PERILLUS My own I willingly would change with thee
And think myself indebted to thy kindness,
But would my friend might keep his garment still.
My friend, I'll give thee this new doublet if thou wilt
Restore his gown unto him back again.

FIRST MARINER Nay, if I do would I might ne'er eat powdered beef and
mustard[4] more, nor drink can of good liquor whilst I live. My friend, you
have small reason to seek to hinder me of my bargain. But the best is, a
bargain's a bargain.

KING LEIR *[to Perillus]* Kind friend, it is much better as it is,
For by this means we may escape unknown
Till time and opportunity do fit.

SECOND MARINER *[to first mariner]*
Hark, hark, they are laying their heads together,[5]
They'll repent them of their bargain anon.
'Twere best for us to go while we are well.

FIRST MARINER God be with you, sir, for your passage back again.
I'll use you as unreasonable as another.[6]

KING LEIR I know thou wilt; but we hope to bring ready money

---

[1] a riverside section of London
[2] I will not charge you for your passage.
[3] coarse clothing worn by shepherds
[4] preserved beef and mustard, a traditional food of simple people
[5] conspiring
[6] treat you as I would any other

With us when we come back again. *Exeunt Mariners.*
Were ever men in this extremity,
In a strange country and devoid of friends,
And not a penny for to help ourselves?
Kind friend, what think'st thou will become of us?

PERILLUS Be of good cheer, my lord, I have a doublet
Will yield us money enough to serve our turns
Until we come unto your daughter's court.
And then, I hope, we shall find friends enough.

KING LEIR Ah, kind Perillus, that is it, I fear,
And makes me faint or ever[1] I come there.
Can kindness spring out of ingratitude?
Or love be reap'd where hatred hath been sown?
Can henbane join in league with mithridate?
Or sugar grow in wormwood's bitter stalk?[2]
It cannot be; they are too opposite,
And so am I to any kindness here.
I have thrown wormwood on the sugared youth
And like to henbane poisoned the fount
Whence flowed the mithridate of a child's goodwill.
I, like an envious thorn, have prick'd the heart
And turned sweet grapes to sour unrelish'd sloes.[3]
The causeless ire of my respectless[4] breast
Hath soured the sweet milk of dame Nature's paps.[5]
My bitter words have galled her honey thoughts
And weeds of rancour chok'd the flower of grace.
Then what remainder is of any hope
But all our fortunes will go quite aslope?[6]

PERILLUS Fear not, my lord, the perfit° good indeed
Can never be corrupted by the bad.
A new fresh vessel still retains the taste

---

[1] if ever
[2] Henbane is a poison, mithridate a magical antidote, and wormwood a proverbially
    bitter plant.
[3] unwanted bitter berries
[4] disrespecting
[5] breasts
[6] downward, awry

Of that which first is poured into the same.
And therefore, though you name yourself the thorn,
The weed, the gall, the henbane and the wormwood,
Yet she'll continue in her former state
The honey, milk, grape, sugar, mithridate.

KING LEIR Thou pleasing orator unto me in woe,
Cease to beguile me with thy hopeful speeches.
O join with me and think of naught but crosses[1]
And then we'll one lament another's losses.

PERILLUS Why, say the worst: the worst can be but death,
And death is better than for to despair.
Then hazard[2] death, which may convert to life;
Banish despair, which brings a thousand deaths.

KING LEIR O'ercome with thy strong arguments, I yield
To be directed by thee, as thou wilt.
As thou yieldest comfort to my crazed thoughts,
Would I could yield the like unto thy body,
Which is full weak, I know, and ill apaid[3]
For want of fresh meat[4] and due sustenance.

PERILLUS Alack, my lord, my heart doth bleed to think
That you should be in such extremity.

KING LEIR Come, let us go, and see what God will send;
When all means fail he is the surest friend. *Exeunt.*

[5.4]   *Enter the Gallian King and Queen, and Mumford with a basket, disguised like country folk.*

GALLIAN KING This tedious journey all on foot, sweet love,
Cannot be pleasing to your tender joints,
Which ne'er were used to these toilsome walks.

CORDELLA I never in my life took more delight

---

[1] nothing but adversity
[2] risk
[3] repaid
[4] lack of food of any sort (see glossary)

In any journey than I do in this:
It did me good whenas° we happ'd to light
Amongst[1] the merry crew of country folk
To see what industry and pains they took
To win them commendations 'mongst their friends.
Lord, how they labour to bestir themselves
And in their quirks to go beyond the moon,
And so take on them with such antic fits,[2]
That one would think they were beside their wits!
Come away, Roger, with your basket.

Enter King Leir and Perillus very faintly.

MUMFORD Soft, dame, here comes a couple of old youths.
I must needs make myself fat with testing at them.[3]

CORDELLA Nay, prithee, do not: they do seem to be
Men much o'ergone[4] with grief and misery.
Let's stand aside, and hearken what they say.

KING LEIR Ah, my Perillus, now I see we both
Shall end our days in this untrustful soil.
Oh, I do faint for want° of sustenance
And thou, I know, in little better case.
No gentle tree affords one taste of fruit,
To comfort us, until we meet with men;
No lucky path conducts our luckless steps
Unto a place where any comfort dwells.
Sweet rest betide unto[5] our happy souls,
For here I see our bodies must have end.

PERILLUS Ah, my dear lord, how doth my heart lament
To see you brought to this extremity!
Oh, if you love me, as you do profess,
Or ever thought well of me in my life, *He strips up his arm.*
Feed on this flesh, whose veins are not so dry

---

[1] when we happened to come among
[2] mad, lunatic shows of frenzy
[3] I will certainly get a laugh by questioning them.
[4] overcome
[5] may sweet rest come unto

But there is virtue left to comfort you.
Oh, feed on this, if this will do you good;
I'll smile for joy to see you suck my blood.

KING LEIR I am no cannibal, that I should delight
To slake my hungry jaws with human flesh.
I am no devil, or ten times worse than so,
To suck the blood of such a peerless friend.
Oh, do not think that I respect my life
So dearly, as I do thy loyal love.
Ah, Britain, I shall never see thee more,
That hast unkindly banished thy king.
And yet not thou dost make me to complain,
But they which were more near to me than thou.[1]

CORDELLA What do I hear? This lamentable[2] voice
Methinks ere now I oftentimes have heard.

KING LEIR Ah, Gonorill, was half my kingdom's gift
The cause that thou didst seek to have my life?
Ah, cruel Ragan, did I give thee all,
And all could not suffice without my blood?
Ah, poor Cordella, did I give thee nought,
Nor never shall be able for to give?
Oh, let me warn all ages that ensueth,
How they trust flattery, and reject the truth.
Well, unkind girls, I here forgive you both—
Yet the just heavens will hardly do the like—
And only crave forgiveness at the end
Of good Cordella and of thee, my friend;
Of God, whose Majesty I have offended,
By my transgression many thousand ways;
Of her, dear heart, whom I for no occasion
Turn'd out of all, through flatterers' persuasion;
Of thee, kind friend, who but for me, I know,
Hadst never come unto this place of woe.

---

[1] The language of this passage underscores the play's theme of loyalty, as Leir addresses Perillus in the familiar *thou* form, while Perillus emphasizes his devotion to the king with the formal or respectful *you*.

[2] lamenting

CORDELLA Alack, that ever I should live to see
My noble father in this misery.

GALLIAN KING Sweet love, reveal not what thou art as yet,
Until we know the ground of this ill.

CORDELLA Oh, but some meat, some meat:° do you not see
How near they are to death for want° of food? [*She shows the basket.*]

PERILLUS Lord, which didst help thy servants at their need,
Or now or never[1] send us help with speed.
Oh, comfort, comfort! Yonder is a banquet
And men and women, my lord. Be of good cheer,
For I see comfort coming very near.
Oh, my lord, a banquet and men and women!

KING LEIR Oh, let kind pity mollify their hearts
That they may help us in our great extremes.

PERILLUS God save you, friends, and if° this blessed banquet
Affordeth any food or sustenance,
Even for His sake that saved us all from death,
Vouchsafe to save us from the grip of famine.

CORDELLA Here father,[2] sit and eat; here, sit and drink,
She bringeth him to the table.
And would it were far better for your sakes.

Perillus takes King Leir by the hand to the table.

PERILLUS I'll give you thanks anon. My friend doth faint
And needeth present comfort. *King Leir drinks.*

MUMFORD I warrant, he ne'er stays to say grace.
Oh, there's no sauce to a good stomach.[3]

---

[1] either now or never
[2] This scene plays strongly on two senses of the word *father*, which could be a general term of respect for any elderly man, and *daughter*, which could also be applied to any young woman or girl (see below).
[3] I declare that he does not pause to say grace. Appetite is the best sauce (proverbial).

PERILLUS The blessed God of Heaven hath thought upon us.

KING LEIR The thanks be His, and these kind courteous folk,
By whose humanity we are preserved. *They eat hungrily. King Leir drinks.*

CORDELLA And may that draught be unto him as was
That which old Aeson drank, which did renew
His withered age and made him young again.
And may that meat be unto him as was
That which Elias ate, in strength whereof
He walked forty days, and never fainted.[1]
[Aside to the Gallian King] Shall I conceal me longer from my father?
Or shall I manifest myself to him?

GALLIAN KING Forbear a while until his strength return,
Lest being overjoyed with seeing thee
His poor weak senses should forsake their office[2]
And so our cause of joy be turn'd to sorrow.

PERILLUS What cheer, my lord? how do you feel yourself?

KING LEIR Methinks I never ate such savoury meat.°
It is as pleasant as the blessed manna
That rained from heaven amongst the Israelites.[3]
It hath recall'd my spirits home again,
And made me fresh as erst° I was before.
But how shall we congratulate[4] their kindness?

PERILLUS In faith, I know not how sufficiently,
But the best mean° that I can think on is this:
I'll offer them my doublet in requital,[5]
For we have nothing else to spare.

---

[1] Aeson was the father of Jason (of the Golden Fleece legend), whose wife Medea
gave him a magic drink that made the old man young again. Elias was
miraculously fed "meat" (food of any sort) by an angel and travelled 40 days
and nights (1 Kings 19:5-8).
[2] proper functions
[3] Exodus 16
[4] express our gratitude for
[5] repayment

342

KING LEIR Nay, stay, Perillus, for they shall have mine.

PERILLUS Pardon, my lord, I swear they shall have mine.
Perillus proffers his doublet: they will not take it.

KING LEIR
Ah, who would think such kindness should remain
Among such strange and unacquainted men
And that such hate should harbour in the breast
Of those which have occasion to be best?

CORDELLA Ah, good old father, tell to me thy grief;
I'll sorrow with thee, if not add relief.

KING LEIR Ah, good young daughter, I may call thee so,
For thou art like a daughter I did owe.[1]

CORDELLA Do you not owe her still? what, is she dead?

KING LEIR No, God forbid, but all my interest's[2] gone
By shewing° myself too much unnatural:
So have I lost the title of a father
And may be call'd a stranger to her rather.

CORDELLA Your title's good still, for 'tis always known
A man may do as him list° with his own.
But have you but one daughter then in all?

KING LEIR Yes, I have more, by two, than would I had.[3]

CORDELLA Oh, say not so, but rather see the end:
They that are bad may have the grace to mend.
But how have they offended you so much?

KING LEIR If from the first I should relate the cause
'T would make a heart of adamant[4] to weep
And thou, poor soul, kind-hearted as thou art,

---

[1] have (literally, own)
[2] relationship, attachment
[3] I wish I had
[4] diamond-like rock

Dost weep already, ere I do begin.

CORDELLA For God's love tell it, and when you have done
I'll tell the reason why I weep so soon.

KING LEIR Then know this first. I am a Britain borne,
And had three daughters by one loving wife.
And though I say it, of beauty they were sped,[1]
Especially the youngest of the three,
For her perfections hardly match'd could be.
On these I doted with a jealous love
And thought to try° which of them lov'd me best
By asking them, which would do most for me.
The first and second flattered me with words
And vow'd they lov'd me better than their lives.
The youngest said she loved me as a child
Might do. Her answer I esteem'd most vild°
And presently in an outrageous mood
I turn'd her from me to go sink or swim.
And all I had, even to the very clothes,
I gave in dowry with the other two
And she that best deserv'd the greatest share
I gave her nothing but disgrace and care.
Now mark the sequel: when I had done thus
I sojourned in my eldest daughter's house,
Where for a time I was entreated well,
And liv'd in state sufficing my content.
But every day her kindness did grow cold,
Which I with patience put up well enough
And seemed not to see the things I saw.
But at the last she grew so far incens'd
With moody fury and with causeless hate
That in most vild° and contumelious[2] terms
She bade me pack and harbour somewhere else.
Then was I fain for refuge to repair[3]
Unto my other daughter for relief,
Who gave me pleasing and most courteous words,

---

[1] endowed
[2] insolent
[3] I had to seek refuge

But in her actions shewed herself so sore,[1]
As never any daughter did before.
She prayed me in a morning out betime[2]
To go to a thicket two miles from the court,
Pointing that there she would come talk with me.
There she had set a shag-haired murd'ring wretch
To massacre my honest friend and me.
Then judge yourself, although my tale be brief,
If ever man had greater cause of grief.

GALLIAN KING Nor never like impiety was done
Since the creation of the world begun.

KING LEIR And now I am constrain'd to seek relief
Of her to whom I have been so unkind,
Whose censure,° if it do award me death,
I must confess she pays me but my due.
But if she shew° a loving daughter's part
It comes of God and her, not my desert.°

CORDELLA No doubt she will. I dare be sworn she will.

KING LEIR How know you that, not knowing what she is?

CORDELLA Myself a father have a great way hence[3]
Used me as ill as ever you did her;
Yet that his reverend age I once might see,
I'd creep along to meet him on my knee.

KING LEIR Oh, no men's children are unkind but mine.

CORDELLA Condemn not all, because of others' crime:
But look, dear father, look, behold and see
Thy loving daughter speaketh unto thee. *She kneels.*

KING LEIR Oh, stand thou up, it is my part to kneel
And ask forgiveness for my former faults. *He kneels.*

---

[1] revealed herself to be so harsh
[2] go out early (betimes)
[3] a long way away

CORDELLA Oh, if you wish I should enjoy my breath,
Dear father rise, or I receive my death. *He riseth.*

KING LEIR Then I will rise, to satisfy your mind,
But kneel again til pardon be resign'd.[1] *He kneels.*

CORDELLA I pardon you? the word beseems not me,[2]
But I do say so for to ease your knee.
You gave me life. You were the cause that I
Am what I am, who else had never been.

KING LEIR But you gave life to me and to my friend,
Whose days had else had an untimely end.

CORDELLA You brought me up whenas° I was but young
And far unable for to help myself.

KING LEIR I cast thee forth whenas thou wast but young,
And far unable for to help thyself.

CORDELLA God, world, and nature say I do you wrong,
That can endure to see you kneel so long.

GALLIAN KING Let me break off this loving controversy,
Which doth rejoice my very soul to see.
Good father, rise: she is your loving daughter,
He riseth. And honours you with as respective[3] duty
As if you were the monarch of the world.

CORDELLA But I will never rise from off my knee
She kneels. Until I have your blessing and your pardon
Of all my faults committed any way
From my first birth unto this present day.

KING LEIR The blessing which the God of Abraham gave
Unto the tribe of Judah light on thee
And multiply thy days, that thou mayst see

---

[1] granted
[2] does not apply to me
[3] respectful

Thy children's children prosper after thee.[1]
Thy faults, which are just none that I do know,
God pardon on high and I forgive below. *She riseth.*

CORDELLA Now is my heart at quiet and doth leap
Within my breast for joy of this good hap.°
And now (dear father) welcome to our court,
And welcome (kind Perillus) unto me,
Mirror° of virtue and true honesty.

KING LEIR Oh, he hath been the kindest friend to me
That ever man had in adversity.

PERILLUS My tongue doth fail to say what heart doth think,
I am so ravish'd with exceeding joy.

GALLIAN KING All you have spoke. Now let me speak my mind
And in few words much matter here conclude. *He kneels.*
If ere my heart do harbour any joy
Or true content repose within my breast,
Till I have rooted out this viperous sect
And repossess'd my father of his crown,
Let me be counted for the perjurdest[2] man
That ever spake word since the world began. *He rises.*

MUMFORD Let me pray too, that never pray'd before.
Mumford kneels. If ere I re-salute the British earth,
As (ere't be long) I do presume I shall,
And do return from thence without my wench,
Let me be gelded for my recompense.[3] *Rise.*

GALLIAN KING Come, let's to arms for to redress this wrong;
Till I am there, methinks, the time seems long. *Exeunt.*

[5.5]   Enter Ragan sola.

RAGAN I feel a hell of conscience in my breast
Tormenting me with horror for my fact,°

---

[1] Genesis 12:2-3.
[2] most perjured
[3] let me be castrated as my reward

And makes me in an agony of doubt,
For fear the world should find my dealing out.
The slave whom I appointed for the act,
I ne'er set eye upon the peasant since.
Oh, could I get him for to make him sure
My doubts would cease and I should rest secure.
But if the old men with persuasive words
Have sav'd their lives and made him to relent,
Then are they fled unto the court of France
And like a trumpet manifest[1] my shame.
A shame on these white-liver'd slaves,[2] say I,
That with fair words so soon are overcome.
O God, that I had been but made a man
Or that my strength were equal with my will!
These foolish men are nothing but mere pity
And melt as butter doth against the sun.
Why should they have pre-eminence over us
Since we are creatures of more brave resolve?
I swear I am quite out of charity
With all the heartless men in Christendom.
A pox upon them, when they are afraid
To give a stab or slit a paltry wind-pipe,
Which are so easy matters to be done.[3]
Well, had I thought the slave would serve me so
Myself would have been executioner.
'Tis now undone and if° that it be known
I'll make as good shift as I can for one.
He that repines at me, howe'er it stands,
'Twere best for him to keep him from my hands. *Exit.*

[5.6]   *Sound Drums and Trumpets: Enter the Gallian King, King Leir,
Mumford and the army.*

GALLIAN KING Thus have we brought our army to the sea,
Whereas° our ships are ready to receive us.
The wind stands fair and we in four hours' sail

---

[1] will publicly reveal
[2] fearful low-born men
[3] This speech probably alludes to a notorious boasting match between two villains
    in Christopher Marlowe's popular play *The Jew of Malta*, first performed
    c.1590.

May easily arrive on British shore,
Where, unexpected, we may them surprise
And gain a glorious victory with ease.
Wherefore, my loving countrymen, resolve,
Since truth and justice fighteth on our sides,
That we shall march with conquest where we go.
Myself will be as forward as the first
And step by step march with the hardiest wight,°
And not the meanest soldier in our camp
Shall be in danger but I'll second[1] him.
[to Mumford] To you, my lord, we give the whole command
Of all the army, next unto our self,
Not doubting of you, but you will extend
Your wonted° valour in this needful case,
Encouraging the rest to do the like
By your approved magnanimity.

MUMFORD My liege, 'tis needless to spur a willing horse
That's apt enough to run himself to death.
For here I swear by that sweet saint's bright eye,
Which are the stars, which guide me to good hap°
Either to see my old lord crown'd anew
Or in his cause to bid the world adieu.

KING LEIR Thanks, good lord Mumford, 'tis more of your good will
Than any merit or desert° in me.

MUMFORD And now to you, my worthy countrymen,
Ye valiant race of Genovestan Gauls,
Surnamed Redshanks, thanks for your chivalry
Because you fight up to the shanks in blood.[2]
Shew yourselves now to be right[3] Gauls indeed
And be so bitter on your enemies
That they may say you are as bitter as gall.
Gall them, brave shot, with your artillery!

---

[1] back up, defend
[2] Genovestan Gauls, natives of Orléans, were reputed for their courage in battle—
    hence Mumford's encouragement for his soldiers to spill enough blood to colour
    their own shanks red.
[3] Now show yourselves to be true Gauls.

Gall them, brave halberts, with your sharp point bills,[1]
Each in their 'pointed[2] place, not one, but all,
Fight for the credit of yourselves and Gaul!

GALLIAN KING Then what should more persuasion need to those
That rather wish to deal than hear of blows?
Let's to our ships, and if that God permit,
In four hours' sail I hope we shall be there.

MUMFORD And in five hours more I make no doubt
But we shall bring our wish'd desires about. *Exeunt.*

[5.7]   *Enter a Captain of the watch, and two watchmen.*

CAPTAIN My honest friends, it is your turn tonight
To watch in this place near about the beacon
And vigilantly have regard
If any fleet of ships pass hitherward,
Which if you do, your office is to fire[3]
The beacon presently and raise[4] the town. *Exit.*

FIRST WATCHMAN Ay, ay, ay, fear nothing. We know our charge, I
warrant. I have been a watchman about this beacon this thirty year, and yet
I ne'er see it stir, but stood as quietly as might be.

SECOND WATCHMAN Faith, neighbour, and° you'll follow my 'vice,[5]
instead of watching the beacon, we'll go to goodman Jennings[6] and watch
a pot of ale and a rasher[7] of bacon: and if we do not drink ourselves drunk,
then so; I warrant, the beacon will see us when we come out again.

FIRST WATCHMAN Ay, but how if somebody excuse[8] us to the captain?

---

[1] Halberds and bills are hand weapons.
[2] appointed, with a pun on pointed weapons
[3] light
[4] warn
[5] if you follow my advice
[6] a tavern-keeper
[7] slice
[8] a verbal slip for "accuse"

SECOND WATCHMAN 'Tis no matter. I'll prove by good reason that we watch the beacon: ass for example.

FIRST WATCHMAN I hope you do not call me ass[1] by craft, neighbour.

SECOND WATCHMAN No, no, but for example. Say here stands the pot of ale—that's the beacon.

FIRST WATCHMAN Ay, Ay, 'tis a very good beacon.

SECOND WATCHMAN Well, say here stands your nose—that's the fire.

FIRST WATCHMAN Indeed, I must confess 'tis somewhat red.

SECOND WATCHMAN I see come marching in a dish half-a-score pieces of salt bacon.

FIRST WATCHMAN I understand your meaning: that's as much to say, half a score ships.

SECOND WATCHMAN True, you conster[2] right. Presently, like a faithful watch man, I fire the beacon and call up the town.

FIRST WATCHMAN Ay, that's as much as to say you set your nose to the pot and drink up the drink.

SECOND WATCHMAN You are in the right. Come, let's go fire the beacon. *Exeunt.*

[5.8]   *Enter the King of Gallia with a still[3] march, Mumford and soldiers.*

GALLIAN KING Now march our ensigns[4] on the British earth
And we are near approaching to the town.
Then look about you, valiant countrymen,
And we shall finish this exploit with ease.
Th' inhabitants of this mistrustful place

---

[1] *Ass* and *as* are pronounced similarly.
[2] interpret
[3] silent, solemn
[4] battle flags

Are dead asleep, as men that are secure.
Here shall we skirmish but with naked men,
Devoid of sense, new waked from a dream,
That know not what our coming doth pretend[1]
Till they do feel our meaning on their skins.
Therefore assail: God and our right for us! *Exeunt.*

*[5.9]   Alarum, with men and women half naked. Enter two Captains
without doublets, with swords.*

FIRST CAPTAIN Where are these villains that were set to watch
And fire[2] the beacon if occasion serv'd,
That thus have suffered us to be surprised,
And never given notice to the town?
We are betrayed and quite devoid of hope
By any means to fortify ourselves.

SECOND CAPTAIN 'Tis ten to one the peasants are o'rcome with drink and
sleep, and so neglect their charge.

FIRST CAPTAIN A whirl-wind carry them quick to a whirlpool,
That there the slaves may drink their bellies full.

SECOND CAPTAIN This 'tis, to have the beacon so near the ale-house.
Enter the watchmen drunk, with each a pot.

FIRST CAPTAIN Out on ye,[3] villains! whither run you now?

FIRST WATCHMAN To fire the town[4] and call up the beacon.

SECOND WATCHMAN No, no, sir, to fire the beacon. *He drinks.*

SECOND CAPTAIN What, with a pot of ale, you drunken rogues?

FIRST CAPTAIN You'll fire the beacon when the town is lost!
I'll teach you how to tend your office better! *He draws to stab them.*

---

[1] signify
[2] set alight
[3] curse you
[4] set fire to the town

Enter Mumford, captains run away.

MUMFORD Yield, yield, yield.
He kicks down their pots.

FIRST WATCHMAN Reel? No, we do not reel:
You may lack a pot of ale ere you die.

MUMFORD But in mean-space I answer: you want none.[1] Well, there's no dealing with you, y'are tall men, and well weaponed. I would there were no worse than you in the town. *Exit.*

SECOND WATCHMAN 'A[2] speaks like an honest man; my choler's[3] past already. Come, neighbour, let's go.

FIRST WATCHMAN Nay, first let's see and° we can stand. *Exeunt.*

Alarum, excursions,[4] Mumford after them, and some half naked.

[5.10]   *Enter the Gallian King, King Leir, Mumford, Cordella, Perillus, [a Noble], and soldiers, with the chief of the town bound.*

GALLIAN KING Fear not, my friends, you shall receive no hurt
If you'll subscribe unto your lawful king
And quite revoke your fealty from Cambria
And from aspiring Cornwall too, whose wives
Have practic'd treason 'gainst their father's life.
We come in justice of your wronged king
And do intend no harm at all to you,
So you submit unto your lawful king.

KING LEIR Kind countrymen, it grieves me that perforce
I am constrained to use extremities.

NOBLE Long have you here been look'd for, good my lord,
And wish'd for by a general consent,
And had we known your highness had arrived,
We had not made resistance to your grace.

---

[1] In the meantime I answer: you lack no pots of ale.
[2] he
[3] anger
[4] raids, sorties

And now, my gracious lord, you need not doubt,
But all the country will yield presently,
Which since your absence have been greatly tax'd
For to maintain their overswelling pride.
We'll presently send word to all our friends
When they have notice, they will come apace.[1]

KING LEIR Thanks, loving subjects, and thanks, worthy son,[2]
Thanks, my kind daughter, thanks to you, my lord,
Who willingly adventured have[3] your blood
(Without desert°) to do me so much good.

MUMFORD Oh, say not so:
I have been much beholding[4] to your grace.
I must confess, I have been in some skirmishes
But I was never in the like to this,
For where I was wont° to meet with armed men,
I was now encountered with naked women.

CORDELLA We that are feeble and want° use of arms
Will pray to God to shield you from all harms.

KING LEIR The while your hands do manage ceaseless toil
Our hearts shall pray the foes may have the foil.[5]

PERILLUS We'll fast and pray whilst you for us do fight
That victory may prosecute the right.[6]

GALLIAN KING Methinks your words do amplify[7] (my friends)
And add fresh vigour to my willing limbs. *Drum.*
But hark, I hear the adverse[8] drum approach.
God and our right, Saint Denis, and Saint George.[9]

---

[1] quickly
[2] son-in-law
[3] have risked
[4] beholden, indebted
[5] suffer defeat
[6] win for the righteous ones
[7] increase
[8] opposing
[9] the patron saints of France and England, respectively

Enter Cornwall, Cambria, Gonorill, Ragan, and the army.

CORNWALL Presumptuous king of Gauls, how dar'st thou
Presume to enter on our British shore?
And more than that, to take our towns perforce[1]
And draw our subjects' hearts from their true king?
Be sure to buy it at as dear a price
As ere you bought presumption in your lives.

GALLIAN KING O'er-daring Cornwall, know we came in right.
And just revengement of the wronged king,
Whose daughters there, fell[2] vipers as they are,
Have sought to murder and deprive of life.
But God protected him from all their spite
And we are come in justice of his right.

CAMBRIA Nor he nor thou have any interest here
But what you win and purchase with the sword.
Thy slanders to our noble virtuous queens,
We'll in the battle thrust them down thy throat,[3]
Except, for fear of our revenging hands,
Thou fly to sea as not secure on lands.

MUMFORD Welshman, I'll so ferret you ere night for that word
That you shall have no mind to crake so well this twelvemonth.[4]

GONORILL They lie that say we sought our father's death.

RAGAN 'Tis merely forged for a colour's sake
To set a gloss on your invasion.[5]
Methinks an old man ready for to die
Should be asham'd to breach[6] so foul a lie.

CORDELLA Fie, shameless sister, so devoid of grace,

---

[1] by force
[2] cruel, ruthless
[3] make you take back the slanders
[4] I'll seek you out for that slander so carefully that you will not boast like a crow this whole year.
[5] It is merely faked in order to cover up your invasion.
[6] broach, suggest

To call our father liar to his face.

GONORILL Peace, puritan,[1] dissembling hypocrite,
Which art so good that thou wilt prove stark naught.[2]
Anon, whenas° I have you in my fingers
I'll make you wish yourself in Purgatory.
PERILLUS Nay, peace thou monster, shame unto thy sex—
Thou fiend in likeness of a humane[3] creature!

RAGAN I never heard a fouler-spoken man.

KING LEIR Out on thee,[4] viper, scum, filthy parricide,
More odious to my sight than is a toad,
Know'st thou these letters? *She snatches them and tears them.*

RAGAN Think you to outface me with your paltry scrawls?
You come to drive my husband from his right,
Under the colour of a forged letter.

KING LEIR Whoever heard the like impiety?

PERILLUS You are our debtor of more patience.[5]
We were more patient when we stayed for you
Within the thicket two long hours and more.

RAGAN What hours? What thicket?

PERILLUS There, where you sent your servant with your letters,
Sealed with your hand, to send us both to heaven,
Where, as I think, you never mean to come.

RAGAN Alas, you are grown a child again with age,
Or else your senses dote for want of sleep.[6]

---

[1] Puritan could mean hypocrite in early modern usage.
[2] will prove to be absolutely nothing
[3] human or humane
[4] Fie upon thee!
[5] You owe us more of your patience.
[6] Your senses suffer from lack of sleep.

PERILLUS Indeed, you made us rise betimes,[1] you know,
Yet had a care we should sleep where you bade us stay,
But never wake more till the latter day.[2]

GONORILL Peace, peace, old fellow; thou art sleepy still.

MUMFORD Faith,[3] and if you reason till tomorrow
You get no other answer at their hands.
'Tis pity two such good faces
Should have so little grace between them.
Well, let us see if their husbands with their hands
Can do as much as they do with their tongues.

CAMBRIA Ay, with their swords they'll make your tongue unsay
What they have said, or else they'll cut them out.

KING LEIR Too't, gallants, too't,[4] let's not stand brawling thus.
Exeunt both armies.

[5.11]   *Sound alarum: excursions.[5] Mumford must chase Cambria away,
then cease. Enter Cornwall.*

CORNWALL The day is lost, our friends do all revolt
And join against us with the adverse part.
There is no means of safety but by flight
And therefore I'll to Cornwall with my queen. *Exit.*

Enter Cambria.

CAMBRIA I think there is a devil in the camp hath haunted me today. He
hath so tired me that in a manner I can fight no more.

Enter Mumford

'Zounds,[6] here he comes; I'll take me to my horse. *Exit.*

---

[1] early
[2] Judgement Day
[3] by my faith
[4] Let them have it!
[5] raids, sorties
[6] by God's wounds (a profanity)

Mumford follows him to the door and returns.

MUMFORD Farewell (Welshman)[1] give thee but thy due:
Thou hast a light and nimble pair of legs!
Thou are more in debt to them than to thy hands.
But if I meet thee once again today,
I'll cut them off and set them to a better heart. *Exit.*
Alarums and excursions, then sound victory.
Enter King Leir, Perillus, the Gallian King, Cordella, and Mumford.

GALLIAN KING Thanks be to God, your foes are overcome
And you again possessed of your right.

KING LEIR First to the heavens, next, thanks to you, my son,[2]
By whose good means I repossess the same,
Which if it please you to accept yourself,
With all my heart I will resign to you,
For it is yours by right and none of mine.
First, have you rais'd, at your own charge,[3] a power
Of valiant soldiers (this comes all from you).
Next have you ventured your own person's scathe.[4]
And lastly, worthy Gallia never stained,[5]
My kingly title I by thee have gained.

GALLIAN KING Thank heavens, not me. My zeal to you is such,
Command my utmost, I will never grutch.[6]

CORDELLA He that with all kind love entreats his queen
Will not be to her father unkind seen.

KING LEIR Ah, my Cordella, now I call to mind
The modest answer, which I took unkind.
But now I see I am no whit beguil'd:
Thou lovedst me dearly and as ought a child.
And thou (Perillus) partner once in woe,

---

[1] Cambria is in the Welsh regions.
[2] son-in-law
[3] cost
[4] risked doing yourself harm
[5] spotless (i.e., blameless and loyal)
[6] complain, begrudge

Thee to requite[1] the best I can, I'll do.
Yet all I can, ay, were it ne'er so much,
Were not sufficient, thy true love is such.
Thanks (worthy Mumford) to the last of all,
Not greeted last 'cause thy desert° was small.
No, thou hast lion-like laid on[2] today,
Chasing the Cornwall king and Cambria,
Who with my daughters (daughters did I say?)
To save their lives the fugitives did play.
Come, son and daughter who did me advance,
Repose with me awhile and then for France.
Sound Drums and Trumpets. Exeunt.

FINIS.

Questions

1. Consider King Leir's opening dialogue with Skallinger: what do we learn about his motives and his style of ruling?

2. The motives of Cordella's sisters are made quite clear in the opening of this play—much clearer than those of Shakespeare's sisters. What is the effect of their forthrightness?

3. Once he reaches the shores of Britain, the Gallian King disguises himself as a pilgrim named Will. Why does he do so? What do other examples of disguise do for the story?

4. This play ends with a military victory and the restoration of King Leir to his throne, if only briefly. What genre of tale does this ending imply?

5. This version of the King Leir legend has no Gloucester family unit, and so no double plot. What do you feel is gained or lost in this story by not having the second plotline?

---

[1] repay, reward
[2] fought

THE HYSTORIE OF HAMBLET (1608)

HAMLET

The definitive account of the sources for Shakespeare's *Hamlet* will never be written. Like many other details concerning Shakespeare's tragic masterpiece, the play's sources remain veiled in mystery to those who have taken pains—and over the centuries many scholars have taken many pains—to unravel from where and by what means Shakespeare drew inspiration for his play.

Although we do not know exactly how Shakespeare encountered and used previous versions of the tale, we actually do know a great deal about the Hamlet story within the broader outlines of the European literary tradition. The first written version comes to us from a Danish author later named Saxo Grammaticus (Saxo the Grammarian, or Saxo the Learned). Probably at the request of Absalon, Archbishop of Lund, he began what would become a sixteen-book Latin history of the Danes now variously titled the *Gesta Danorum*, meaning "Deeds of the Danes," or *Historiae Danicae*, the "Stories of the Danes." Though most of the text was probably written in the last years of the twelfth century, the work was not completed until at least 1208. Saxo freely combined oral and written sources in his history of the Danes, with the first nine books devoted to Norse legend and mythology and the last seven to medieval history, which is to say the history of his own recent past. Originally circulated in manuscript form (we must remember that printing is a mid-fifteenth-century innovation in Europe, starting some two hundred and fifty years after Saxo), it was first printed in Latin in 1514 and reprinted twice more during the sixteenth century. In each of the following centuries the text or parts of it was also translated into Danish, German, French, Italian, Russian, and other languages. However, it was not translated into English until the late nineteenth century, and even then only in part.

If Shakespeare read the *Historiae Danicae*, he would have done so in Latin, something he was quite capable of doing. But whether he actually did remains a matter of debate among scholars: the evidence is not necessarily compelling that he resorted to Europe's first version of the Hamlet story, found in Books 3 and 4. Saxo's story is tightly written, spare, ironic, and very violent. It is a document attesting to the values and outlooks of a warrior culture, where plunder and battle were ways of life and lines of family and kinship, especially from male to male, were what bound society together. No wonder, then, that avenging the harms done to family members constituted a nearly sacred duty and accounts like this one made for exciting narratives. Although the story was composed by a Christian, there is little in it to suggest the beliefs and values of the Christianity practiced in Shakespeare's time.

The story opens with an extended description that includes a genealogy of Denmark's rulers, the alliances they formed, and the battles they fought. The Hamlet character, named Amleth in this version, is introduced only after the narrator establishes a sense of place and purpose within an elaborately described network of kinship and clan. Amleth is bound by filial obligation and a sense of honour to take revenge on his uncle Feng who, like Shakespeare's Claudius, murdered his own brother and married his sister-in-law, Amleth's mother Gerutha. In order to buy time to exact his revenge, Amleth dons a guise of stupidity and insanity in all his public behaviour, so as to deflect the suspicions of Feng, Gerutha, and the Danish court. His eventual revenge is accomplished after a long series of clever, patiently timed manoeuvres and deceptions. The wily protagonist eventually burns the entire Danish court on his way to killing the sleeping Feng with his own sword. Just after the murder is described, the narrator pauses to praise Amleth's bravery and commend the clever disguises and subtlety that allowed him to achieve complete revenge.

Many of the major plot points in Shakespeare's *Hamlet* can be found in Saxo's story: a son's father murdered by his own brother, that brother's tainted re-marriage to his widowed sister-in-law, and a son's solemn sense of duty to avenge his father. It also contains smaller plot details such as a prying counsellor to the king who is stabbed to death while spying on Amleth and his mother (the basis for Polonius in the so-called Closet Scene of Shakespeare's play) and an exchange of letters to the English king that saves Amleth from execution and sends his two handlers (the prototypes of Rosencrantz and Guildenstern) to their deaths.

There are major differences, however. Saxo's story has no Laertes figure, no swordfight, no poisoned sword, and most significantly, Amleth lives on as a hero. At least for a while: after burning the Danish court alive and killing Feng, he summons the Danish people together and asserts his right to the throne, which they grant him by "prompt and general acclaim." He goes on to marry twice, achieves more victories using more clever deceptions, and plunders his enemies before finally falling victim to his kinsman Wiglek, who mounts an insurrection against Amleth and then marries his widow. A notable point of difference is that whereas Shakespeare's story ends with Hamlet's death as part of the general collapse of the Danish court, Saxo's saga contains several additional episodes; it finally ends with a warrior's death in battle—a fitting end to the hero he created in his Amleth.

François de Belleforest (1530-1583) translated Saxo's Amleth story into French, placing it within a long collection of tragic tales specifically moralised for the more thoroughly Christianised readers of sixteenth-century France. This collection, called the *Histoires Tragiques*, was immensely popular, with at least six editions of the fifth volume, the one containing the Amleth story, appearing between 1570 and 1601. Shakespeare would have had several opportunities to read the French translation (something he would have been capable of doing), but as with the Latin editions of the sixteenth century, whether he did or not is still a matter of debate.

Belleforest was not merely a translator, however. In addition to Christianising and moralising the Saxo story, he added several significant plot points to Saxo's tale and left several others out. For example, even beyond additional plot points, on one occasion Belleforest seems to change the nature of Saxo's protagonist. He credits his Hamleth (the spelling of the hero changes in the translation) with a superabundance of "melancholy," suggesting that he has both a philosophical bent and a near-supernatural ability to foretell future events. Hamlet's melancholy is a character attribute that appears with great force in Shakespeare's play but has no part in Saxo's portrait of his hero Amleth.

As part of his general tendency to moralise the story, which can seem tedious to modern readers, Belleforest also introduces a misogynistic undercurrent far stronger than that found in Saxo's story, taking nearly every opportunity to criticise and denigrate women as he tells this tale of male heroism. Did these additions somehow influence the character of Shakespeare's Hamlet, who famously asserts, "frailty thy name is woman" and who, unjustly it seems, charges Ophelia with infidelity? Belleforest's version also strikes a different general tone from Saxo's, especially in two overarching moral lessons not present in his source. The first is his plea that the actions of even rude and "unchristened" peoples hardly worth the notice of the civilised French can in fact illustrate important moral lessons. In this regard, Belleforest encourages a certain cultural distance between the actions of his story and his readers, suggesting that the story's exoticism and remoteness offer a means for measuring the superiority of modern culture. His version relies upon a kind of cultural chauvinism that is absent from the more immediate and unselfconscious account of Saxo. And second,

Belleforest frames the entire Hamblet story as an object lesson showing that the desire for political power is the root of most human discord and misery, asserting in his opening that "desire of rule causeth men to become traitors and murtherers" and that peoples of times past lived in moral darkness. This particular emphasis upon the story's value as moral instruction, very typical of writers trained in the humanist thought of the sixteenth century, cannot be found in his source, but is something that Belleforest's learning and intellectual tendencies bring to the older tale.

Even though there is a great deal in the Belleforest translation to suggest that it, rather than Saxo's, was Shakespeare's direct source, there is no evidence that Shakespeare actually used it, beyond circumstantial similarities in the two plots. But even Saxo and Belleforest are not the whole story. The missing link to Shakespeare in this history of textual transmission is a play from the late 1580s which scholars know was performed, and apparently to some general acclaim, into the 1590s. This lost work has taken on the status of the Holy Grail of *Hamlet* studies, among the most sought-after missing artifacts in all of Shakespeare scholarship. It is usually called the *Ur-Hamlet*, which is to say, the "original *Hamlet*."

Although no printed or manuscript version of the play survives, we know something about it through indirect means. It must have been performed several times by 1589 because Thomas Nashe, an Elizabethan playwright and writer, made reference to it in a preface he wrote for Robert Greene's romance *Menaphon.* This is the same Robert Greene who would later call Shakespeare an "upstart crow'—see the general introduction to this volume—and whose prose story *Pandosto* served Shakespeare as his primary source for *The Winter's Tale.* Nashe wrote, "English Seneca by candlelight yields many good sentences, as *Blood is a begger*, and so forth; and if you entreat fair in a frosty morning, he will afford you whole Hamlets, I should say handfuls of tragical speeches."

For Nashe to have taken notice of the play and quoted directly from it would seem to indicate that it was popular enough by 1589 that his allusion would find readers who could recognise it. In effect, he mocks the play for trying to out-Seneca Seneca, the Roman playwright admired by Elizabethans for his violent tragedies and heightened language. In addition, a June 1594 performance of the play was recorded in Henslowe's diary, another of the most significant artifacts of early modern stage history. And in 1596 Thomas Lodge, another playwright and writer whose prose romance *Rosalynde* formed the basis of *As You Like It*, also alluded to the play when describing a devil "as pale as the vizard of the ghost which cried so miserably at the Theatre, like an oyster-wife, 'Hamlet, revenge.'"

These passing references to a Hamlet play of the 1580s and 1590s, powerful as the work seems to have been to Elizabethan audiences, cannot refer to the play we know to be by Shakespeare. His version was written sometime between 1599 and 1603—scholars still debate exactly when within that range. And although some have occasionally proposed that Shakespeare might have written both the *Ur-Hamlet* and the *Hamlet* we know, scholarly consensus favours the view that the *Ur-Hamlet* was the work of another playwright, perhaps Thomas Kyd. If so, and if Shakespeare saw it, which would seem almost certain in the tight world of Elizabethan theatre, he was clearly influenced by what he saw. His Hamlet story contains a number of key plot details not found in either the Saxo or Belleforest versions, among the most significant of these the addition of the Ghost, who directs Prince Hamlet to avenge his murder and revisits him during the course of the son's delays; a character in whom Hamlet confides his intentions to behave erratically and who provides his eulogy (Horatio in Shakespeare's play); two sons of slain fathers who provide different kinds of dramatic foils to Prince Hamlet (Laertes and Fortinbras); a woman with whom he had a prior and intense love relationship that he breaks off (Ophelia); a play-within-a-play performed ostensibly for the benefit (but actually the entrapment) of the king; and perhaps most obviously and importantly, the death of the protagonist at the end of the play.

From where did these major changes to the story come? Scholars typically offer two possible lines of interpretation for how Shakespeare's play developed from previous versions of the story. The first theory is that the author of the *Ur-Hamlet* knew the received story from either Saxo or Belleforest (or both) and added a number of key details to it. But Shakespeare may not even have known the story in *any* written form, even though it was available to him in both Latin and French versions. Of course, without the text of the *Ur-Hamlet*, we will never be able to compare what he saw on stage with what he wrote in his own version because we are left to conjecture what the *Ur-Hamlet* might have contained, based on only a few contemporary references to it.

The second theory gives less importance to the *Ur-Hamlet* and posits that Shakespeare himself was responsible for the major changes to the Hamlet story—that the alterations which transformed a fairly primitive folk tale of strategy, violence, and revenge into one of literature's most compelling portraits of human psychology and moral reflection came from his imagination. Although this theory cannot be proved or disproved any more than the first, it is complicated by some compelling circumstantial evidence and several facts of Elizabethan literary history. Ghosts, revenge plots, soliloquies, and long, philosophical speeches were staples of late

Elizabethan tragedy. Plays like Thomas Kyd's immensely popular *The Spanish Tragedy*, probably written before 1587, would have had an influence upon Shakespeare, irrespective of the particulars of which Hamlet story he inherited. Likewise, one would not have to look far in Elizabethan letters to find models for the smouldering melancholy, sardonic wit, and misogyny of his protagonist. So even if Shakespeare brought much new to the old tale first written by Saxo some four hundred years before, his cultural moment had many significant influences upon his imagination.

This brief history of the pre-Shakespearean story now takes us to the anonymous 1608 publication entitled *The Hystorie of Hamblet*. We might well ask: how can a translation published after the play was performed possibly be a *source* for it? The answer lies in the fact that *The Hystorie of Hamblet* is a translation of a 1582 edition of Belleforest's French text. Thus, if the scholarly conjectures that Belleforest was in some way an influence upon Shakespeare have any validity, the English translation of 1608 is a very suitable document: it is written in the language of Shakespeare's own age and it assumes many of the mental horizons of his time. The *Ur-Hamlet* is the document we would all wish most to examine, but the odds that a manuscript or surreptitiously printed version will ever emerge are essentially nil, and so we are left with only the options available to us. The story told by Belleforest is closer in many details to Shakespeare's than is Saxo's, so it makes the better case for being a possible source for Shakespeare. And an English translation from the age of Shakespeare better captures the reading experience of the period than a modern English translation of Belleforest's sixteenth-century French ever could.

This said, the text of *The Hystorie of Hamblet* that follows is offered with two cautions. First, it is likely that this now-anonymous translation was influenced by Shakespeare's *Hamlet*, which was published in 1603, five years before the translation appeared, and was first performed, scholars believe, a few years before the play appeared in print. This is more than enough time for the anonymous translator to work remembered details of a performance or even sections of the printed play into Belleforest's text. Unless new details could be shown to come from the *Ur-Hamlet* (we will probably never know), we are left to conclude that the translator of *The Hystorie of Hamblet* was influenced by the stage version that was, some years before, influenced by the story he translates. Second, we have to remember that the Holy Grail in this analysis of sources and influences is missing and will almost certainly never be found. Almost everything about the transmission of the Hamlet story from Saxo to Shakespeare is conjectural, and so the 1608 text, though it cannot be a source in the strict sense, may be the closest we will ever come to one.

A Note on the Text

The Hystorie of Hamblet appears in an anonymous translation of 1608 (London: Thomas Pavier). As I explain in the introduction above, this English version is a translation of François de Belleforest's French text, with some obvious changes that may be based on Shakespeare's play. The translator also added chapter divisions and summaries not present in Belleforest's version. Belleforest's text is not an original story, either, but a liberal translation of Saxo Grammaticus's version of the story. I added notes and glosses and modernised the original spelling and punctuation. My text retains the marginal notes of the 1608 edition, which I have reproduced as footnotes beginning with the notation *"In margin."* Whenever it seemed possible, I kept early modern forms that present no difficulties for modern readers (*causeth* for *caused*, *murtherer* for *murderer*, *shew* for *show*, etc). Frequently repeated archaic words are footnoted on their first occurrence and thereafter noted with °, which refers readers to the glossary at the end of this volume.

The Hystorie of Hamblet (1608)

The Argument

It is not at this present, neither yet a small[1] time since that envy reigning in
the world hath in such sort[2] blinded men that without respect of
consanguinity,[3] friendship, or favour whatsoever they forget themselves so
much as that they spared not to defile their hands with the blood of those
men who by all law and right they ought chiefly to defend and cherish. For
what other impression was it that entered into Romulus's heart when under
pretence of I know not what law he defiled his hands with the blood of his
own brother, but the abominable vice of desire to reign? Which if in all the
occurrences, prosperities, and circumstances thereof it were well weighed and
considered, I know not any man that had not rather live at his ease and
privately without charge[4] than, being feared and honoured of all men, to bear
all the charge and burden upon his shoulders[5] to serve and please the fantasies
of the common people, to live continually in fear, and to see himself exposed
to a thousand occasions of danger; and most commonly assailed and spoiled
when he thinks verily to hold Fortune as slave to his fantasies and will and yet
buys such and so great misery for the vain and frail pleasures of this world,
with the loss of his own soul, making so large a measure of his conscience
that it is not once moved at any murther, treason, deceit, nor wickedness
whatsoever he committed, so the way may be opened and made plain unto
him whereby he may attain to that miserable felicity to command and govern
a multitude of men (as I said of Romulus) who by a most abominable action[6]
prepared himself a way to heaven (but not by virtue).

The ambitious and seditious orator of Rome supposed the degrees and
steps to heaven, and the ways to virtue to consist in the treasons, ravishments
and massacres committed by him that first laid the foundations of that city.[7]

---

[1] short. *In margin:* The desire of rule, causeth men to become traitors and murtherers.
 [The original text has many marginal notes and glosses, which I have reproduced
 in footnotes, starting with the notation *In margin:*]

[2] such a way (see glossary)

[3] blood relationship

[4] burden

[5] *In margin:* The miserable condition of such as rule over others.

[6] *In margin:* Romulus for small or no cause, killed his brother.

[7] *In margin:* Cicero in his Paradoxes. [Marcus Tullius Cicero (106-43 BCE), here
 called "the ambitious and seditious orator of Rome," was Europe's most
 influential Latin stylist, studied and imitated throughout the early modern
 period.]

And not to leave the histories of Rome:[1] what, I pray you, incited Ancius Martinus to massacre Tarquin the elder, but the desire of reigning, as a king who before had been the only man to move and solicit the said Tarquinius to bereave[2] the right heirs and inheritors thereof? What caused Tarquinius the proud[3] traitorously to imbrue[4] his hands in the blood of Servius Tullius, his father-in-law, but only that fumish[5] and unbridled desire to be commander over the city of Rome? Which practice never ceased nor discontinued in the said principal city of the empire as long as it was governed by the greatest and wisest personages chosen and elected by the people.[6] For therein have been seen infinite numbers of seditions, troubles, pledges, ransomings, confiscations and massacres only proceeding from this ground and principle which entereth into men's hearts and maketh them covet and desirous to be heads and rulers of a whole commonwealth. And after the people were deprived of that liberty of election, and that the empire became subject to the pleasure and fantasy of one man commanding all the rest, I pray you peruse their books and read diligently their histories and do but look into the means used by the most part of their kings and emperors[7] to attain to such power and authority: and you shall see how poisons, massacres, and secret murthers were the means to push them forwards that durst[8] not openly attempt it or else could not compass[9] to make open wars.

And for that the history (which I pretend to shew[10] unto you) is chiefly grounded upon treason committed by one brother against the other I will not err far out of the matter,[11] thereby desiring to shew you that it is and hath been a thing long since practised and put in use by men to spill the blood of their nearest kinsmen and friends to attain to the honour of being great and in authority, and that there hath been some that, being impatient of staying till their just time of succession, have hastened the death of their own parents,[12] as Absalom would have done to the holy king David his father,

---

[1] *In margin:* Tarquin the elder slain in Rome.
[2] strip away, rob (see glossary)
[3] *In margin:* Servius Tullius slain by his son in law.
[4] soak
[5] fuming, intemperate
[6] *In margin:* Wherefore Rome was subject to seditions.
[7] *In margin:* Divers attained to the empire, by murther. [*divers*: see glossary]
[8] dared (see glossary)
[9] plan, plot
[10] presume to show (see glossary)
[11] wander far off topic
[12] *In margin:* Absalom conspired against David his father.

and as we read of Domitian, that poisoned his brother Titus, the most courteous and liberal prince that ever swayed the empire of Rome.

And God knows we have many the like examples in this our time, where the son conspired against the father: for that Sultan Zelin, Emperour of Turks,[1] was so honest a man, that fearing Bajazeth his father would die of his natural death and that thereby he should have stayed too long for the empire, bereaved° him of his life: and Sultan Soliman his successor,[2] although he attempted not anything against his father, yet being moved with a certain fear to be deposed from his empery and bearing a hatred to Mustapha his son (incited thereunto by Rustain Bassa, whom the Jews' enemies to the young prince had by gifts procured thereunto), caused him to be strangled with a bow string, without hearing him (that never had offended his father) once speak to justify his innocence.

But let us leave the Turks, like barbarians as they are, whose throne is ordinarily established by the effusion of the blood of those that are nearest of kindred and consanguinity to the empire, and consider what tragedies have been played to the like effect in the memory of our ancestors and with what charity and love the nearest kindreds and friends among them have been entertained one of the other.[3] If you had not the histories extant before you, if the memory were not in a manner fresh and known almost to every man, I would make a long discourse thereof: but things being so clear and evident, the truth so much discovered[4] and the people almost as it were glutted with such treasons, I will omit them and follow my matter to shew° you that if the iniquity of a brother caused his brother to lose his life, yet that vengeance was not long after delayed: to the end that traitors may know although the punishment of their trespasses committed be stayed[5] for awhile, yet that they may assure themselves that without all doubt they shall never escape the puissant[6] and revenging hand of God, who being slow to anger, yet in the end doth not fail to shew some signs and evident tokens of his fearful judgement upon such as, forgetting their duties, shed innocent blood and betray their rulers, whom they ought chiefly to honour, serve, and reverence.

---

[1] *In margin:* Zelin slew his father Bajazeth

[2] *In margin:* Soliman caused Mustapha his son to be hanged.

[3] *In margin:* Great mischief in our age.

[4] *In margin:* God stayeth his wrath, but yet revengeth wrong: read Plutarch Opuscules of the slowness of God's judgements. [The "Opuscules of Plutarch" are the minor works; the author probably had in mind the edition *Cinq opuscules de Plutarch cheronné* (Paris, 1546).]

[5] delayed

[6] powerful

The Preface

Although in the beginning of this history, I had determined not to have troubled you with any other matter than a history of our own time, having sufficient tragical matter to satisfy the minds of men, but because I cannot well discourse thereof without touching many personages whom I would not willingly displease, and partly because the argument[1] that I have in hand seemed unto me a thing worthy to be offered to our French nobility for the great and gallant occurrences therein set down, I have somewhat strayed from my course as touching the tragedies of this our age: and starting out of France and over Netherlanders countries, I have ventured to visit the histories of Denmark, that it may serve for an example of virtue and contentment to our nation (whom I specially seek to please) and for whose satisfaction I have not left any flower whatsoever untasted, from whence I have not drawn the most perfect and delicate honey,[2] thereby to bind them to my diligence herein, not caring for the ingratitude of the time present that leaveth (and as it were rejecteth) without recompense such as serve the commonwealth and by their travail and diligence honour their country and illustrate[3] the realm of France, so that often times the fault proceedeth rather from them than from the great personages that have other affairs which withdraw them from things that seem of small consequence.

Withal,[4] esteeming myself more than satisfied in this contentment and freedom which I now enjoy, being loved of the nobility, for whom I travail without grudging; favoured of men of learning and knowledge for admiring and reverencing them according to their worthiness; and honoured of the common people, of whom although I crave not their judgement, as not esteeming them of ability to eternise the name of a worthy man, yet I account myself sufficiently happy to have attained to this felicity that few or no men refuse or disdain to read my works, many admiring and wondering thereat, as there are some that, provoked by envy, blame and condemn it. To whom I confess myself much bound and beholding, for that by their means I am the more vigilant and so by my travail much more beloved and honoured than ever I was: which to me is the greatest pleasure that I can enjoy and the most abundant treasures in my coffers, wherewith I am more satisfied and contented than (if without comparison) I enjoyed the

---

[1] topic
[2] The metaphor of gathering honey from different flowers was a traditional way to describe the practice of "commonplacing," or gathering written notes from earlier authors as material for future arguments.
[3] make illustrious, glorify
[4] all considered (see glossary)

greatest treasures in all Asia. Now returning to our matter, let us begin to declare the history.

Chapter 1

How Horvendile and Fengon were made governors of the Province of Ditmarsse[1] and how Horvendile married Geruth, daughter to Roderick,[2] chief king of Denmark, by whom he had Hamblet: and how after his marriage his brother Fengon slew him traitorously and married his brother's wife; and what followed.

You must understand that long time before the kingdom of Denmark received the faith of Jesus Christ and embraced the doctrine of the Christians,[3] that the common people in those days were barbarous and uncivil and their princes cruel, without faith or loyalty, seeking nothing but murther and deposing (or at the least) offending each other either in honours, goods, or lives, not caring to ransom such as they took prisoners,[4] but rather sacrificing them to the cruel vengeance naturally imprinted in their hearts in such sort° that if there were sometime[5] a good prince or king among them, who being adorned with the most perfect gifts of nature, would addict himself to virtue and use courtesy, although the people held him in admiration (as virtue is admirable to the most wicked), yet the envy of his neighbours was so great that they never ceased until that virtuous man were dispatched out of the world.[6]

King Roderick as then reigning in Denmark, after he had appeased the troubles in the country and driven the Sweathlanders and Slaveans[7] from thence, he divided the kingdom into diverse provinces, placing governors therein who after (as the like happened in France) bare[8] the names of dukes, marquises, and earls, giving the government of Jutie (at this present called Ditmarsse),[9] lying upon the country of the Cimbrians, in the straight or narrow part of land that sheweth° like a point or cape of ground upon the sea which northward bordereth upon the country of Norway, two valiant

---

[1] Dithmarschen, a province of northern Germany, formerly Danish lands
[2] Rørik, a legendary seventh-century Danish king
[3] *In margin:* The Danes in times past barbarous and uncivil.
[4] *In margin:* The cruelty of the Danes.
[5] occasionally, at times
[6] *In margin:* Roderick King of Denmark.
[7] Swedes and Slavs
[8] bore (see glossary)
[9] *In margin:* Jutie at this time, called then Ditmarsse. [The Jutland Peninsula is part of modern-day Denmark and Germany.]

and warlike lords, Horvendile and Fengon, sons to Gervendile, who likewise had been governor of that province.

Now the greatest honour that men of noble birth could at that time win and obtain was in exercising the art of piracy upon the seas, assailing their neighbours and the countries bordering upon them:[1] and how much the more they used to rob, pill,[2] and spoil other provinces and islands far adjacent, so much the more their honours and reputation increased and augmented: wherein Horvendile obtained the highest place in his time, being the most renowned pirate that in those days scoured the seas and havens of the north parts: whose great fame, so moved the heart of Collere, king of Norway[3] that he was much grieved to hear that Horvendile, surmounting him in feats of arms, thereby obscuring the glory by him already obtained upon the seas, honour more than covetousness of riches (in those days) being the reason that provoked those barbarian princes to overthrow and vanquish one the other, not caring to be slain by the hands of a victorious person.

This valiant and hardy king, having challenged Horvendile to fight with him body to body, the combat was by him accepted, with conditions that he which should be vanquished should lose all the riches he had in his ship and that the vanquisher should cause the body of the vanquished (that should be slain in the combat) to be honourably buried, death being the prize and reward of him that should lose the battle. And to conclude, Collere, king of Norway (although a valiant, hardy and courageous prince) was in the end vanquished and slain by Horvendile,[4] who presently caused a tomb to be erected and therein (with all honourable obsequies[5] fit for a prince) buried the body of King Collere according to their ancient manner and superstitions in those days and the conditions of the combat, bereaving the king's ships of all their riches and having slain the king's sister, a very brave and valiant warrior, and overrun all the coast of Norway and the northern islands, returned home again laden with much treasure, sending the most part thereof to his sovereign King Roderick, thereby to procure his good liking and so to be accounted one of the greatest favourites about his majesty.

The king, allured by those presents and esteeming himself happy to have so valiant a subject, sought by a great favour and courtesy to make him become bounden unto him perpetually, giving him Geruth, his daughter, to his wife,[6] of whom he knew Horvendile to be already much enamoured.

---

[1] *In margin:* Horvendile a king and a pirate.
[2] pillage
[3] *In margin:* Collere king of Norway.
[4] *In margin:* Horvendile slew Collere.
[5] funeral rites
[6] King Collere gave his daughter Geruth as wife to Horvendile

And the more to honour him, determined himself in person to conduct her into Jutie, where the marriage was celebrated according to the ancient manner: and to be brief, of this marriage proceeded Hamblet,[1] of whom I intend to speak, and for his cause have chosen to renew this present history.

Fengon, brother to this Prince Horvendile, who only fretting and despiting[2] in his heart at the great honour and reputation won by his brother in warlike affairs, but solicited and provoked by a foolish jealousy to see him honoured with royal alliance[3] and fearing thereby to be deposed from his part of the government, or rather desiring to be only governor, thereby to obscure the memory of the victories and conquests of his brother Horvendile, determined (whatsoever happened) to kill him, which he effected in such sort° that no man once so much as suspected him, every man esteeming that from such and so firm a knot of alliance and consanguinity,[4] there could proceed no other issue[5] than the full effects of virtue and courtesy. But (as I said before) the desire of bearing sovereign rule and authority respecteth neither blood nor amity, nor caring for virtue as being wholly without respect of laws or majesty divine, for it is not possible that he which invadeth the country and taketh away the riches of another man without cause or reason should know or fear God. Was not this a crafty and subtle counsellor? But he might have thought that the mother, knowing her husband's case, would not cast her son into the danger of death.

But Fengon having secretly assembled certain men and perceiving himself strong enough to execute his enterprise, Horvendile his brother being at a banquet with his friends, suddenly set upon him,[6] where he slew him as traitorously, as cunningly he purged himself of so detestable a murther to his subjects, for that before he had any violent or bloody hands or once committed parricide upon his brother he had incestuously abused his wife, whose honour he ought as well to have sought and procured as traitorously he pursued and effected his destruction. And it is most certain that the man that abandoneth himself to any notorious and wicked action whereby he becometh a great sinner, he careth not to commit much more heinous and abominable offences, and covered his boldness and wicked practise with so great subtlety and policy[7] and under a veil of mere simplicity, that being favoured for the honest love that he bare° to his sister-

---

[1] *In margin:* Hamblet son to Horvendile.
[2] not only being vexed and sullen
[3] *In margin:* Fengon his conspiracy against his brother.
[4] nearness of blood
[5] outcome
[6] *In margin:* Fengon killeth his brother.
[7] strategy, cunning (see glossary)

in-law, for whose sake he affirmed he had in that sort murthered his brother, that his sin found excuse among the common people and of the nobility was esteemed for justice.

For that Geruth being as courteous a princess as any then living in the north parts and one that had never once so much as offended any of her subjects, either commons or courtiers, this adulterer and infamous murtherer slandered his dead brother, that he would have slain his wife, and that he by chance finding him upon the point ready to do it, in defence of the lady had slain him, bearing off the blows which as then he struck at the innocent princess, without any other cause of malice whatsoever, wherein he wanted no false witnesses to approve his act, which deposed in like sort, as the wicked calumniator[1] himself protested, being the same persons that had borne him company and were participants of his treason. So that instead of pursuing him as a parricide and an incestuous person,[2] all the courtiers admired and flattered him in his good fortune, making more account of false witnesses and detestable wicked reporters, and more honouring the calumniators than they esteemed of those that seeking to call the matter in question, and admiring the virtues of the murthered prince would have punished the massacrers and bereavers of his life.[3]

Which was the cause that Fengon, boldened and encouraged by such impunity durst° venture to couple himself in marriage with her whom he used as his concubine during good Horvendile's life, in that sort spotting his name with a double vice, and charging his conscience with abominable guilt and twofold impiety, as incestuous adultery and parricide murther; and that the unfortunate and wicked woman that had received the honour to be the wife of one of the valiantest and wisest princes in the north imbased[4] herself in such vile sort as to falsify her faith unto him and, which is worse, to marry him that had been the tyrannous murtherer of her lawful husband, which made diverse men think that she had been the causer of the murther, thereby to live in her adultery without control.

But where shall a man find a more wicked and bold woman than a great personage, once having loosed the bands of honour and honesty? This princess who at the first for her rare virtues and courtesy[5] was honoured of all men and beloved of her husband, as soon as she once gave ear to the tyrant Fengon forgot both the rank she held among the greatest names and the duty of an honest wife on her behalf. But I will not stand to gaze and

---

[1] slanderer
[2] *In margin:* Slanderers more honoured in court then virtuous persons.
[3] those who massacred him and stole his life from him
[4] debased
[5] courtly or refined behaviour

mervail[1] at women, for that there are many which seek to blase[2] and set them forth: in which their writings they spare not to blame them all for the faults of some one, or few, women. But I say that either nature ought to have bereaved° man of that opinion to accompany with women,[3] or else to endow them with such spirits as that they may easily support the crosses they endure without complaining so often and so strangely, seeing it is their own beastliness that overthrows them. For if it be so, that a woman is so imperfect a creature as they make her to be and that they know this beast to be so hard to be tamed as they affirm, why then are they so foolish to preserve them and so dull and brutish as to trust their deceitful and wanton embracings?

But let us leave her in this extremity of lasciviousness and proceed to shew you in what sort° the young Prince Hamblet behaved himself to escape the tyranny of his uncle.

Chapter 2

How Hamblet counterfeited the madman to escape the tyranny of his uncle, and how he was tempted by a woman (through his uncle's procurement) who thereby thought to undermine the prince, and by that means to find out whether he counterfeited madness or not: and how Hamblet would by no means be brought to consent unto her; and what followed.

Geruth having (as I said before) so much forgotten herself, the Prince Hamblet perceiving himself to be in danger of his life, as being abandoned of his own mother and forsaken of all men, and assuring himself that Fengon would not detract[4] the time to send him the same way his father Horvendile was gone, to beguile the tyrant in his subtleties (that esteemed him to be of such a mind that if he once attained to man's estate he would not long delay the time to revenge the death of his father) counterfeiting the madman with such craft and subtle practises that he made shew° as if he had utterly lost his wits. And under that veil he covered his pretence and defended his life from the treasons and practises of the tyrant his uncle. And although he had been at the school of the Roman prince who because he counterfeited himself to be a fool was called Brutus, yet he imitated his fashions and his

---

[1] marvel
[2] proclaim
[3] *In margin:* If man be deceived by a woman, it is his own beastliness.
[4] delay

wisdom.[1] For every day being in the queen's palace (who as then was more careful to please her whoremaster than ready to revenge the cruel death of her husband or to restore her son to his inheritance), he rent and tore his clothes, wallowing and lying in the dirt and mire, his face all filthy and black, running through the streets like a man distraught, not speaking one word but such as seemed to proceed of madness and mere frenzy, all his actions and gestures being no other than the right countenances of a man wholly deprived of all reason and understanding, in such sort° that as then he seemed fit for nothing but to make sport to the pages and ruffling courtiers[2] that attended in the court of his uncle and father in law. But the young prince noted them well enough, minding one day to be revenged in such manner that the memory thereof should remain perpetually to the world.

Behold, I pray you, a great point of a wise and brave spirit in a young prince, by so great a shew° of imperfection in his person for advancement and his own imbasing[3] and despising, to work the means and to prepare the way for himself to be one of the happiest kings in his age. In like sort, never any man was reputed by any of his actions more wise and prudent than Brutus,[4] dissembling a great alteration in his mind, for that the occasion of such his device of foolishness proceeded only of a good and mature counsel and deliberation not only to preserve his goods and shun the rage of the proud tyrant, but also to open a large way to procure the banishment and utter ruin of wicked Tarquinius and to enfranchise the people (which were before oppressed) from the yoke of a great and miserable servitude. And so not only Brutus, but this man and worthy prince, to whom we may also add King David that counterfeited the madman among the petty kings of Palestina to preserve his life from the subtle practises of those kings.[5] I shew

---

[1] The author alludes to Lucius Junius Brutus (flourished 6th century BCE), who in order to overthrow the regime of the tyrannical Tarquin family feigned inability or madness. This story was well known in the period (and is retold in Shakespeare's narrative poem *The Rape of Lucrece*). The allusion develops below.

[2] page boys and elaborately dressed courtiers

[3] lowering

[4] *In margin:* Brutus esteemed wise, for counterfeiting the fool. Read Titus Livius, and Halicarnassus. [Titus Livius (or Livy) was an important first-century BCE Roman historian; Dionysius of Halicarnassus was a Greek historian and rhetorician of the same period.]

[5] *In margin:* David counterfeited the madman, before King Athes. [King David pretended to be mad before Achish, king of Gath in Palestine (1 Samuel 21). The author's combination of Brutus and David is an instance of his Christian humanist approach to his version of the Hamblet story. See introduction.]

this example unto such, as being offended with any great personage, have not sufficient means to prevail in their intents or revenge the injury by them received; but when I speak of revenging any injury received upon a great personage or superior it must be understood by such an one as is not our sovereign, against whom we may by no means resist, nor once practise any treason nor conspiracy against his life. And he that will follow this course must speak and do all things whatsoever that are pleasing and acceptable to him whom he meaneth to deceive, practise his actions, and esteem him above all men, clean contrary to his own intent and meaning. For that is rightly to play and counterfeit the fool, when a man is constrained to dissemble and kiss his hand whom in heart he could wish an hundred foot depth under the earth so he might never see him more, if it were not a thing wholly to be disliked in a Christian, who by no means ought to have a bitter gall or desires infected with revenge.

Hamblet, in this sort° counterfeiting the madman, many times did diverse actions of great and deep consideration and often made such and so fit answers that a wise man would soon have judged from what spirit so fine an invention might proceed, for that standing by the fire and sharpening sticks like poignards and pricks,[1] one in smiling manner asked him wherefore[2] he made those little staves so sharp at the points. I prepare (saith he) piercing darts and sharp arrows to revenge my father's death.[3] Fools, as I said before, esteemed those his words as nothing, but men of quick spirits and such as had a deeper reach began to suspect somewhat, esteeming that under that kind of folly there lay hidden a great and rare subtlety such as one day might be prejudicial to their prince, saying that under colour of such rudeness he shadowed a crafty policy° and by his devised simplicity he concealed a sharp and pregnant spirit, for which cause they counselled the king to try and know if it were possible how to discover the intent and meaning of the young prince, and they could find no better nor more fit invention[4] to entrap him than to set some fair and beautiful woman in a secret place, that with flattering speeches and all the craftiest means she could use should purposely seek to allure his mind to have his pleasure of her. For the nature of all young men[5] (specially such as are brought up wantonly) is so transported with the desires of the flesh and entereth so greedily into the pleasures thereof that it is almost impossible to cover the foul affection neither yet to dissemble or hide the same by art or industry,

---

[1] daggers and pointed sticks
[2] why (see glossary)
[3] *In margin:* A subtle answer of Prince Hamblet.
[4] plan
[5] *In margin:* subtleties used to discover Hamblet's madness.

much less to shun it. What cunning or subtlety soever they use to cloak their pretence, seeing occasion offered, and that in secret, specially in the most enticing sin that reigneth in man, they cannot choose (being constrained by voluptuousness) but fall to natural effect and working.

To this end certain courtiers were appointed to lead Hamblet into a solitary place within the woods, whither they brought the woman, inciting him to take their pleasures together and to embrace one another, but the subtle practises used in these our days, not to try if men of great account be extract out of their wits but rather to deprive them of strength, virtue, and wisdom by means of such devilish practitioners and infernal spirits their domestical servants and ministers of corruption: and surely the poor prince at this assault had been in great danger if a gentleman (that in Horvendile's time had been nourished with him) had not shown himself more affectioned[1] to the bringing up he had received with Hamblet than desirous to please the tyrant, who by all means sought to entangle the son in the same nets wherein the father had ended his days. This gentleman bare° the courtiers (appointed as aforesaid of this treason) company, more desiring to give the prince instructions what he should do than to entrap him, making full account that the least show of perfect sense and wisdom that Hamblet should make would be sufficient to cause him to lose his life. And therefore by certain signs he gave Hamblet intelligence in what danger he was like to fall if by any means he seemed to obey or once like the wanton toys and vicious provocations of the gentlewoman sent thither by his uncle.

Which much abashed[2] the prince, as then wholly being in affection to the lady, but by her he was likewise informed of the treason, as being one that from her infancy loved and favoured him and would have been exceeding sorrowful for his misfortune, and much more to leave his company without enjoying the pleasure of his body, whom she loved more than herself. The prince in this sort° having both deceived the courtiers and the lady's expectation, that affirmed and swore that he never once offered to have his pleasure of the woman, although in subtlety he affirmed the contrary. Every man thereupon assured themselves that without all doubt he was distraught of his senses, that his brains were as then wholly void of force and incapable of reasonable apprehension so that as then Fengon's practise took no effect. But for all that he left not off, still seeking by all means to find out Hamblet's subtlety, as in the next chapter you shall perceive.

---

[1] affectionately disposed. *In margin:* Corrupters of young gentlemen in prince's courts and great houses.
[2] surprised, disturbed (see glossary)

Chapter 3

How Fengon, uncle to Hamblet, a second time to entrap him in his politic[1] madness, caused one of his counsellors to be secretly hidden in the queen's chamber, behind the arras, to hear what speeches passed between Hamblet and the queen, and how Hamblet killed him and escaped that danger; and what followed.

Among the friends of Fengon there was one that above all the rest doubted of[2] Hamblet's practices in counterfeiting the madman, who for that cause said that it was impossible that so crafty a gallant as Hamblet that counterfeited the fool should be discovered with so common and unskillful practices, which might easily be perceived, and that to find out his politic pretence[3] it were necessary to invent some subtle and crafty means more attractive: whereby the gallant might not have the leisure to use his accustomed dissimulation, which to effect he said he knew a fit way and a most convenient mean[4] to effect the king's desire and thereby to entrap Hamblet in his subtleties and cause him of his own accord to fall into the net prepared for him and thereby evidently shew° his secret meaning.

His device was thus, that King Fengon should make as though he were to go some long voyage concerning affairs of great importance, and that in the meantime Hamblet should be shut up alone in a chamber with his mother, wherein some other should secretly be hidden behind the hangings, unknown either to him or his mother, there to stand and hear their speeches, and the complots by them to be taken concerning the accomplishments of the dissembling fool's pretence, assuring the king that if there were any point of wisdom and perfect sense in the gallant's spirit that without all doubt he would easily discover it to his mother as being devoid of all fear that she would utter or make known his secret intent, being the woman that had borne him in her body and nourished him so carefully, and withal° offered himself to be the man that should stand to harken[5] and bear witness of Hamblet's speeches with his mother, that he might not be esteemed a counsellor in such a case, wherein he refused to be the executioner, for the behoof[6] and service of his prince.

This invention pleased the king exceeding well, esteeming it as the only and sovereign remedy to heal the prince of his lunacy, and to that end

---

[1] strategic, cunning
[2] suspected. *In margin:* Another subtlety used to deceive Hamblet.
[3] uncover his strategic ruse
[4] means
[5] listen to
[6] benefit

making a long voyage issued out of his palace and rode to hunt in the forest. Meantime, the counsellor entered secretly into the queen's chamber, and there hid himself behind the arras[1] not long before the queen and Hamblet came thither,[2] who being crafty and politic, as soon as he was within the chamber doubting[3] some treason and, fearing if he should speak severely and wisely to his mother touching his secret practises he should be understood and by that means intercepted, used his ordinary manner of dissimulation and began to crow like a cock beating with his arms (in such manner as cocks use to strike with their wings) upon the hangings of the chamber, whereby feeling something stirring under them, he cried "a rat, a rat," and presently drawing his sword thrust it into the hangings, which done, pulled the counsellor (half dead) out by the heels, made an end of killing him, and being slain, cut his body in pieces, which he caused to be boiled and then cast it into an open vault or privy,[4] that so it might serve for food to the hogs.

By which means, having discovered the ambush and given the inventor thereof his just reward, he came again to his mother, who in the meantime wept and tormented herself to see all her hopes frustrate. For that what fault soever she had committed, yet was she sore grieved to see her only child made a mere mockery, every man reproaching her with his folly, one point whereof she had as then seen before her eyes, which was no small prick to her conscience, esteeming that the gods sent her that punishment[5] for joining incestuously in marriage with the tyrannous murtherer of her husband, who likewise ceased not to invent all the means he could to bring his nephew to his end, accusing his own natural indiscretion as being the ordinary guide of those that so much desire the pleasures of the body, who shutting up the way to all reason respect not what may ensue of their lightness[6] and great inconstancy, and how a pleasure of small moment is sufficient to give them cause of repentance during their lives and make them curse the day and time that ever any such apprehensions entered into their minds or that they closed their eyes to reject the honesty requisite in ladies of her quality, and to despise the holy institution of those dames that had gone before her both in nobility and virtue, calling to mind the great praises and commendations given by the Danes to Rinde, daughter to King Rothere, the chastest lady in

---

[1] wall tapestry

[2] *In margin:* Hamblet's subtlety.

[3] suspecting

[4] toilet or sewer. *In margin:* A cruel revenge taken by Hamblet upon him that would have betrayed him.

[5] *In margin:* Queen Geruth's repentance.

[6] fickleness or lewdness

her time and withal so shamefast[1] that she would never consent to marriage
with any prince or knight whatsoever, surpassing in virtue all the ladies of
her time, as she herself surmounted them in beauty, good behaviour and
comeliness.

And while in this sort° she sat tormenting herself, Hamblet entered into
the chamber, who having once again searched every corner of the same,
distrusting his mother as well as the rest, and perceiving himself to be alone,
began in sober and discreet manner to speak unto her, saying "What treason
is this, O most infamous woman! Of all that ever prostrated themselves to
the will of an abominable whoremonger who under the veil of a dissembling
creature covereth the most wicked and detestable crime that man could ever
imagine, or was committed. How may I be assured to trust you, that like a
vile wanton adulteress altogether impudent and given over to her pleasure,
runs spreading forth her arms joyfully to embrace the traitorous villainous
tyrant that murthered my father and most incestuously receivest the villain
into the lawful bed of your loyal spouse, imprudently entertaining him
instead of the dear father of your miserable and discomforted son, if the
gods grant him not the grace speedily to escape from a captivity so unworthy
the degree he holdeth and the race and noble family of his ancestors. Is this
the part of a queen and daughter to a king to live like a brute beast (and like
a mare that yieldeth her body to the horse that hath beaten her companion
away), to follow the pleasure of an abominable king that hath murthered a
far more honester and better man than himself in massacring Horvendile,
the honour and glory of the Danes, who are now esteemed of no force nor
valour at all, since the shining splendour of knighthood was brought to an
end by the most wickedest and cruellest villain living upon earth? I for my
part will never account him for my kinsman, nor once know him for mine
uncle, nor you my dear mother for not having respect to the blood that ought
to have united us so straightly together and who neither with your honour
nor without suspicion of consent to the death of your husband could ever
have agreed to have married with his cruel enemy.

O, Queen Geruth, it is the part of a bitch to couple with many and desire
acquaintance of diverse mastiffs;[2] it is licentiousness only that hath made
you deface out of your mind the memory of the valour and virtues of the
good king your husband and my father. It was an unbridled desire that
guided the daughter of Roderick to embrace the tyrant Fengon and not to
remember Horvendile (unworthy of so strange entertainment), neither that
he killed his brother traitorously, and that she being his father's wife

---

[1] in all ways meek or submissive. *In margin:* Rinde a princess of an admirable
  chastity.
[2] various dogs

betrayed him, although he so well favoured and loved her that for her sake he utterly bereaved° Norway of her riches and valiant soldiers to augment the treasures of Roderick and make Geruth wife to the hardiest prince in Europe. It is not the part of a woman, much less of a princess, in whom all modesty, courtesy, compassion and love ought to abound, thus to leave her dear child to fortune in the bloody and murtherous hands of a villain and traitor. Brute beasts do not so: for lions, tigers, ounces,[1] and leopards fight for the safety and defence of their whelps, and birds that have beaks, claws and wings resist such as would ravish them of their young ones; but you to the contrary expose and deliver me to death, whereas ye should defend me. Is not this as much as if you should betray me, when you knowing the perverseness of the tyrant and his intents, full of deadly counsel as touching the race and image of his brother, have not once sought nor desired to find the means to save your child (and only son) by sending him into Swethland,[2] Norway or England, rather than to leave him as a prey to your infamous adulterer? Be not offended, I pray you, madam, if transported with dolour and grief I speak so boldly unto you and that I respect you less than duty requireth, for you, having forgotten me and wholly rejected the memory of the deceased king, my father, must not be abashed° if I also surpass the bounds and limits of due consideration. Behold into what distress I am now fallen, and to what mischief my fortune and your over-great lightness[3] and want of wisdom have induced me, that I am constrained to play the madman to save my life instead of using and practising arms, following adventures, and seeking all means to make myself known to be the true and undoubted heir of the valiant and virtuous King Horvendile. It was not without cause and just occasion that my gestures, countenances and words seem all to proceed from a madman, and that I desire to have all men esteem me wholly deprived of sense and reasonable understanding because I am well assured that he that hath made no conscience to kill his own brother (accustomed to murthers, and allured with desire of government without control in his treasons) will not spare to save himself with the like cruelty in the blood and flesh of the loins of his brother by him massacred.

And therefore it is better for me to feign madness than to use my right senses as nature hath bestowed them upon me, the bright shining clearness thereof I am forced to hide under this shadow of dissimulation, as the sun doth her beams under some great cloud when the weather in summertime overcasteth: the face of a madman serveth to cover my gallant countenance and the gestures of a fool are fit for me, to the end that guiding myself wisely

---

[1] lynxes or pumas
[2] Sweden
[3] fickleness

therein I may preserve my life for the Danes and the memory of my late deceased father. For yet the desire of revenging his death is so engraven in my heart that if I die not shortly I hope to take such and so great vengeance that these countries shall for ever speak thereof.

Nevertheless, I must stay[1] the time, means, and occasion, lest by making over-great haste I be now the cause of mine own sudden ruin and overthrow and by that means end before I begin to effect my heart's desire. He that hath to do with a wicked, disloyal, cruel, and discourteous man must use craft and politic inventions, such as a fine wit can best imagine, not to discover his enterprise.[2] For seeing that by force I cannot effect my desire, reason alloweth me by dissimulation, subtlety, and secret practises to proceed therein. To conclude, weep not (madam) to see my folly, but rather sigh and lament your own offence, tormenting your conscience in regard of the infamy that hath so defiled the ancient renown and glory that (in times past) honoured Queen Geruth: for we are not to sorrow and grieve at other men's vices, but for our own misdeeds, and great follies, desiring you, for the surplus[3] of my proceedings, above all things (as you love your own life and welfare) that neither the king, nor any other may by any means know mine intent, and let me alone with the rest, for I hope in the end to bring my purpose to effect."

Although the queen perceived herself nearly touched and that Hamblet moved her to the quick, where she felt herself interested,[4] nevertheless she forgot all disdain and wrath which thereby she might as then have had, hearing herself so sharply chidden and reproved, for the joy she then conceived to behold the gallant spirit of her son and to think what she might hope and the easier expect of his so great policy° and wisdom. But on the one side she durst° not lift up her eyes to behold him, remembering her offence. And on the other side she would gladly have embraced her son, in regard of the wise admonitions by him given unto her, which as then quenched the flames of unbridled desire that before had moved her to affect King Fengon, to engraft in her heart the virtuous actions of her lawful spouse, whom inwardly she much lamented, when she beheld the lively image and portraiture of his virtue and great wisdom in her child, representing his father's haughty and valiant heart. And so overcome and vanquished with this honest passion and weeping most bitterly, having long time fixed her eyes upon Hamblet, as being ravished into some great and

---

[1] delay

[2] *In margin:* We must use subtleties to a disloyal person.

[3] remainder, final part. *In margin:* We must weep for our own faults and not for other men's.

[4] the core of her being, where she was most concerned

deep contemplation and as it were wholly amazed, at the last embracing him in her arms (with the like love that a virtuous mother may or can use, to kiss and entertain her own child) she spake unto him in this manner:

"I know well (my Son) that I have done thee great wrong in marrying with Fengon, the cruel tyrant and murtherer of thy father, and my loyal spouse: but when thou shalt consider the small means of resistance and the treason of the palace, with the little cause of confidence we are to expect or hope for of the courtiers, all wrought to his will, as also the power he made ready if I should have refused to like of him, thou wouldst rather excuse than accuse me of lasciviousness or inconstancy, much less offer me that wrong to suspect that ever thy mother Geruth once consented to the death and murther of her husband: swearing unto thee (by the majesty of the gods) that if it had lain in my power to have resisted the tyrant, although it had been with the loss of my blood, yea and of my life, I would surely have saved the life of my lord and husband with as good a will and desire as since that time I have often been a means to hinder and impeach the shortening of thy life, which being taken away, I will no longer live here upon earth. For seeing that thy senses are whole and sound, I am in hope to see an easy means invented for the revenging of thy father's death. Nevertheless, mine own sweet son, if thou hast pity of thy self or care of the memory of thy father (although thou wilt do nothing for her that deserveth not the name of a mother in this respect) I pray thee carry thine affairs wisely. Be not hasty nor over-furious in thy enterprises, neither yet advance thyself more than reason shall move thee to effect thy purpose. Thou seest there is not almost any man wherein thou mayest put thy trust nor any woman to whom I dare utter the least part of my secrets that would not presently report it to thine adversary, who although in outward shew° he dissembleth to love thee, the better to enjoy his pleasures of me, yet he distrusteth and feareth me for thy sake and is not so simple to be easily persuaded that thou art a fool or mad. So that if thou chance to do anything that seemeth to proceed of wisdom or policy° (how secretly soever it be done) he will presently be informed thereof and I am greatly afraid that the devils have shewed him what hath passed at this present between us (Fortune so much pursueth and contrarieth[1] our ease and welfare) or that this murther that now thou hast committed be not the cause of both our destructions, which I by no means will seem to know, but will keep secret both thy wisdom and hardy enterprise. Beseeching the gods (my good son) that they guiding thy heart, directing thy counsels and prospering thy enterprise, I may see thee possess and enjoy that which is thy right, and wear the crown of Denmark by the

---

[1] impedes, crosses

tyrant taken from thee: that I may rejoice in thy prosperity and therewith content myself, seeing with what courage and boldness thou shalt take vengeance upon the murtherer of thy father, as also upon all those that have assisted and favoured him in his murtherous and bloody enterprise."

"Madam (said Hamblet) I will put my trust in you, and from henceforth mean not to meddle further with your affairs, beseeching you (as you love your own flesh and blood) that you will from henceforth no more esteem of the adulterer mine enemy, whom I will surely kill or cause to be put to death, in despite of all the devils in hell. And have he never so many flattering courtesans[1] to defend him, yet will I bring him to his death, and they themselves also shall bear him company therein, as they have been his perverse counsellors in the action of killing my father and his companions in his treason, massacre, and cruel enterprise. And reason requireth, that even as traitorously as they then caused their prince to be put to death that with the like (nay well much more) justice they should pay the interest of their felonious actions.

You know (madam) how Hother your grandfather[2] and father to the good king Roderick, having vanquished Guimon, caused him to be burnt, for that the cruel villain had done the like to his lord Gevare, whom he betrayed in the nighttime.[3] And who knoweth not that traitors and perjured persons deserve no faith nor loyalty to be observed towards them, and that conditions[4] made with murtherers ought to be esteemed as cobwebs and accounted as if they were things never promised nor agreed upon. But if I lay hands upon Fengon it will neither be felony nor treason, he being neither my king nor my lord: but I shall justly punish him as my subject that hath disloyally behaved himself against his lord and sovereign prince. And seeing that glory is the reward of the virtuous, and the honour and praise of those that do service to their natural prince, why should not blame and dishonour accompany traitors and ignominious death all those that dare be so bold as to lay violent hands upon sacred kings, that are friends and companions of the gods, as representing their majesty and persons?

To conclude, glory is the crown of virtue and the price of constancy, and seeing that it never accompanieth with infelicity but shunneth cowardice and spirits of base and traitorous conditions, it must necessarily follow that either a glorious death will be mine end, or with my sword in hand (laden with triumph and victory) I shall bereave° them of their lives that made mine unfortunate and darkened the beams of that virtue which I possessed from

---

[1] courtiers

[2] *In margin:* Hother father to Roderick. Guimon burnt his lord Gevare.

[3] *In margin:* We must observe neither faithfulness or fidelity to traitors or parricides.

[4] agreements

the blood and famous memory of my predecessors. For why should men desire to live when shame and infamy are the executioners that torment their consciences and villainy is the cause that withholdeth the heart from valiant enterprises and diverteth the mind from honest desire of glory and commendation, which endureth forever? I know it is foolishly done to gather fruit before it is ripe and to seek to enjoy a benefit not knowing whether it belong to us of right, but I hope to effect it so well and have so great confidence in my fortune (that hitherto hath guided the action of my life) that I shall not die without revenging myself upon mine enemy, and that himself shall be the instrument of his own decay, and to execute that which of myself I durst° not have enterprised."

After this Fengon (as if he had been out some long journey) came to the court again, and asked for him that had received the charge to play the intelligencer[1] to entrap Hamblet, in his dissembled wisdom was abashed° to hear neither news nor tidings of him, and for that cause asked Hamblet what was become of him, naming the man. The prince, that never used lying[2] and who in all the answers that ever he made (during his counterfeit madness) never strayed from the truth (as a generous mind is a mortal enemy to untruth), answered and said that the counsellor he sought for was gone down through the privy,[3] where being choked by the filthiness of the place, the hogs meeting him had filled their bellies.

Chapter 4

How Fengon the third time devised to send Hamblet to the king of England, with secret letters to have him put to death: and how Hamblet, when his companions slept, read the letters and instead of them counterfeited others, willing the king of England to put the two messengers to death, and to marry his daughter to Hamblet, which was effected; and how Hamblet escaped out of England.

A man would have judged anything rather than that Hamblet had committed that murther; nevertheless, Fengon could not content himself, but still his mind gave him[4] that the fool would play him some trick of legerdemain[5] and willingly would have killed him, but he feared King Roderick, his grandfather, and further durst° not offend the queen, mother to the fool, whom she loved and much cherished, shewing° great grief and heaviness to

---

[1] spy
[2] who never lied
[3] sewer
[4] suggested or intimated to him
[5] sleight of hand, trickery

see him so transported out of his wits. And in that conceit,[1] seeking to be rid of him, determined to find the means to do it by the aid of a stranger, making the king of England minister of his massacring resolution, choosing rather that his friend should defile his renown with so great a wickedness than himself to fall into perpetual infamy by an exploit of so great cruelty, to whom he purposed to send him and by letters desire him to put him to death.

Hamblet, understanding that he should be sent into England, presently doubted[2] the occasion of his voyage and for that cause speaking to the queen, desired her not to make any shew° of sorrow or grief for his departure, but rather counterfeit a gladness as being rid of his presence, who although she loved, yet she daily grieved to see him in so pitiful estate deprived of all sense and reason: desiring her further that she should hang the hall with tapestry and make it fast with nails upon the walls and keep the brands for him which he had sharpened at the points then, when as he said he made arrows to revenge the death of his father. Lastly, he counselled her that the year after his departure being accomplished she should celebrate his funerals, assuring her that at the same instant she should see him return with great contentment and pleasure unto her for that his voyage. Now, to bear him company were assigned two of Fengon's faithful ministers bearing letters engraved in wood that contained Hamblet's death, in such sort as he had advertised[3] the king of England.

But the subtle Danish prince (being at sea) whilst his companions slept, having read the letters and known his uncle's great treason, with the wicked and villainous minds of the two courtiers that led him to the slaughter, raced[4] out the letters that concerned his death, and instead thereof graved others, with commission to the king of England to hang his two companions.[5] And not content to turn the death they had devised against him upon their own necks, wrote further that King Fengon willed him to give his daughter to Hamblet in marriage. And so arriving in England, the messengers presented themselves to the king, giving him Fengon's letters, who having read the contents said nothing as then but stayed[6] convenient time to effect Fengon's desire. Meantime, using the Danes familiarly, doing them that honour to sit at his table (for that kings as then were not so curiously[7] nor solemnly served as in these our days) for in these days mean

---

[1] with that thought
[2] suspected
[3] in such a way that he had warned (see glossary)
[4] erased
[5] *In margin:* Hamblet's craft to save his life.
[6] awaited
[7] fastidiously

kings and lords of small revenue are as difficult and hard to be seen as in times past the monarchs of Persia used to be: or as it is reported of the great king of Ethiopia who will not permit any man to see his face, which ordinarily he covereth with a veil.

And as the messengers sat at the table with the king, subtle Hamblet was so far from being merry with them that he would not taste one bit of meat, bread, nor cup of beer whatsoever as then set upon the table not without great wondering of the company, abashed° to see a young man and a stranger, not to esteem of the delicate meats and pleasant drinks served at the banquet, rejecting them as things filthy, evil of taste and worse prepared. The king, who for that time dissembled what he thought, caused his guests to be conveyed into their chamber, willing one of his secret servants to hide himself therein and so to certify him what speeches passed among the Danes at their going to bed.

Now they were no sooner entered into the chamber and those that were appointed to attend upon them gone out, but Hamblet's companions asked him why he refused to eat and drink of that which he found upon the table, not honouring the banquet of so great a king that entertained them in friendly sort° with such honour and courtesy as it deserved, saying further that he did not well, but dishonoured him that sent him as if he sent men into England that feared to be poisoned by so great a king. The prince, that had done nothing without reason and prudent consideration, answered them and said: "What, think you, that I will eat bread dipped in human blood, and defile my throat with the rust of iron, and use that meat that stinketh and savoureth of man's flesh, already putrefied and corrupted and that senteth[1] like the savour of a dead carrion long since cast into a vault?[2] And how would you have me to respect the king that hath the countenance of a slave and the queen who instead of great majesty hath done three things more like a woman of base parentage and fitter for a waiting gentlewoman than beseeming a lady of her quality and estate?" And having said so, used many injurious and sharp speeches as well against the king and queen as others that had assisted at that banquet for the entertainment of the Danish ambassadors, and therein Hamblet said truth, as hereafter you shall hear, for that in those days the north parts of the world, living as then under Sathan's laws, were full of enchanters, so that there was not any young gentleman whatsoever that knew not something therein sufficient to serve his turn if need required.

---

[1] smells
[2] sewer

As yet in those days in Gothland and Biarmy[1] there are many that knew not what the Christian religion permitteth, as by reading the histories of Norway and Gothland you may easily perceive: and so Hamblet, while his father lived, had been instructed in that devilish art whereby the wicked sprite[2] abuseth mankind and advertiseth° him (as he can) of things past.

It toucheth not the matter herein to discover the parts of divination in man and whether this prince by reason of his over-great melancholy had received those impressions, divining that which never any but himself had before declared, like the philosophers who, discoursing of diverse deep points of philosophy, attribute the force of those divinations[3] to such as are Saturnists by complexion[4] who oftentimes speak of things which, their fury ceasing, they then already can hardly understand who are the pronouncers. And for that cause Plato saith, many diviners and many poets, after the force and vigour of their fire beginneth to lessen, do hardly understand what they have written, although entreating of such things while the spirit of divination continueth upon them they do in such sort° discourse thereof that the authors and inventers of the arts themselves by them alleged commend their discourses and subtle disputations. Likewise, I mean not to relate that which divers men believe: that a reasonable soul becometh the habitation of a meaner sort of devils, by whom men learn the secrets of things natural. And much less do I account of the supposed governors of the world feigned[5] by magicians by whose means they brag to effect marvellous things. It would seem miraculous that Hamblet should divine in that sort, which after proved so true (if as I said before) the devil had not knowledge of things past, but to grant it he knoweth things to come.

I hope you shall never find me in so gross an error you will compare and make equal derivation and conjecture with those that are made by the spirit of God and pronounced by the holy prophets that tasted of that marvellous science, to whom only was declared the secrets and wondrous works of the Almighty. Yet there are some imposturious companions that impute so much divinity to the Devil, the father of lies, that they attribute unto him the truth of the knowledge of things that shall happen unto men, alleging the conference of Saul with the witch, although one example out of the Holy Scriptures specially set down for the condemnation of wicked man is not of

---

[1] modern Gotland and Bjarmaland
[2] spirit (i.e., Satan)
[3] predictions
[4] saturnine, ill-tempered by one's inherent nature
[5] deceived

force to give a sufficient law to all the world.[1] For they themselves confess that they can divine not according to the universal cause of things, but by signs borrowed from such like causes, which are always alike, and by those conjectures they can give judgement of things to come. But all this being grounded upon a weak support (which is a simple conjecture) and having so slender a foundation, as some foolish or late[2] experience, the fictions being voluntary, it should be a great folly in a man of good judgement, specially one that embraceth the preaching of the gospel and seeketh after no other but the truth thereof, to repose upon any of these likelihoods or writings full of deceit.

As touching magical operations, I will grant them somewhat therein, finding divers histories that write thereof and that the Bible maketh mention and forbiddeth the use thereof. Yea, the laws of the gentiles and ordinances of emperors have been made against it, in such sort° that Mahomet the great heretic and friend of the Devil by whose subtleties he abused most part of the east countries hath ordained great punishments for such as use and practise those unlawful and damnable arts, which for this time leaving off, let us return to Hamblet, brought up in these abuses, according to the manner of his country, whose companions, hearing his answer, reproached him full of folly, saying that he could by no means show a greater point of indiscretion than in despising that which is lawful and rejecting that which all men received as a necessary thing and that he had not grossly so forgotten himself as in that sort to accuse such and so excellent a man as the king of England and to slander the queen, being then as famous and wise a princess as any at that day reigning in the islands thereabouts, to cause him to be punished according to his deserts.[3]

But he, continuing in his dissimulation, mocked him, saying that he had not done anything that was not good and most true. On the other side, the king, being advertised° thereof by him that stood to hear the discourse, judged presently that Hamblet speaking so ambiguously was either a perfect fool or else one of the wisest princes in his time, answering so suddenly and so much to the purpose upon the demand by his companions made touching his behaviour. And the better to find the truth caused the baker[4] to be sent

---

[1] Saul conferred with the Witch of Endor in order to summon the spirit of the prophet Samuel (1 Samuel 28). The episode later provoked a series of theological debates over its meaning.

[2] recent

[3] deserving, merit (see glossary)

[4] The 1608 text erroneously reads *babler*, though Belleforest clearly intended a baker (*boulanger*).

for, of whom inquiring in what place the corn¹ grew whereof he made bread
for his table and whether in that ground there were not some signs or news
of a battle fought whereby human blood had therein been shed. The baker
answered that not far from thence there lay a field full of dead men's bones,
in times past slain in a battle, as by the great heaps of wounded sculls might
well appear, and for that the ground in that part was become fertiler than
other grounds by reason of the fat and humours² of the dead bodies, that
every year the farmers used there to have in³ the best wheat they could find
to serve his majesty's house. The king perceiving it to be true, according to
the young prince's words, asked where the hogs had been fed that were
killed to be served at his table, and answer was made him that those hogs
getting out of the said field wherein they were kept had found the body of a
thief that had been hanged for his demerits and had eaten thereof. Whereat
the king of England, being abashed,° would needs know with what water
the beer he used to drink of⁴ had been brewed. Which, having known, he
caused the river to be digged somewhat deeper and therein found great store
of swords and rusty armours that gave an ill savour to the drink.

It were good I should here dilate somewhat of Merlin's prophesies which
are said to be spoken of him before he was fully one year old, but if you
consider well what hath already been spoken it is no hard matter to divine
of things past, although the minister of Sathan therein played his part, giving
sudden and prompt answers to this young prince, for that herein are nothing
but natural things such as were well known to be true and therefore not
needful to dream of things to come.

This known, the king, greatly moved with a certain curiosity to know
why the Danish prince said that he had the countenance of a slave,
suspecting thereby that he reproached the baseness of his blood and that he
would affirm that never any prince had been his sire, wherein to satisfy
himself he went to his mother and leading her into a secret chamber, which
he shut as soon as they were entered, desired her of her honour to shew° him
of whom he was engendered in this world. The good lady well assured⁵ that
never any man had been acquainted with her love, touching any other man
than her husband, swear⁶ that the king her husband only was the man that
had enjoyed the pleasures of her body. But the king her son, all ready with

---

¹ any kind of grain used for baking bread
² In seventeenth-century medical thought, the four humours (fluids) were believed
    to be the constituent parts of the human body.
³ harvest
⁴ customarily drank
⁵ promised
⁶ swore

the truth of the Danish prince's answers, threatened his mother to make her tell by force if otherwise she would not confess it, who for fear of death acknowledged that she had prostrated her body to a slave and made him father to the king of England, whereat the king was abashed° and wholly ashamed.

I give them leave to judge who, esteeming themselves honester than their neighbours and supposing that there can be nothing amiss in their houses, make more enquiry than is requisite to know it which they would rather not have known, nevertheless dissembling what he thought and biting upon the bridle rather than he would deprive himself by publishing[1] the lasciviousness of his mother, thought better to leave a great sin unpunished than thereby to make himself contemptible to his subjects, who peradventure would have rejected him as not desiring to have a bastard to reign over so great a kingdom.

But as he was sorry to hear his mother's confession, on the other side he took great pleasure in the subtlety and quick spirit of the young prince and for that cause went unto him to ask him why he had reproved three things in his queen convenient for a slave and savouring more of baseness than of royalty and far unfit for the majesty of a great prince. The king, not content to have received a great displeasure by knowing himself to be a bastard and to have heard with what injuries he charged her whom he loved best in all the world, would not content himself until he also understood that which displeased him, as much as his own proper disgrace, which was that his queen was the daughter of a chambermaid, and withal° noted certain foolish countenances she made which not only shewed° of what parentage she came, but also yet her humours[2] savoured of the baseness and low degree of her parents, whose mother he assured the king was as then yet holden[3] in servitude. The king, admiring the young prince and beholding in him some matter of greater respect than in the common sort° of men, gave him his daughter in marriage, according to the counterfeit letters by him devised and the next day caused the two servants of Fengon to be executed to satisfy as he thought the king's desire.

But Hamblet, although the sport pleased him well and that the king of England could not have done him a greater favour made as though he had been much offended, threatening the king to be revenged, but the king to appease him gave him a great sum of gold which Hamblet caused to be molten and put it into two staves made hollow for the same purpose, to serve

---

[1] The king of England keeps this information to himself for fear of diminishing his reputation and authority over his people.

[2] boldily (and by extension, mental and spiritual) composition

[3] held

his turn therewith as need should require, for of all other the king's treasures he took nothing with him into Denmark but only those two staves. And as soon as the year began to be at an end, having somewhat before obtained licence of the king his father-in-law to depart, went for Denmark, then, with all the speed he could, to return again into England to marry his daughter and so set sail for Denmark.

Chapter 5

How Hamblet, having escaped out of England, arrived in Denmark the same day that the Danes were celebrating his funerals, supposing him to be dead in England, and how he revenged his father's death upon his uncle and the rest of the courtiers; and what followed.

Hamblet in that sort° sailing into Denmark, being arrived in the country, entered into the palace of his uncle the same day that they were celebrating his funerals; and going into the hall, procured[1] no small astonishment and wonder to them all, no man thinking other but that he had been dead, among the which many of them rejoiced not a little, for the pleasure which they knew Fengon would conceive for so pleasant a loss. And some were sad, as remembering the honourable king Horvendile, whose victories they could by no means forget, much less deface out of their memories that which appertained unto him, who as then greatly rejoiced to see a false report spread of Hamblet's death, and that the tyrant had not as yet obtained his will of the heir of Jutie, but rather hoped God would restore him to his senses again for the good and welfare of that province.

Their amazement at the last being turned into laughter, all that as then were assistant[2] at the funeral banquet of him whom they esteemed dead mocked each at other, for having been so simply deceived and wondering at the prince that in his so long a voyage he had not recovered any of his senses asked what was become of them that had borne him company into great Britain, to whom he made answer (shewing° them the two hollow staves wherein he had put his molten gold, that the king of England had given him to appease his fury concerning the murther of his two companions) and said here they are both. Whereat many that already knew his humours presently conjectured that he had played some trick of legerdemain[3] and to deliver himself out of danger had thrown them into the pit prepared for him, so that fearing to follow after them and light upon some

---

[1] provided
[2] in attendance
[3] sleight of hand, trickery

evil adventure they went presently out of the court. And it was well for them that they did so, considering the tragedy acted by him the same day, being accounted his funeral but in truth their last days, that as then rejoiced for their overthrow.

For when every man busied himself to make good cheer and Hamblet's arrival provoked them more to drink and carouse, the prince himself at that time played the butler and a gentleman attending on the tables, not suffering the pots nor goblets to be empty whereby he gave the noble men such store of liquor that all of them, being full laden with wine and gorged with meat, were constrained to lay themselves down in the same place where they had supped, so much their senses were dulled and overcome with the fire of over-great drinking (a vice common and familiar among the Almaines[1] and other nations inhabiting the north parts of the world). Which when Hamblet perceiving and finding so good opportunity to effect his purpose and be revenged of his enemies and, by it, means to abandon the actions, gestures and apparel of a madman, occasion so fitly finding his turn and as it were effecting itself failed not to take hold thereof. And seeing those drunken bodies filled with wine lying like hogs upon the ground, some sleeping, others vomiting the over-great abundance of wine which without measure they had swallowed up, made the hangings about the hall to fall down and cover them all over, which he nailed to the ground, being boarded, and at the ends thereof he stuck the brands whereof I spake before by him sharpened, which served for pricks, binding and tying the hangings in such sort° that what force soever they used to loose themselves it was unpossible to get from under them.

And presently he set fire in the four corners of the hall in such sort that all that were as then therein not one escaped away, but were forced to purge their sins by fire and dry up the great abundance of liquor by them received into their bodies, all of them dying in the unevitable and merciless flames of the hot and burning fire: which the prince perceiving, became wise, and knowing that his uncle before the end of the banquet had withdrawn himself into his chamber,[2] which stood apart from the place where the fire burnt, went thither, and entering into the chamber, laid hand upon the sword of his father's murtherer, leaving his own in the place, which while he was at the banket[3] some of the courtiers had nailed fast into the scabbard. And going to Fengon said, "I wonder, disloyal king, how thou canst sleep here at thine ease: and all thy palace is burnt the fire thereof having burnt the greatest

---

[1] Germans or Germanic peoples. *In margin:* Drunkenness a vice overcommon in the north parts of the world.

[2] *In margin:* A strange revenge taken by Hamblet.

[3] banquet

part of thy courtiers and ministers of thy cruelty[1] and detestable tyrannies. And which is more, I cannot imagine how thou shouldst well assure thyself and thy estate, as now to take thy ease, seeing Hamblet so near thee armed with the shafts by him prepared long since and at this present is ready to revenge the traitorous injury by thee done to his lord and father."

Fengon, as then knowing the truth of his nephew's subtle practise and hearing him speak with stayed[2] mind, and which is more, perceived a sword naked in his hand, which he already lifted up to deprive him of his life, leaped quickly out of the bed, taking hold of Hamblet's sword that was nailed into the scabbard, which as he sought to pull out, Hamblet gave him such a blow upon the chine[3] of the neck that he cut his head clean from his shoulders, and as he fell to the ground said: "This just and violent death is a first reward for such as thou art; now go thy ways and when thou comest in hell, see thou forget not to tell thy brother (whom thou traitorously slewest) that it was his son that sent thee thither with the message, to the end that being comforted thereby, his soul may rest among the blessed spirits and quit me of the obligation that bound me to pursue his vengeance upon mine own blood, that seeing it was by thee that I left the chief thing that tied me to this alliance and consanguinity."[4]

A man (to say the truth) hardy, courageous, and worthy of eternal commendation, who arming himself with a crafty, dissembling and strange shew° of being distract out of his wits, under that pretence deceived the wise, politick and crafty, thereby not only preserving his life from the treasons and wicked practises of the tyrant,[5] but (which is more) by an new and unexpected kind of punishment revenged his father's death many years after the act committed: in no such sort° that directing his courses with such prudence and effecting his purposes with so great boldness and constancy, he left a judgement[6] to be decided among men of wisdom which was more commendable in him, his constancy or magnanimity, or his wisdom in ordering his affairs according to the premeditable[7] determination he had conceived. If vengeance ever seemed to have any shew of justice, it is then,[8] when piety and affection constraineth us to remember our fathers unjustly murdered, as the things whereby we are dispensed withal° and which seek

---

[1] *In margin*: A mock but yet sharp and stinging given by Hamblet to his uncle.
[2] steady
[3] back
[4] blood relation
[5] *In margin:* Commendation of Hamblet for killing the Tyrant.
[6] matter or question
[7] premeditated
[8] *In margin:* How just vengeance ought to be considered.

the means not to leave treason and murther unpunished: seeing David a holy and just king and of nature simple, courteous and debonair, yet when he died he charged his son Solomon (that succeeded him in his throne) not to suffer certain men that had done him injury to escape unpunished.[1]

Not that this holy king (as then ready to die and to give account before God of all his actions) was careful[2] or desirous of revenge, but to leave this example unto us that where the prince or country is interested the desire of revenge cannot by any means (how small soever) bear the title of condemnation, but is rather commendable and worthy of praise. For otherwise the good kings of Judah nor others had not pursued them to death that had offended their predecessors if God himself had not inspired and engraven that desire within their hearts. Hereof the Athenian laws bear witness, whose custom was to erect images in remembrance of those men that, revenging the injuries of the commonwealth, boldly massacred tyrants and such as troubled the peace and welfare of the citizens.

Hamblet, having in this manner revenged himself, durst° not presently declare his action to the people, but to the contrary determined to work by policy° so to give them intelligence what he had done and the reason that drew him thereunto; so that being accompanied with such of his father's friends that then were rising, he stayed to see what the people would do, when they should hear of that sudden and fearful action. The next morning the towns bordering thereabouts, desiring to know from whence the flames of fire proceeded the night before they had seen, came thither; and perceiving the king's palace burnt to ashes and many bodies (most part consumed) lying among the ruins of the house, all of them were much abashed,° nothing being left of the palace but the foundation. But they were much more amazed to behold the body of the king all bloody and his head cut off lying hard by[3] him, whereat some began to threaten revenge, yet not knowing against whom. Others beholding so lamentable a spectacle armed themselves, the rest rejoicing, yet not daring to make any shew° thereof, some detesting the cruelty, others lamenting the death of their prince, but the greatest part calling Horvendile's murther to remembrance, acknowledging a just judgement from above that had thrown down the pride of the tyrant. And in this sort° the diversities of opinions among that multitude of people being many, yet every man ignorant what would be the

---

[1] *In margin:* David's intent in commanding Solomon to revenge him of some of his enemies. [On his deathbed, King David commanded Solomon to take revenge on his enemies (1 Kings 2:1-8).]
[2] circumspect, cautious
[3] immediately next to

issue[1] of that tragedy, none stirred from thence, neither yet attempted to move any tumult, every man fearing his own skin and distrusting his neighbour, esteeming each other to be consenting to the massacre.

Chapter 6

How Hamblet, having slain his uncle and burnt his palace, made an oration to the Danes to shew° them what he had done, and how they made him king of Denmark; and what followed.

Hamblet, then seeing the people to be so quiet and most part of them not using any words, all searching only and simply the cause of this ruin and destruction, not minding to lose any time, but aiding himself with the commodity thereof,[2] entered among the multitude of people and standing in the middle spake unto them as followeth.

"If there be any among you (good people of Denmark) that as yet have fresh within your memories the wrong done to the valiant king Horvendile, let him not be moved nor think it strange to behold the confused, hideous and fearful spectacle of this present calamity: if there be any man that affecteth fidelity and alloweth of the love and duty that man is bound to shew his parents and find it a just cause to call to remembrance the injuries and wrongs that have been done to our progenitors, let him not be ashamed beholding this massacre, much less offended to see so fearful a ruin both of men and of the bravest[3] house in all this country: for the hand that hath done this justice, could not effect it by any other means, neither yet was it lawful for him to do it otherwise than by ruinating[4] both sensible and unsensible things, thereby to preserve the memory of so just a vengeance.

I see well (my good friends) and am very glad to know so good attention and devotion in you, that you are sorry (before your eyes) to see Fengon so murthered and without a head, which heretofore you acknowledged for your commander. But I pray you remember, this body is not the body of a king but of an execrable tyrant and a parricide most detestable. O, Danes, the spectacle was much more hideous when Horvendile your king was murthered by his brother. What, should I say a brother? Nay, rather by the most abominable executioner that ever beheld the same. It was you that saw Horvendile's members massacred and that with tears and lamentations accompanied him to the grave: his body disfigured, hurt in a thousand places

---

[1] outcome
[2] seizing upon the opportunity of it
[3] most noble
[4] destroying

and misused in ten times as many fashions. And who doubteth (seeing experience hath taught you) that the tyrant (in massacring your lawful king) sought only to infringe the ancient liberties of the common people? And it was one hand only that, murthering Horvendile, cruelly despoiled him of life and by the same means unjustly bereaved° you of your ancient liberties and delighted more in oppression than to embrace the pleasant countenance of prosperous liberty without adventuring for the same. And what madman is he that delighteth more in the tyranny of Fengon than in the clemency and renewed courtesy of Horvendile?

If it be so, that by clemency and affability the hardest and stoutest hearts are mollified and made tractable, and that evil and hard usage causeth subjects to be outrageous and unruly, why behold you not the debonair carriage of the first, to compare it with the cruelties and insolence of the second, in every respect as cruel and barbarous as his brother was gentle, meek and courteous? Remember, O you Danes, remember what love and amity Horvendile shewed° unto you, with what equity and justice he swayed the great affairs of this kingdom, and with what humanity and courtesy he defended and cherished you, and then I am assured that the simplest man among you will both remember and acknowledge that he had a most peaceable, just and righteous king taken from him, to place in his throne a tyrant and murtherer of his brother: one that hath perverted all right, abolished the ancient laws of our fathers, contaminated the memories of our ancestors and by his wickedness polluted the integrity of this kingdom, upon the neck thereof having placed the troublesome yoke of heavy servitude, abolishing that liberty wherein Horvendile used to maintain you and suffered[1] you to live at your ease.

And should you now be sorry to see the end of your mischiefs and that this miserable wretch, pressed down with the burthen of his offences, at this present payeth the usury of the parricide committed upon the body of his brother and would not himself be the revenger of the outrage done to me, whom he sought to deprive of mine inheritance, taking from Denmark a lawful successor to plant[2] a wicked stranger and bring into captivity those that my father had enfranchised and delivered out of misery and bondage? And what man is he that, having any spark of wisdom, would esteem a good deed to be an injury and account pleasures equal with wrongs and evident outrages? It were then great folly and temerity in princes and valiant commanders in the wars to expose themselves to perils and hazards of their lives for the welfare of the common people if that for a recompense they

---

[1] permitted
[2] place on the throne

should reap hatred and indignation of the multitude. To what end should Hother have punished Balder,[1] if instead of recompense, the Danes and Swethlanders[2] had banished him to receive and accept the successors of him that desired nought but his ruin and overthrow? What is he that hath so small feeling of reason and equity that would be grieved to see treason rewarded with the like and that an evil act is punished with just demerit in the party himself that was the occasion? Who was ever sorrowful to behold the murtherer of innocents brought to his end, or what man weepeth to see a just massacre done upon a tyrant, usurper, villain and bloody personage?

I perceive you are attentive and abashed° for not knowing the author of your deliverance and sorry that you cannot tell to whom you should be thankful for such and so great a benefit as the destruction of a tyrant and the overthrow of the place that was the storehouse of his villainies and the true receptacle of all the thieves and traitors in this kingdom. But behold (here in your presence) him that brought so good an enterprise to effect. It is I (my good friends), it is I that confess I have taken vengeance for the violence done unto my lord and father and for the subjection and servitude that I perceived in this country, whereof I am the just and lawful successor. It is I alone that have done this piece of work, whereunto you ought to have lent me your hands and therein have aided and assisted me. I have only accomplished that which all of you might justly have effected by good reason without falling into any point of treason or felony. It is true that I hope so much of your good wills toward the deceased king Horvendile and that the remembrances of his virtues is yet so fresh within your memories that if I had required your aid herein you would not have denied it, specially to your natural prince. But it liked[3] me best to do it myself alone, thinking it a good thing to punish the wicked without hazarding the lives of my friends and loyal subjects, not desiring to burthen other men's shoulders with this weight, for that I made account to effect it well enough without exposing any man into danger, and by publishing[4] the same, should clean have overthrown the device which at this present I have so happily brought to pass.[5]

I have burnt the bodies of the courtiers to ashes, being companions in the mischiefs and treasons of the tyrant, but I have left Fengon whole, that

---

[1] The brothers Hodr and Balder are gods of the Norse pantheon. Hodr was tricked into killing his brother by the god Loki.
[2] Swedes
[3] pleased
[4] making public
[5] Had Hamblet let others know beforehand of his strategy he would have exposed it and ruined it.

you might punish his dead carcass (seeing that when he lived you durst° not lay hands upon him) to accomplish the full punishment and vengeance due unto him and so satisfy your choler upon the bones of him that filled his greedy hands and coffers with your riches and shed the blood of your brethren and friends. Be joyful, then, (my good friends): make ready the nose-gay[1] for this usurping king, burn his abominable body, boil his lascivious members, and cast the ashes of him that hath been hurtful to all the world into the air; drive from you the sparks of pity, to the end that neither silver, nor crystal cup, nor sacred tomb may be the restful habitation of the relics and bones of so detestable a man. Let not one trace of a parricide be seen, nor your country defiled with the presence of the least member of this tyrant without pity, that your neighbours may not smell the contagion nor our land the polluted infection of a body condemned for his wickedness.

I have done my part to present him to you in this sort;° now it belongs to you to make an end of the work and put to the last hand of duty, whereunto your several functions call you, for in this sort you must honour abominable princes. And such ought to be the funeral of a tyrant, parricide, and usurper both of the bed and patrimony that no way belonged unto him, who having bereaved° his country of liberty, it is fit that the land refuse to give him a place for the eternal rest of his bones.

O my good friends, seeing you know the wrong that hath been done unto me, what my griefs are and in what misery I have lived since the death of the king, my lord and father, and seeing that you have both known and tasted these things then, when as I could not conceive the outrage that I felt. What need I recite it unto you? What benefit would it be to discover[2] it before them that, knowing it, would burst (as it were with despite) to hear of my hard chance and curse Fortune for so much imbasing[3] a royal prince as to deprive him of his majesty, although not any of you durst° so much as shew° one sight of sorrow or sadness?

You know how my father-in-law[4] conspired my death and sought by divers means to take away my life, how I was forsaken of the queen my mother, mocked of my friends, and despised of mine own subjects. Hitherto I have lived laden with grief and wholly confounded in tears, my life still accompanied with fear and suspicion, expecting the hour when the sharp

---

[1] Bouquet of flowers or herbs (for his funeral): the translator misread the French *bucher* (funeral pyre or burning at the stake) as *bouquet*, which he rendered in English as "nosegay." However, the mistake produced another instance of Hamblet's sardonic wit.

[2] reveal

[3] debasing, lowering

[4] step-father

sword would make an end of my life and miserable anguishes, how many times counterfeiting the madman, have I heard you pity my distress and secretly lament to see me disinherited, and yet no man sought to revenge the death of my father nor to punish the treason of my incestuous uncle, full of murthers and massacres? This charity ministered comfort and your affectionate complaints made me evidently see your good wills, that you had in memory the calamity of your prince and within your hearts engraven the desire of vengeance for the death of him that deserved a long life. And what heart can be so hard and so intractable, or spirit so severe, cruel and rigorous that would not relent at the remembrance of my extremities,[1] and take pity of an orphan child so abandoned of the world? What eyes were so void of moisture but would distil a field of tears to see a poor prince assaulted by his own subjects, betrayed by his mother, pursued by his uncle and so much oppressed that his friends durst° not shew° the effects of their charity and good affection? O (my good friends) shew pity to him whom you have nourished and let your hearts take some compassion upon the memory of my misfortunes. I speak to you that are innocent of all treason and never defiled your hands, spirits, nor desires with the blood of the great and virtuous king Horvendile. Take pity upon the queen, sometime[2] your sovereign lady and my right honourable mother, forced by the tyrant and rejoice to see the end and extinguishing of the object of her dishonour, which constrained her to be less pitiful to her own blood so far as to embrace the murtherer of her own dear spouse, charging herself with a double burthen of infamy and incest, together with injuring and disanulling[3] of her house and the ruin of her race.

This hath been the occasion that made me counterfeit folly and cover my intents under a veil of mere madness, which hath wisdom and policy° thereby to enclose the fruit of this vengeance which that it hath attained to the full point of efficacy and perfect accomplishment you yourselves shall be judges, for touching this and other things concerning my profit and the managing of great affairs, I refer myself to your counsels and thereunto am fully determined to yield, as being those that trample under your feet the murtherers of my father and despise the ashes of him that hath polluted and violated the spouse of his brother, by him massacred, that hath committed felony against his lord, traitorously assailed the majesty of his king and odiously thralled[4] his country under servitude and bondage. And you his loyal subjects from whom he, bereaving° your liberty, feared not to add

---

[1] suffering
[2] formerly, at one time
[3] nullifying, wiping out
[4] enslaved

incest to parricide, detestable to all the world, to you also it belongeth by duty and reason commonly to defend and protect Hamblet the minister and executor of just vengeance, who being jealous[1] of your honour and your reputation hath hazarded himself, hoping you will serve him for fathers, defenders, and tutors, and, regarding him in pity, restore him to his goods and inheritances.

It is I that have taken away the infamy of my country and extinguished the fire that embraced your fortunes. I have washed the spots that defiled the reputation of the queen, overthrowing both the tyrant and the tyranny and beguiling the subtleties of the craftiest deceiver in the world, and by that means brought his wickedness and impostures to an end. I was grieved at the injury committed both to my father and my native country, and have slain him that used more rigorous commandments over you than was either just or convenient to be used unto men that have commanded the valiantest nations in the world. Seeing, then, he was such a one to you, it is reason that you acknowledge the benefit and think well of for the good[2] I had done your posterity, and admiring my spirit and wisdom, choose me your king if you think me worthy of the place. You see I am the author of your preservation, heir of my father's kingdom, not straying in any point from his virtuous action, no murtherer, violent parricide, nor man that ever offended any of you, but only the vicious. I am lawful successor in the kingdom and just revenger of a crime above all others most grievous and punishable. It is to me that you owe the benefit of your liberty received and of the subversion of that tyranny that so much afflicted you, that hath trodden under feet the yoke of the tyrant and overwhelmed his throne and taken the sceptre out of the hands of him that abused a holy and just authority, but it is you that are to recompense those that have well deserved. You know what is the reward of so great desert,° and being in your hands to distribute the same, it is of you that I demand the price of my virtue and the recompense of my victory."

This oration of the young prince so moved the hearts of the Danes and wan[3] the affections of the nobility that some wept for pity, other[4] for joy to see the wisdom and gallant spirit of Hamblet; and having made an end of their sorrow, all with one consent proclaimed him king of Jutie and Chersonnese,[5] at this present the proper° country of Denmark. And having

---

[1] protective

[2] think well upon the good deed

[3] won

[4] others

[5] Jutland was also known as the Cimbric Peninsula (*Chersonnese* here), a region now shared by modern Denmark and Germany.

celebrated his coronation[1] and received the homages and fidelities of his subjects, he went into England to fetch his wife, and rejoiced with his father-in-law, touching his good fortune. But it wanted little[2] that the king of England had not accomplished that which Fengon with all his subtleties could never attain.

Chapter 7

How Hamblet after his coronation went into England, and how the king of England secretly would have put him to death, and how he slew the king of England and returned again into Denmark with two wives; and what followed.

Hamblet, being in England, shewed° the king what means he had wrought to recover his kingdom, but when the king of England understood of Fengon's death he was both abashed° and confused in his mind, at that instant feeling himself assailed with two great passions. For that in times past he and Fengon, having been companions together in arms, had given each other their faith and promises by oath that if either of them chanced to be slain by any man whatsoever, he that survived (taking the quarrel upon him as his own) should never cease till he were revenged or at the least do his endeavour. This promise incited the barbarous king to massacre Hamblet, but the alliance presenting itself before his eyes, and beholding the one dead, although his friend, and the other alive and husband to his daughter made him deface[3] his desire of revenge. But in the end the conscience of his oath and promise obtained the upper hand and secretly made him conclude the death of his son-in-law, which enterprise after that was cause of his own death and overrunning of the whole country of England by the cruelty and despite conceived by the king of Denmark. I have purposely omitted the discourse of that battle as not much pertinent to our matter, as also not to trouble you with too tedious a discourse, being content to shew you the end of this wise and valiant king Hamblet who, revenging himself upon so many enemies and discovering all the treasons practiced against his life, in the end served for a sport[4] to fortune and an example to all great personages that trust overmuch to the felicities of this world, that are of small moment and less continuance.

The king of England perceiving that he could not easily effect his desire upon the king, his son-in-law, as also not being not willing to break the laws

---

[1] *In margin:* Hamblet king of one part of Denmark.
[2] lacked
[3] obliterate, forget
[4] source of amusement or diversion

and rights of hospitality, determined to make a stranger the revenger of his injury and so accomplish his oath made to Fengon without defiling his hands with the blood of the husband of his daughter and polluting his house by the traitorous massacring of his friend. In reading of this history it seemeth Hamblet should resemble another Hercules, sent into divers° places of the world by Euristheus (solicited by Juno), where he knew any dangerous adventure, thereby to overthrow and destroy him, or else Bellerophon set to Ariobatus to put him to death, or (leaving profane histories) another Urias by King David appointed to be placed in the forefront of the battle and the man that should be first slain by the Barbarians.[1]

For the king of England's wife being dead not long before (although he cared not for marrying another woman), desired his son-in-law to make a voyage for him into Scotland, flattering him in such sort° that he made him believe that his singular wisdom caused him to prefer him to that embassage,[2] assuring himself that it were impossible that Hamblet, the subtlest and wisest prince in the world, should take anything in the world in hand without effecting the same.

Now, the queen of Scots, being a maid and of a haughty courage, despised marriage with all men, as not esteeming any worthy to be her companion, in such manner that by reason of this arrogant opinion there never came any man to desire her love but she caused him to lose his life. But the Danish king's fortune was so good that Hermetrude (for so was the queen's name), hearing that Hamblet was come thither to entreat at a marriage between her and the king of England, forgot all her pride and despoiling herself of her stern nature, being as then determined to make him (being the greatest prince as the living) her husband and deprive the English princess of her spouse whom she thought fit for no men but herself. And so this Amazon without love, disdaining Cupid, by her free will submitted her haughty mind to her concupiscence.

The Dane, arriving in her court, desired she to see the old king of England's letters and mocking at his fond[3] appetites, whose blood as then was half congealed, cast her eyes upon the young and pleasant Adonis of the north, esteeming herself happy to have such a prey fallen into her hands

---

[1] Encouraged by Juno, King Eurystheus arranged for the twelve labours of Hercules, intending that he would not survive them. King Proteus attempted to have ancient Greek hero Bellerophon killed by King Iobates, who instead sent the hero on a quest to kill the Chimera. King David arranged for Uriah the Hittite to be killed in battle (2 Samuel 11:14-17). The author again draws upon his humanist education for examples of heroes betrayed by those who know them.

[2] choose him for that mission

[3] foolish (see glossary)

whereof she made her full account to have the possession. And to conclude, she that never had been overcome by the grace, courtesy, valour or riches of any prince nor lord whatsoever was as then vanquished with the only report of the subtleties of the Dane, who knowing that he was already fianced to the daughter of the king of England, spake unto him and said, "I never looked for so great a bliss, neither from the gods nor yet from fortune, as to behold in my countries the most complete prince in the north and he that hath made himself famous and renowned through all the nations of the world, as well neighbours as strangers, for the only respect of his virtue, wisdom and good fortune, serving him much in the pursuit and effect of divers° things by him undertaken, and think myself much beholding[1] to the king of England (although his malice seeketh neither my advancement nor the good of you my lord) to do me so much honour as to send me so excellent a man to entreat of a marriage (he being old and a mortal enemy to me and mine) with me that am such a one as every man seeth, is not desirous to couple with a man of so base quality as he, whom you have said to be the son of a slave. But on the other side I marvel at the son of Horvendile and grand-child to king Roderick, he that by his foolish wisdom and feigned madness surmounted the forces and subtleties of Fengon and obtained the kingdom of his adversary, should so much embase[2] himself (having otherwise been very wise and well advised in all his actions) touching his bedfellow, and he that for his excellency and valour surpasseth humane capacity should stoop so low as to take to wife, her that issuing from a servile race hath only the name of a king for her father, for that the baseness of her blood will always cause her to shew° what are the virtues and noble qualities of her ancestors."

"And you my lord," said she, "are you so ignorant as not to know that marriage should not be measured by any foolish opinion of an outward beauty, but rather by virtues and antiquity of race, which maketh the wife to be honoured for her prudence and never degenerating from the integrity of his ancestors? Exterior beauty also is nothing where perfection of the mind doth not accomplish and adorn that which is outwardly seen to be in the body and is lost by an accident and occurrence of small moment: as also such toys have deceived many men and drawing the like enticing baits, have cast them headlong into the gulf of their ruin, dishonour, and utter overthrow. It was I to whom this advantage belonged, being a queen and such a one, as for nobility, may compare myself with the greatest princes in Europe, being nothing inferior unto any of them, neither for antiquity of

---

[1] beholden
[2] lower

blood, nobility of parents, nor abundance of riches, and am not only a queen but such a one as that, receiving whom I will for my companion in bed, can make him bear the title of a king and with my body give him possession of a great kingdom and goodly province.

Think, then, my lord, how much I account of your alliance, who being accustomed with the sword to pursue such as durst° embolden themselves to win my love, it is to you only to whom I make a present both of my kisses, embracings, sceptre and crown. What man is he, if he be not made of stone, that would refuse so precious a pawn as Hermetrude with the kingdom of Scotland? Accept, sweet king, accept this queen, who with so great love and amity desireth your so great profit and can give you more contentment in one day than the princess of England would yield you pleasure during her life. And although she surpass me in beauty, her blood being base, it is fitter for such a king as you are to choose Hermetrude, less beautiful but noble and famous, rather than the English lady with great beauty but issuing from an unknown race, without any title of honour."

Now think if the Dane, hearing such forcible reasons, and understand it by her which he half doubted,[1] as also moved with choler for the treason of his father-in-law, that purposely sent him thither to lose his life, and being welcomed, kissed and played withal° by this queen, young and reasonable fair, if he were not easy enough to be converted and like to forget the affection of his first wife, with this to enjoy the realm of Scotland and so open the way to become king of all great Britain, that, to conclude, he married her and led her with him to the king of England's court, which moved the king from that time forward much more to seek the means to bereave° him of his life, and had surely done it if his daughter, Hamblet's other wife, more careful[2] of him that had rejected her than of her father's welfare, had not discovered[3] the enterprise to Hamblet, saying "I know well, my lord, that the allurements and persuasions of a bold and altogether shameless woman, being more lascivious than the chaste embracements of a lawful and modest wife, are of more force to entice and charm the senses of young men; but for my part I cannot take this abuse, for satisfaction to leave me in this sort° without all cause, reason, or precedent fault once known in me your loyal spouse and take more pleasure in the alliance of her who one day will be the cause of your ruin and overthrow. And although a just cause of jealousy and reasonable motion of anger dispense with me at this time, to make no more account of you than you do of me, that am not worthy to be so scornfully rejected. That matrimonial charity shall have

---

[1] her, whom he half suspected
[2] solicitous of
[3] revealed

more force and vigour in my heart than the disdain which I have justly conceived to see a concubine hold my place and a strange woman before my face enjoy the pleasures of my husband. This injury, my lord, although great and offensive, which to revenge divers° ladies of great renown have in times past sought and procured the death of their husbands, cannot so much restrain my good will, but that may not choose but advertise° you what treason is devised against you, beseeching you to stand upon your guard for that my father's only seeking is to bereave° you of your life, which if it happen, I shall not long live after you.

Many reasons induce me to love and cherish you, and those of great consequence, but specially and above all the rest, I am and must be careful of you,[1] when I feel your child stirring in my womb, for which respect, without so much forgetting yourself, you ought to make more account of me than of your concubine, whom I will love because you love her, contenting myself that your son hateth her, in regard of the wrong she doth to his mother. For it is impossible that any passion or trouble of the mind whatsoever can quench those fierce passions of love that made me yours, neither that I should forget your favours past when loyally you sought the love of the daughter of the king of England; neither is it in the power of that thief that hath stolen your heart nor my father's choler to hinder me from seeking to preserve you from the cruelty of your dissembling friend (as heretofore by counterfeiting the madman, you prevented the practices and treasons of your uncle Fengon), the complot[2] being determined to be executed upon you and yours."

Without this advertisement,° the Dane had surely been slain and the Scots that came with him, for the king of England, inviting his son-in-law to a banquet with the greatest courtesies that a friend can use to him whom he loved as himself, had the means to entrap him and cause him dance a pitiful galliard in that sort[3] to celebrate the marriage between him and his new lady. But Hamblet went thither with armour under his clothes and his men in like sort,° by which means he and his escaped with little hurt, and so after that happened the battle before spoken of, wherein the king of England, losing his life, his country was the third time sacked by the barbarians of the islands and country of Denmark.

---

[1] concerned for you

[2] conspiracy, plot

[3] a lively style of dance on that occasion

Chapter 8

How Hamblet being in Denmark, was assailed by Wiglerus, his uncle, and after betrayed by his last wife, called Hermetrude, and was slain: after whose death she married his enemy Wiglerus.

Hamblet, having obtained the victory against the king of England and slain him, laden with great treasures and accompanied with his two wives, set forward to sail into Denmark, but by the way he had intelligence that Wiglere his uncle and son to Roderick, having taken the royal treasure from his sister Geruth (mother to Hamblet), had also seized upon the kingdom, saying that neither Horvendile nor any of his held it but by permission and that it was in him (to whom the property belonged) to give the charge thereof to whom he would. But Hamblet, not desirous to have any quarrel with the son of him[1] from whom his predecessors had received their greatness and advancement, gave such and so rich presents to Wiglere, that he being contented withdrew himself out of the country and territories of Geruth's son. But within certain time after Wiglere, desirous to keep all the country in subjection, enticed by the conquest of Scanie and Sialandie,[2] and also that Hermetrude (the wife of Hamblet, whom he loved more than himself) had secret intelligence[3] with him and had promised him marriage, so he would take her out of the hands of him that held her, sent to defy Hamblet and proclaimed open war against him.

Hamblet, like a good and wise prince, loving especially the welfare of his subjects, sought by all means to avoid that war, but again refusing it, he perceived a great spot and blemish in his honour; and accepting the same, he knew it would be the end of his days, by the desire of preserving his life on the one side and his honour on the other side pricking him forward. But at the last, remembering that never any danger whatsoever had once shaken his virtues and constancy, chose rather the necessity of his ruin than to lose the immortal fame that valiant and honourable men obtained in the wars: and there is as much difference between a life without honour and an honourable death, as glory and renown is more excellent than dishonour and evil report.

But the thing that spoiled this virtuous prince was the over-great trust and confidence he had in his wife Hermetrude and the vehement love he bare° unto her, not once repenting the wrong in that case done to his lawful

---

[1] *In margin:* Hermetrude betrayeth Hamblet her husband.

[2] Scania, now a province of Sweden, was once under Danish control; Zealand is the major island of continental Denmark.

[3] communication, conference

spouse, and for the which (peradventure that misfortune had never happened unto him, and it would never have been thought that she whom he loved above all things would have so villainously betrayed him), he not once remembering his first wife's speeches, who prophesied unto him that the pleasures he seemed to take in his other wife would in the end be the cause of his overthrow, as they had ravished him of the best part of his senses and quenched in him the great prudence that made him admirable in all the countries in the ocean seas and through all Germany. Now the greatest grief that this king (besotted on[1] his wife) had was the separation of her whom he adored, and assuring himself of his overthrow, was desirous either that she might bear him company at his death or else to find her a husband that should love her (he being dead) as well as ever he did.

But the disloyal queen had already provided herself of a marriage to put her husband out of trouble and care for that, who perceiving him to be sad for her sake when she should have absented herself from him, she, to blind him the more and to encourage him to set forward to his own destruction, promised to follow him whither soever he went and to take the like fortune that befell to him, were it good or evil, and that so she would give him cause to know how much she surpassed the English woman in her affection towards him, saying that woman is accursed that feareth to follow and accompany her husband to the death. So that to hear her speak, men would have said that she had been the wife of Mithridates or Zenobia, queen of Palmira,[2] she made so great a show of love and constancy.[3] But by the effect it was after easily perceived how vain the promise of this inconstant and wavering princess was and how uncomparable the life of this Scottish queen was to the vigour of her chastity, being a maid before she was married. For that Hamblet had no sooner entered into the field, but she found means to see Wiglere, and the battle begun wherein the miserable[4] Danish prince was slain.

But Hermetrude presently yielded herself with all her dead husband's treasons[5] into the hand of the tyrant who, more than content with that metamorphosis so much desired, gave order that presently the marriage (bought with the blood and treason of the son of Horvendile) should be celebrated.

---

[1] foolishly or madly in love with

[2] Laodice (c. 130-c.90 BCE), sister and wife to Mithridates VI of Pontus and the Syrian Queen Zenobia (c.240-c.274 CE) were frequently used, as the author does here, as examples of treacherous powerful women.

[3] *In margin:* Hamblet slain.

[4] unfortunate

[5] Belleforest's text has *desponilles*, probably a typographic error for *despouilles* (spoils).

Thus you see that there is no promise or determination of a woman, but that a very small discommodity[1] of Fortune mollifieth and altereth the same, and which time doth not pervert: so that the misfortunes subject to a constant man shake and overthrow the natural slippery loyalty of the variable[2] steps of women, wholly without any faithful assurance of love or true unfeigned constancy. For as a woman is ready to promise, so is she heavy and slow to perform and effect that which she hath promised, as she that is without end or limit in her desires, flattering herself in the diversity of her wanton delights and taking pleasure in diversity and change of new things, which as soon she doth forget and grow weary of. And to conclude, such she is in all her actions; she is rash, covetous, and unthankful, whatsoever good or service can be done unto her.

But now I perceive I err in my discourse, vomiting such things unworthy of this sects,[3] but the vices of Hermetrude have made me say more than I meant to speak, as also the author from whence I take this history hath almost made me hold his course. I find so great a sweetness and liveliness in this kind of argument,[4] and the rather because it seemeth so much the truer, considering the miserable success[5] of poor king Hamblet.

Such was the end of Hamblet, son to Horvendile, Prince of Jutie, to whom if this Fortune had been equal with his inward and natural gifts I know not which of the ancient Grecians and Romans had been able to have compared with him for virtue and excellency, but hard fortune following him in all his actions. And yet he, vanquishing the malice of his time with the vigour of constancy, hath left us a notable example of haughty[6] courage worthy of a great prince, arming himself with hope in things that were wholly without any colour or shew° thereof, and in all his honourable actions made himself worthy of perpetual memory, if one only spot had not blemished and darkened a good part of his praises. For that the greatest victory that a man can obtain is to make himself victorious and lord over his own affections, and that restraineth the unbridled desires of his concupiscence: for if a man be never so princely, valiant, and wise, if the desires and enticements of his flesh prevail and have the upper hand, he will

---

[1] inconvenience
[2] inconstant
[3] The French version reads "de ce sexe." The spelling of *sex* and *sect* were sometimes confused in the early modern period, leading the English translator to render the French as "this sects."
[4] topic, subject
[5] outcome, conclusion
[6] noble

embase his credit[1] and, gazing after strange beauties, become a fool and (as it were), incensed, dote on the presence of women. This fault was in the great Hercules, Sampson, and the wisest man that ever lived upon the earth following this train, therein impaired his wit; and the most noble, wise, valiant and discreet personages of our time, following the same course, have left us many notable examples of their worthy and notable virtues.[2]

But I beseech you that shall read this history not to resemble the spider that feedeth of the corruption that she findeth in the flowers and fruits that are in the gardens, whereas the bee gathereth her honey out of the best and fairest flower she can find. For a man that is well brought up should read the lives of whoremongers, drunkards, incestuous, violent and bloody persons not to follow their steps and so to defile himself with such uncleanness, but to shun paliardise,[3] abstain the superfluities and drunkenness in banquets, and follow the modesty, courtesy, and continency that recommendeth Hamblet in this discourse, who while other made good cheer continued sober. And where all men sought as much as they could to gather together riches and treasure, he, simply accounting riches nothing comparable to honour, sought to gather a multitude of virtues that might make him equal to those that by them were esteemed as gods, having not as then received the light of the Gospel, that men might see among the barbarians and them that were far from the knowledge of one only God that nature was provoked to follow that which is good and those forward to embrace virtue. For that there was never any nation how rude or barbarous soever that took not some pleasure to do that which seemed good, thereby to win praise and commendations, which we have said to be the reward of virtue and good life. I delight to speak of these strange histories and of people that were unchristened, that the virtue of the rude people may give more splendour to our nation, who, seeing them so complete, wise, prudent, and well advised in their actions, might strive not only to follow (imitation being a small matter) but to surmount them as our religion surpasseth their superstition and our age more purged, subtle, and gallant than the season[4] wherein they lived and made their virtues known.

FINIS

---

[1] make base his reputation

[2] Hercules and Samson ("Sampson") were both conventional images of powerful men betrayed or tricked by women. The author might have had in mind England's Henry VIII, among others, as an example of "personages of our time" who were impaired by "the desires and enticements of the flesh."

[3] debauchery

[4] more purified, refined, noble than the age

Questions

1. How are bravery and masculinity portrayed in this story? What part does cleverness play in heroic behaviour?

2. How important is the overt moralising of this story to its plot? Do we gain any insights into the cultural values of the world described in this tale?

3. One of the classic questions often asked about Shakespeare's Hamlet is whether he remains in control of his own mental facilities, even after he vows merely to feign madness by putting on an "antic disposition" (see act 1, scene 5). How does this story represent Hamblet's real or feigned madness?

4. The plot of this story includes several major events after the death of the protagonist's uncle Feng. How do these later episodes fit into the full story? Is anything lost when Shakespeare excludes them from his story?

5. Women come in for some very harsh treatment in this story: by whom, and why?

GLOSSARY OF ARCHAIC AND UNFAMILIAR TERMS

This list includes high-frequency words, which are footnoted on their first occurrence within each text and thereafter marked with a ° within that text. Extremely high-frequency words such as *eke* ("also"), *ere* ("before"), *ne* ("not," "nor," "no"), and *wherefore* ("for that reason") are not marked with a ° in their respective texts but are included in this list.

abash(ed)	(v) to astonish, startle; (adj) amazed, startled, confused
abode	(n) place of sojourn or lodging; (v) to stay, live, endure
accompt	(n) account; (v) to count, to account for
advertise	to warn
algate(s)	in any case
alway	always
ambassage	diplomatic mission or embassy
and / and if	if
appeach	to accuse
assay	(n) attempt, trial; (v) to try, test
aught	anything, something
ay	yes, indeed (used as a general term of affirmation)
aye	ever, at one time
bare	bore
bereave	to steal, take, or strip away (see reave)
betide	to occur, happen (past tense: *betid*)
betime(s)	early, in good time
bin	been
bewray	to betray, reveal
boot	profit, success (n); (v) to profit, succeed
bootless	useless, unprofitable, in vain
break	to open or begin a conversation
brake	broke (see break)
brook	to tolerate
busy	anxious, worried
careful	concerned, worried
censure	judgement

clepe(d)	(v) to name or call; (adj) named
corse	corpse, body
desert	deserving, merit, worth
device	plan, plot, strategy
divers	various, several, many
doubt	(n) fear or uncertainty, or both; (v) to suspect
dower	dowry
durst	dared
eft	quickly, early (also *eftsoons*)
eke	also
enthrall	to enslave (see thrall)
ere	ever, before
erst	(adj) first, prior, earlier; (adv) formerly, before
except	unless
eyne	eyes
fact	deed
fain	rather, prefer to; in some contexts, must
fare	to go, behave, perform
fere	companion, friend; in some contexts, partner or lover
fond	foolish, especially doting in love
gan	began
geast	guest
ghostly	spiritual
handsome	fitting, suitable, gracious; in context, gallant
hap	(n) fortune, fate; (v) to occur by chance
haply	by chance, by fortune, perhaps
hest	command
hie	to go, hurry
hire	gain, profit
hugy	huge
leech	medical doctor
list	to prefer to do, rather do, wish to do (see lust)
lore	advice, knowledge
lour	to look or behave sullenly
lust	(n) will or desire in general; (v) wanted to (see list)
maze	to amaze
mean	(n) means; (v) to mean
meat	food of any sort, nourishment
meet	fitting, suitable
mirror	model, paragon
naught	nothing

ne	not, neither, nor, no
nought	nothing
perfit	perfect
perforce	of necessity
policy	strategy, plot, plan; in context, cunning
press	crowd
proper	own, selfsame
reave	to steal, take away, rob (see also bereave)
rest	to remain
rout	crowd
ruth	pity, compassion
seely, silly	innocent, defenceless
shew	(n) show, pretense; (v) to show, reveal
shrift, shrive	(n) confession; (v) to confess
sith	since
smart	(n) injury, pain; (v) to injure
sometime	sometimes, at one time, for a time
sort	(n) kind, style, type, way; (v) to agree, concur
speed	(n) success, achievement; (v) to succeed, prosper
sprite	spirit
stay	(n) hindrance; (v) to stop, hesitate, make hesitate
sterve	to die
thrall	(n) servitude, bondage, slave; (v) to enslave, bind
trow	to believe or assert as true
try	to test
vild	vile
want(ing)	(n) lack; (adj) lacking
ware(ly)	(n) care, caution; (adj) cautious; (adv) cautiously
weal	good, well-being; in some contexts, (common)wealth
weed(s)	clothing, garment(s)
ween	to believe, guess
whenas	when, seeing that
whereas	where
wherefore	why, for that reason; therefore
wight	person, human being
wise, -wise	(n) way, manner; in such a way (e.g., in friendly wise)
wis	to know
withal	with, by which, by such means, all things considered
withouten	without
wont(ed)	(n) habit, custom; (adj) habitual, customary
wot	to know, believe

wroth   (n) wrath, intense anger; (adj) intensely angry
y- + verb   *y-* marks a past tense (e.g. *y-cleped*: named)

SUGGESTIONS FOR FURTHER READING

This very brief list offers some starting places for students and general readers interested in learning more about Shakespeare's borrowing and the age in which he worked.

Overviews and Introductions

Leah Scragg's "Mouldy Tales and Renaissance Attitudes to Originality," serves as the introduction to her book *Shakespeare's Mouldy Tales: Recurrent Plot Motifs in Shakespearian Drama* (New York and London: Longman, 1992), 1-11. In fewer than a dozen pages, she describes the principles of literary artistry in the early modern period, offering examples from Shakespeare and several of his contemporaries. Scragg also wrote an essay called "Source Study" in *Shakespeare: An Oxford Guide*, edited by Stanley Wells and Lena Cowen Orlin (Oxford: Oxford University Press, 2003), pp. 373-83.

Leonard Barkan's "What Did Shakespeare Read?" in *The Cambridge Companion to Shakespeare*, ed. Margreta de Grazia and Stanley Wells (Cambridge: Cambridge University Press, 2001), 31-47 offers a useful brief overview of what we can reconstruct of Shakespeare's reading and reading habits.

Sources and Source Studies

The most comprehensive work concerning Shakespeare's sources is Geoffrey Bullough's eight-volume *Narrative and Dramatic Sources of Shakespeare* (London: Routledge Kegan Paul and New York: Columbia University Press, 1957-75). It includes some complete works and large sections of works acknowledged by scholars to have been directly used by Shakespeare. It also includes works that might have been used or are close analogues to certain elements in the plays. Although scholarship has advanced since his project was completed, the introductions to each section remain valuable accounts of the prior stories that went into, or may have contributed to, the making of each play. Non-specialist readers should be aware that Bullough's texts are in their original spelling and punctuation, and that the project is directed more to specialists than general readers.

Stuart Gillespie's *Shakespeare's Books: A Dictionary of Shakespeare Sources.* 2nd edition. (London: Bloomsbury, 2016) is an encyclopedia-style handbook offering high-quality entries on Shakespeare's major sources, the authors of those sources, and in some cases their publishers. The introductory material for the volume is also very useful.

Jonathan Bate's *Shakespeare and Ovid* (Oxford: Clarendon Press, 1993) describes how Shakespeare re-imagined Ovid's works in his plays and poems.

T. W. Baldwin's *William Shakespere's Small Latine & Lesse Greeke* 2 vols (Champaign-Urbana, IL: University of Illinois Press, 1944) contains information on Shakespeare's education and his reading tastes as an adult. An online version is searchable: http://durer.press.illinois.edu/baldwin/index.html.

Creativity and Intellectual Property in the Early Modern Period

The first chapter of John Kerrigan's *Shakespeare's Originality* (Oxford: Oxford University Press, 2018) is very informative; subsequent chapters focus on *Much Ado About Nothing*, *Richard III*, *King Lear*, and *The Tempest*.

Robert S. Miola, *Shakespeare's Reading* (Oxford: Oxford University Press, 2000) covers a good deal of ground concerning the ways Shakespeare re-purposed his source material.

Mark Rose, *Authors and Owners: The Invention of Copyright* (Cambridge, MA: Harvard University Press, 1993) surveys copyright laws and changing attitudes toward intellectual property.

Several essays in *The Construction of Authorship: Textual Appropriation in Law and Literature*, edited by Peter Jaszi and Martha Woodmansee (Durham: Duke University Press, 1994) touch on relevant topics.

So do several essays, especially those of Part I, in the collection *Plagiarism in Early Modern England*, edited by Paulina Kewes (New York: Palgrave, 2003).

Linda Hutcheon with Siobhan O'Flynn's *A Theory of Adaptation.* 2nd edition (London: Routledge, 2016), though not specifically devoted to Shakespeare, is good introduction to adaptation as a literary and cultural practice.

Another good introduction to adaptation in general is Julie Sanders's *Adaptation and Appropriation.* 2nd edition. The New Critical Idiom (London: Routledge, 2016). Chapters 1-3 may prove most useful.